Introduction to
STRUCTURAL PROBLEMS
in
Nuclear Reactor Engineering

Edited by

J. R. RYDZEWSKI

Department of Civil Engineering,
The University, Southampton

PERGAMON PRESS

OXFORD · LONDON · NEW YORK · PARIS

1962

PERGAMON PRESS LTD.
Headington Hill Hall, Oxford
*4 & 5 Fitzroy Square, London, W.*1

PERGAMON PRESS INC.
122 *East 55th Street, New York 22, N.Y.*

PERGAMON PRESS G.m.b.H.
Kaiserstrasse 75, Frankfurt-am-Main

GAUTHIER-VILLARS
55 *Quai des Grands-Augustins, Paris 6*ᵉ

Library of Congress Card Number 62–17649

*Set in Times New Roman 10/12 pt and
Made and Printed in Great Britain by
the Villafield Press, Bishopbriggs, Glasgow*

CONTENTS

Chapter   Page

CONTRIBUTORS

DR. J. M. ALEXANDER: Reader in Plasticity, Mechanical Engineering Dept., Imperial College of Science and Technology, London.

DR. R. W. BAILEY: Head of Reactor Core Design and Structural Analysis Group, G.E.C.–Simon Carves Atomic Energy Group, Erith, Kent.

MR. G. H. BROOMFIELD: Metallurgy Division, U.K.A.E.A., Harwell, Bucks.

DR. A. H. CHILVER: Chadwick Professor of Civil and Municipal Engineering, University College, London University.

DR. P. B. MORICE: Professor of Civil Engineering, Southampton University.

DR. N. W. MURRAY: Senior Lecturer, Dept. of Engineering, Monash University, Clayton, Victoria, Australia; *formerly* G.E.C., Erith, Kent.

MR. R. W. PAGE: Lecturer, Mechanical Engineering Dept., Southampton University.

MR. J. F. POYNOR: Design Engineer, Atomic Energy Dept., Babcock and Wilcox Ltd., London.

DR. J. PRZEMIENIECKI: Professor of Aircraft Structures, Department of Mechanics, Air Force Institute of Technology, Wright-Patterson Air Force Base, Ohio, U.S.A.; *formerly* Head of the Structures Research and Development Group, Bristol Aircraft Ltd., Bristol.

MR. E. A. RICHARDS: Mathematics Group, Mechanical Engineering Laboratory, The English Electric Co., Ltd., Whetstone, Leicester.

MR. D. F. T. ROBERTS: Head of Engineering, Metallurgy and Welding Division, G.E.C., Erith, Kent.

DR. J. R. RYDZEWSKI: Lecturer, Civil Engineering Dept., Southampton University.

MR. H. TOTTENHAM: Reader in Structural Engineering, Southampton University.

ACKNOWLEDGMENTS

Chapter 1

R. W. Page—to the General Electric Company for permission to reproduce Figs. 1.7 and 1.8, and to the editors of "Nuclear Power" for Fig. 1.10.

Chapter 3

D. F. T. Roberts—to the directors and management of the Atomic Energy Division of the General Electric Company for permission to publish the chapter and to Mr. A. Prince, Mr. F. Perry and members of the Engineering Metallurgy and Welding Group, A.E.D., Erith, Kent.

Chapter 5

E. A. Richards—to the author's colleagues, both in the Mechanical Engineering Laboratory of the English Electric Company and in the Civil Engineering Department of the Company's Atomic Power Division, where the numerical example originated.

Chapter 9

J. M. Alexander—to Dr. H. G. Hopkins of the Armament Research and Development Establishment, Fort Halstead, Kent, for helpful discussion.

Chapter 12

J. F Poynor—to Mr. M. B. Bickell of the Atomic Energy Department, Babcock & Wilcox Ltd., for his valuable assistance with the more mathematical aspects of the text. Also, to the Research Department of the Company for Fig. 12.6.

Chapter 13

J R. Rydzewski—to Dr. R. W. Bailey, Mr. H. V. Hickson and Mr. C. Snell for assistance with illustrations to the text.

EDITOR'S PREFACE

NUCLEAR power left the hands of the physicists as a successful experiment and passed to those of the engineers. The engineers who received it were, quite naturally, not the civil engineers who were then designing the structures of conventional power stations, but the mechanical engineers experienced in the design of steam raising units.

As reactors grew in size and complexity, the teams of engineers engaged in various commercial establishments on their structural design not only rapidly absorbed the advances in the theory of structures made by civil and aeronautical engineers but initiated, on their own, valuable research in this field.

From this a situation has tended to arise in which the structural expert in the nuclear reactor industry is now in the front line of the structural engineering profession, while the "traditional" structural engineer has been left largely unaware of the opportunities in reactor engineering. To draw attention to these it was decided that it was time to make an attempt at presenting the problems involved, as they affect the structural engineer. With this object in view, I was given all encouragement to organise a week's residential course at Southampton University in Spring 1960. On all sides I met with willingness and enthusiasm and was gratified to find it possible to assemble an impressive team of experts from industry and the universities to deliver lectures on specialist topics.

The course proved very successful and it was then decided to keep the team together for the preparation of this volume, making full use of the experience gained during the course.

The policy for the course, as well as for the present volume, has been to concentrate on the fundamentals. Once these are fully developed for any particular subject, it is only necessary to indicate where the reader can find details of their application. Only by strict adherence to this principle has it been possible to present the subject in a volume of this size.

As the book is intended to be read by those who can appreciate the practical aspects of engineering, the first three chapters are intended to "set the scene" and to define the problems that have to be solved in the light of physical, metallurgical and constructional requirements.

The six chapters that follow aim at giving an up-to-date introduction to the analytical and computational techniques which singly or in combination can be used to solve the various problems. As these problems occur in many types of structures, I hope they will find readers outside the ranks of those directly concerned in the design of nuclear power stations. Chapter 7, for instance, contains the first presentation of a very powerful method of structural analysis.

In the next three chapters experienced designers from the nuclear reactor industry outline the methods they favour for the design of different reactor components. The final chapter discusses the use of experimental stress analysis.

Since the original course was held, the possibility of prestressed concrete pressure vessels for nuclear reactors has become very real. This is discussed in the Appendix.

At the expense of a certain lack of uniformity, I have considered it best to leave each author to use his preferred technique in developing his subject. Since, in each chapter, care has been taken to define all terms used, slight differences of notation should not create difficulties for the reader.

In a work of this kind a fully comprehensive Index with cross-references between chapters is of doubtful value. The Index provided is, in fact, broadly based on the very detailed Table of Contents, which should serve as a guide to the reader.

The whole venture would have been impossible without the active support and encouragement of Professor P. B. Morice, Head of the Department of Civil Engineering at Southampton University.

J. R. RYDZEWSKI

Southampton
July 1962

CHAPTER 1

AN INTRODUCTION TO NUCLEAR REACTORS

R. W. PAGE

THE field of nuclear reactor engineering is one which embraces a wide range
of applied sciences. For this reason, the design of a nuclear reactor is
necessarily the result of the combined efforts of a number of specialists.
But, in order that their efforts can be smoothly co-ordinated, it is essential
that each one should be aware of how the general principles and features of
a nuclear reactor affect his problems. Consequently this first chapter is
concerned with a simple description of the physical processes occurring in
a reactor, followed by a discussion of some existing reactor systems. In this
way the structural engineer will at least become acquainted with how the
structural and other problems arise in the design of a nuclear reactor. For
those readers concerned with acquiring a deeper understanding, Refs. 1 and
2 should be consulted.

Before any of the processes which occur in a reactor can be discussed, it
is first necessary briefly to describe the composition of an atom.

1.1. ATOMIC COMPOSITION

An atom consists of a central massive nucleus around which negatively
charged particles of matter called electrons revolve, as indicated in Fig. 1.1.

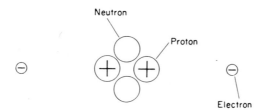

FIG. 1.1. Composition of an atom.

The nucleus is composed of a cluster of matter particles, these being of
two types, namely protons and neutrons. A proton has a positive electric
charge whereas a neutron is electrically neutral and has a mass slightly

1

greater than a proton. Because the electric charge possessed by an electron and a proton is equal in magnitude and the number of protons in the nucleus is equal to the number of orbiting electrons, an atom is electrically neutral.

Because of the repulsive forces existing between protons due to their positive electric charge, it is evident that other forces must exist within the nucleus in order for it to hold together. Experiment shows that the range of action of these forces is confined to within the nucleus. The exact nature of these short-range nuclear forces is unknown at the present time.

In order to indicate the composition of any atom or nucleus, the total number of protons and neutrons in the nucleus is represented by a mass number A, the number of protons by an atomic number Z. Thus an atom or nucleus of an element having a chemical symbol, say X, is represented by $_Z X^A$.

Not all the atoms of one element are necessarily identical. Different atomic species of the same element sometimes exist, the difference being that the atoms of one species contain more or less neutrons than the atoms of the other species. These different atomic species of the same element are called isotopes, e.g. naturally occurring oxygen has three isotopes these being $_8 O^{16}$, $_8 O^{17}$ and $_8 O^{18}$. The isotopic abundance of $_8 O^{16}$ atoms, i.e. the percentage of naturally occurring oxygen atoms which are $_8 O^{16}$ atoms, is 99·76 per cent, whilst that for $_8 O^{17}$ and $_8 O^{18}$ is 0·04 per cent and 0·20 per cent, respectively.

Having acquainted the reader with atomic composition and some of the terminology which will be used later, consideration can now be given to nuclear reactions.

1.2. NUCLEAR REACTIONS

It has been found that some naturally occurring elements, particularly the very high mass number elements emit radiation in the form of particles. Such elements are called natural radioactive elements. The radiation arises from the disintegration of the elements nuclei. Each disintegration consists in the ejection of a particle from a nucleus causing its composition to change, so producing a nucleus of a different element. The ejected particle may be either an alpha- or a beta-particle. An alpha-particle is the nucleus of a helium atom whilst a beta-particle is an electron.

In a manner similar to the way in which chemical reactions are represented, so nuclear reactions may be represented by a nuclear reaction equation. One side of the equation indicates the nucleus which undergoes the reaction, the other side the nucleus and particle arrived at as a result of the reaction. Thus an alpha-disintegration is represented by

$$_Z X^A \rightarrow {}_{Z-2} Y^{A-4} + \alpha$$

or
$$_Z X^A \rightarrow {}_{Z-2} Y^{A-4} + {}_2 He^4$$

and a beta-disintegration by
$$_Z X^A \rightarrow {}_{Z+1} Y^A + \beta$$
or
$$_Z X^A \rightarrow {}_{Z+1} Y^A + {}_{-1} e^0$$

The emission of these particles is sometimes accompanied by the emission of high-frequency electromagnetic radiation called gamma-rays.

These reactions result in an energy release, the kinetic energy of the emitted particles and the energy of any gamma-rays eventually appearing as heat.

The existence of atoms which disintegrate of their own accord led, in the early part of this century, to investigations to determine whether or not normally stable atoms could be caused to disintegrate and so result in the transmutation of one element into another. It was argued that if say an alpha-particle could be fired at a nucleus it might enter the nucleus and cause so violent a disruption that the nucleus would disintegrate. This supposition was confirmed by the first artificially induced nuclear disintegration in which nitrogen gas was bombarded by alpha-particles, producing nuclei of $_8 O^{17}$ and protons according to the equation,

$$_7 N^{14} + {}_2 He^4 \rightarrow {}_8 O^{17} + {}_1 H^1$$

Many similar reactions have been induced since the time the above reaction was first achieved. An important feature of many of these reactions is that the nucleus formed by the reaction is radioactive. An example of such a reaction is that in which an isotope of boron is bombarded by alpha-particles to produce a radioactive isotope of carbon. The reaction is

$$_5 B^{11} + {}_2 He^4 \rightarrow {}_6 C^{14} + {}_1 H^1$$

The $_6 C^{14}$ disintegrates by emitting a beta-particle, i.e.

$$_6 C^{14} \rightarrow {}_7 N^{14} + {}_{-1} e^0$$

In the type of nuclear reaction mentioned so far, they are characterized by the product nucleus having mass and atomic numbers little different to that of the initial nucleus. However, the reaction called nuclear fission consists in the splitting of a nucleus, producing two nuclei having mass and atomic numbers differing considerably from those of the initial nucleus. This reaction mainly occurs with high mass number elements, in particular uranium. Because of its importance in the working of a nuclear reactor, the nuclear fission of uranium will be considered in some detail.

A fission reaction commences with a neutron entering a uranium nucleus. Now uranium has two isotopes, $_{92} U^{238}$ (isotopic abundance 99·3 per cent) and $_{92}U^{235}$ (isotopic abundance 0·7 per cent). Assuming that the neutron enters a $_{92}U^{235}$ nucleus, a $_{92}U^{236}$ nucleus will be produced. It will, however, be a nucleus with an internal energy in excess of that which a $_{92}U^{236}$ nucleus normally has. For, it has been shown that to any mass m there must be associated an energy E according to the equation

$$E = mc^2$$

where c is the speed of light in a vacuum. Then assuming that the neutron has no kinetic energy the excess of internal energy is

$$E = \{M(U^{235}) + M(n^1) - M(U^{236})\}c^2$$

where $M(U^{235})$ = mass of a U^{235} nucleus in normal state,

$\qquad M(U^{236})$ = mass of a U^{236} nucleus in normal state,

$\qquad M(n^1)$ = mass of a neutron.

This excess internal energy or excitation energy, as it is usually called, may be considered to cause the nucleus to oscillate.[1] If the excitation energy is sufficiently great, a neck is formed in the nucleus as seen in Fig. 1.2(c). If, however, the excitation energy is insufficient to cause a neck to form, the oscillations are damped out and the nucleus attains its normal energy state by emitting the excitation energy in the form of a γ-ray. This process is referred to as radioactive capture. But, if a neck is formed, fission of the nucleus in one of many different ways will occur producing two nuclei or fission fragments which because of their positive electric charge will move apart with a total kinetic energy of approximately 167 MeV.* These nuclei possess an excitation energy which causes neutrons to be immediately ejected from them. On an average, approximately 2·5 neutrons are ejected per fission, the average kinetic energy of any neutron being 2 MeV. A possible fission mode for a $_{92}U^{235}$ nucleus is

$$_{92}U^{235} + {_0}n^1 \rightarrow {_{56}}Ba^{141} + {_{36}}Kr^{92} + 3{_0}n^1$$

The nuclei remaining after neutron emission still possess excitation energy and this is emitted in the form of gamma-rays. The nuclei arrived at as a result of neutron and gamma-emission are radioactive, disintegrating mainly by emission of beta-particles and gamma-rays. Radioactive disintegration continues until stable nuclei are obtained. For example, the $_{56}Ba^{141}$ pro-

---

* The energy of nuclei and nuclear particles is measured in terms of a unit called the electron-volt (eV). An electron-volt is defined as the energy which would be acquired by an electron when passing through a potential difference of 1 volt.

Units which are multiples of the electron-volt are commonly used, these being

$$1 \text{ keV} = 10^3 \text{ eV} \quad \text{and} \quad 1 \text{ MeV} = 10^6 \text{ eV}.$$

duced by the fission reaction mentioned above disintegrates in the following way:

$$_{56}\text{Ba}^{141} \rightarrow {}_{57}\text{La}^{141} + {}_{-1}e^0$$

$$_{57}\text{La}^{141} \rightarrow {}_{58}\text{Ce}^{141} + {}_{-1}e^0$$

$$_{58}\text{Ce}^{141} \rightarrow {}_{59}\text{Pr}^{141} + {}_{-1}e^0$$

$_{59}\text{Pr}^{141}$ is a stable isotope of praseodymium.

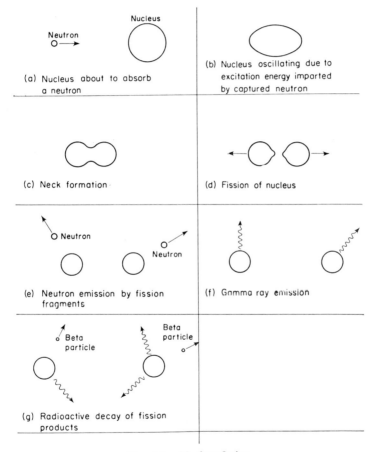

FIG. 1.2. Nuclear fission.

So far, reference has only been made to the fission of $_{92}\text{U}^{235}$ nuclei. $_{92}\text{U}^{238}$ nuclei can also be fissioned but only by neutrons having an energy of at least 1·1 MeV. $_{92}\text{U}^{235}$ nuclei may be fissioned by neutrons of any energy.

An important feature of nuclear fission is the large amount of energy that is released compared to other reactions. Most of the energy is in the form of kinetic energy of the fission fragments. The rest is distributed in the kinetic energy of the neutrons and radiation energy. The distribution of the energy release is given in Table 1.1.

TABLE 1.1.   ENERGY RELEASE FROM AN AVERAGE FISSION

Form	Energy (MeV)
Kinetic energy of fission fragments	167
Prompt* gamma-rays	6
Kinetic energy of neutrons	5
Fission products decay	26
Total energy release	204

Two other reactions are of importance in the working of a reactor. The first is that of elastic scattering. In this reaction a neutron collides with a nucleus, so losing kinetic energy, the loss in kinetic energy increasing as the mass of the scattering nucleus decreases. The other reaction is inelastic scattering in which a nucleus absorbs a neutron and then ejects a neutron having a kinetic energy less than the neutron which entered. The excitation energy possessed by the nucleus is then emitted in the form of a γ-ray.

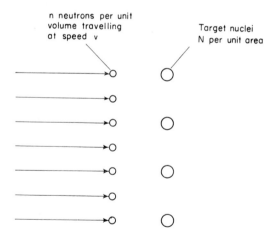

FIG. 1.3.   Neutron irradiation.

From the preceding discussion, it is evident that a neutron may cause one of a number of different reactions to occur. The probability of any one reaction occurring may be measured in terms of a *neutron cross-section*. In

* The gamma rays emitted immediately after neutron emission are called the prompt gamma-rays in order to distinguish them from those which are emitted by the radioactive fission products.

order to understand this term, consider a sample of material having a thickness equivalent to the diameter of one atom being irradiated by a beam of monoenergetic neutrons, as illustrated in Fig. 1.3. Then if the reactions of a particular type occurring per unit area and time is R, it is evident that

$$R \propto N$$

also

$$R \propto \phi$$

where $\phi = nv$,

$$R = \sigma N \phi$$

where σ is some quantity dependent upon the type of reaction, the element being irradiated and the neutron energy,

and

$$\frac{R}{\phi} = \sigma N$$

Clearly not every neutron will react with a nucleus and so R/ϕ represents the fraction of the maximum possible number of reactions. σ may then be regarded as the area presented by a nucleus to an oncoming neutron. For this reason σ is called the neutron cross-section. It is usually measured in terms of a unit called the barn, where 1 barn $= 10^{-24}$ cm^2.

When a number of different reactions is possible the total reaction rate is

$$R_t = \sigma_t N \phi$$

where σ_t, the total neutron cross-section is the sum of the neutron cross-section for each reaction. Then the probability of any one reaction occurring is simply σ/σ_t.

Attention can now be turned to discussing how nuclear fission may be utilized for the generation of power.

1.3. THE NEUTRON CHAIN REACTION

Since in the fission of a uranium nucleus approximately 2·5 neutrons are released, it appears possible that if in a sample of uranium one fission were to occur, a continuous self-sustaining chain of fission reactions would proceed, each reaction being caused by a neutron released by the preceding reaction in the chain. The possibility of this chain reaction occurring is dependent upon the production and absorption of neutrons in the uranium, also upon the leakage of neutrons across the boundaries of the sample. For the total neutron population in the sample will clearly be governed by an equation which will state that

$$\left. \begin{matrix} \text{rate of change of} \\ \text{neutron population} \end{matrix} \right\} = \left. \begin{matrix} \text{production} \\ \text{rate} \end{matrix} \right\} - \left. \begin{matrix} \text{absorption} \\ \text{rate} \end{matrix} \right\} - \begin{matrix} \text{leakage} \\ \text{rate} \end{matrix}$$

In considering whether a self-sustaining neutron chain reaction is possible in natural uranium, consider the sample to be of infinite extent so that the leakage rate is zero. Since the isotopic abundance of $_{92}U^{235}$ is only 0·7 per cent, its presence can for the moment be ignored. Then if a fission of a $_{92}U^{238}$ nucleus occurs, a released neutron may indulge in either fission, elastic and inelastic scattering or radiative capture reactions. However, at neutron energies of about 2 MeV the neutron cross-section of $_{92}U^{238}$ for inelastic scattering is much greater than that for the other reactions. Because of this, the neutron rapidly loses energy. At around 10 eV to 500 eV, the neutron cross-section for radiative capture in $_{92}U^{238}$ is very high, causing the probability of the neutron being captured in this region to be high. This causes a self-sustaining neutron chain reaction in natural uranium to be impossible. However, if the high capture energy region in the $_{92}U^{238}$ could be avoided, a self-sustaining chain reaction would be possible. This is because at neutron energies of around 0·025 eV, the neutron cross-section for fission of $_{92}U^{235}$ is sufficiently high to overcome the effect of its low isotopic abundance and so fission in $_{92}U^{235}$ at these energies becomes a significant reaction. The capture of neutrons in $_{92}U^{238}$ can be partly eliminated by embedding bars of natural uranium in a material which is highly effective at slowing neutrons down but not at capturing them. Such materials are called moderators. Then, provided the cross-section dimensions of the uranium bars is not too great and that they are not too near or too far apart, a neutron released by a fission in a uranium bar may emerge from the bar and be slowed down to an energy of approximately 0·025 eV by elastic scattering reactions in the moderator. In this way it will not be captured by a $_{92}U^{238}$ nucleus when it has an energy at which capture by $_{92}U^{238}$ is high. The neutron now has a high probability of entering a uranium bar and fissioning a $_{92}U^{235}$ nucleus, so producing a continuous chain of fission reactions.

At the low energy at which neutrons cause fission the neutron energy is comparable to the energy of thermal vibration of atoms in the moderator. Because of this and the arrangement of fuel and moderator, nuclear reactors working on this principle are referred to as thermal heterogeneous reactors.

A more obvious way of overcoming neutron capture in $_{92}U^{238}$ is to increase the $_{92}U^{235}$ content, i.e. to use enriched uranium. Fission of $_{92}U^{235}$ nuclei by high-energy neutrons then becomes comparable to the neutron capture in $_{92}U^{238}$. In this way a self-sustaining chain reaction can be achieved. A nuclear reactor adopting this principle is called a fast reactor. The reason for the term " fast " is that neutrons colliding with uranium nuclei are not slowed down to any great extent due to the very much greater mass of a uranium nucleus as compared to a neutron's mass.

So far, the system has been assumed infinite in extent so that the leakage rate is zero. If a self-sustaining chain reaction is possible in a system of finite extent, then it is evident that in one of infinite extent the neutron population will increase with time. But if the system is made finite in size the leakage rate will attain some value other than zero. As the size of the system is reduced so the leakage rate will increase until a particular size is reached such that

$$\text{production rate} = \text{absorption rate} + \text{leakage rate}$$

The system is then said to be critical and the corresponding size is called the critical size. If the system is made smaller than the critical size, the neutron population will decrease with time and so render it impossible to establish a self-sustaining chain reaction.

Immediately a reactor commences operation several things happen, these being:

(1) the temperature of the fuel and moderator increases causing the nuclear characteristics of the system to change;
(2) fission products begin to accumulate in the fuel, some of which have the undesirable property of having high neutron capture cross-sections;
(3) fuel is consumed (for each megawatt day of heat produced by a reactor, approximately 1 g of $_{92}U^{235}$ is consumed).

If the reactor were initially just critical these effects would rapidly cause the chain reaction to cease. To overcome these effects it is necessary to load the reactor with more fuel than that required for it to be critical. In this way the neutron population would rapidly increase and so some means of controlling the chain reaction is required. This is usually achieved in thermal reactors by inserting bars of a material which has a high neutron absorption cross-section into the reactor core.* Thus the neutron absorption rate in the core may be varied, enabling the reactor to be held critical despite temperature changes and fuel consumption. Due to the low neutron absorption cross-sections at high neutron energies, the control of fast reactors is usually achieved by moving parts of the core, the effect of this being to change the neutron leakage and absorption rates.

Having indicated the basic physical processes occurring in a reactor and the principles underlying the achievement of a self-sustaining neutron chain reaction, the discussion can now turn to considering how the principles have been applied in the design and construction of some reactor systems.

1.4. NUCLEAR REACTOR SYSTEMS

The design of a nuclear reactor is greatly dependent upon the purpose for which the reactor is to be used. These uses may be classified as in the Table 1.2.

* The assembly of fuel and moderator is often referred to as the reactor core.

TABLE 1.2.   USE OF NUCLEAR REACTORS

Nuclear reactor type	Use
Reactor experiment	To obtain information concerning a specific design or concept.
Research reactor	To provide a source of neutrons for nuclear physics and engineering experiments.
Production reactor	To produce fissionable material.
Power reactor	The generation of electrical or shaft output.

This discussion will be limited to a consideration of power reactors.

Power generation is usually achieved by the use of a plant as illustrated in Fig. 1.4. The heat produced by nuclear fission in the reactor core is

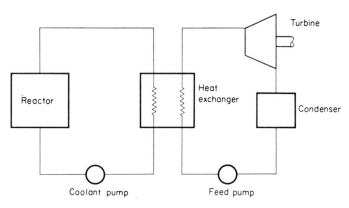

FIG. 1.4.   Nuclear reactor power plant.

transferred to a coolant which is pumped through the core. The coolant then passes through a heat exchanger where heat is rejected from the coolant to water, producing steam which is used to drive turbines or turbo-alternators.

In the following, the features of some power reactor systems will be discussed.

1.5. THE GRAPHITE MODERATED GAS-COOLED REACTOR

This reactor is of the thermal heterogeneous type. Fig. 1.5 shows the essentials of the system.

It is seen to consist of a core contained within a pressure vessel which in turn is surrounded by a biological shield. Ducts from the pressure vessel pass the coolant into heat exchangers.

The fuel in this system is in the form of bars of natural uranium metal. These are sheathed in a metal can, the purpose of this being to prevent corrosion of the uranium by the coolant, also to prevent fission products from passing into the coolant and so contaminating the coolant circuit with radioactive material. The material from which any can is made must

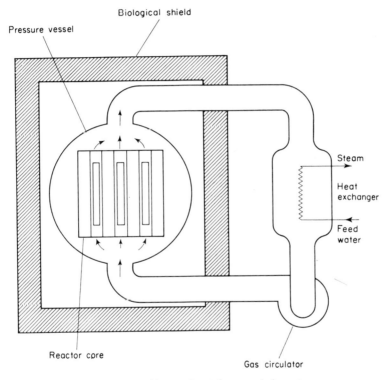

Fig. 1.5. Graphite moderated gas-cooled reactor.

obviously be capable of withstanding the stresses and temperature conditions imposed upon it by reactor operation. Further, it must be chemically compatible with the coolant and uranium and be a low absorber of neutrons. These requirements have been met by a specially developed magnesium alloy called Magnox.

This type of fuel element* has a severe temperature limitation imposed upon it by a phase change in uranium. This phase change occurs at 662°C and results in a volume increase. If this temperature were execcded, the

---
* The combined fuel and can is usually referred to as a fuel element.

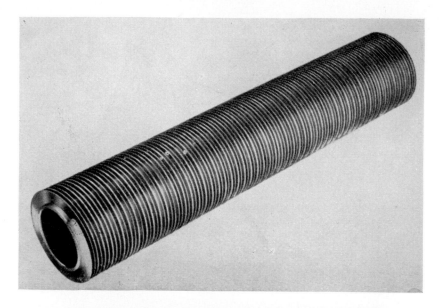

FIG. 1.6.   Gas-cooled reactor fuel cans.

resulting volume change could cause rupture of the can, so releasing fission products into the coolant stream. It is therefore important that the temperature of the uranium should never exceed 662°C. In this way, the maximum surface temperature of the can is limited to about 450°C. Any increase in the heat transfer rate from a fuel element must result from an increase in the heat transfer surface area or by increasing the degree of turbulence in the coolant flow. Both of these results have been achieved without an excessive increase in the power required to pump the coolant around its circuit by using cans of the form shown in Fig. 1.6.

A further limitation on this type of fuel element is that gaseous fission products accumulate within the uranium and produce swelling of the bars. This swelling can produce considerable deformation of the can, ultimately leading to its rupture. Because of this, these fuel elements can only be irradiated to the extent of 3000 MWD/tonne. This corresponds to fissioning only 45 per cent of the available $_{92}U^{235}$ nuclei.

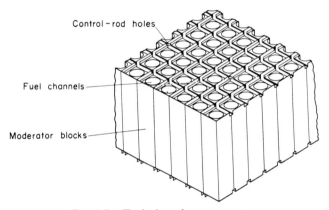

FIG. 1.7. Typical moderator structure.

The moderator of this reactor system is graphite. The graphite is in the form of a large number of blocks fitted together to form a structure pierced by channels into which are placed the fuel elements. The design of such a structure poses some unique structural problems. For, the dimensions of each block will change due to neutron irradiation and thermal expansion. This must not result in the structure becoming unstable or channels becoming misaligned, since fuel elements have to be inserted and removed from the core. Further, neutron streaming and coolant leakage between the blocks must be minimized. One way in which these problems have been solved is illustrated in Fig. 1.7. The graphite structure is supported on a steel grid framework or grillage within the pressure vessel.

The choice of the gas to serve as a coolant in this type of reactor is governed by several factors. For the gas should be:

(a) chemically compatible with the can material, moderator and uranium;
(b) effective as a heat transfer medium;
(c) a low absorber of neutrons;
(d) readily available and of low cost.

On the first three points helium is excellent. It is, however, of limited availability and expensive. Carbon dioxide emerges as the best compromise.

The coolant is contained in its circuit at a pressure of around 100–200 lb./ in^2. The reason for this is that the power required to pump the coolant around its circuit represents a loss of useful power output and so is required to be made as small as possible. It can be shown[3] that the pumping power required is approximately inversely proportional to the square of the coolant's density. For this reason the coolant circuit is pressurized, requiring the reactor core to be contained within a pressure vessel.

It is well known that nuclear radiations can produce harmful effects within a human body.[4] To protect persons from the radiations produced in a nuclear reactor it is necessary to surround the reactor with a biological shield. The function of the shield is to absorb most of the radiations which emerge from the reactor core so that at the outside surface of the shield the intensity of the radiation will produce no significant biological damage to any person.

The most penetrating radiations emerging from the reactor core are neutrons and gamma-rays. The neutrons incident upon the biological shield may be divided into two groups these being:

  (a) fast neutrons—energy > 100 eV,
  (b) slow neutrons—energy < 100 eV.

Slow neutrons are in general easily absorbed by atomic nuclei whereas fast neutrons are not. So the shield has first to slow down the fast neutrons and then to absorb them. This is achieved by having in the shield iron and hydrogen. Iron will inelastically scatter the fast neutrons, reducing their energy to about 0·5 MeV. Hydrogen then completes the slowing down process by elastically scattering the neutrons and then eventually absorbing them. Thus the ingredients required to attenuate neutrons could be provided by plates of iron or steel immersed in water. Iron–water shields are used for some reactor systems but for the system under discussion, concrete provides the most economical shield. Special so-called heavy concretes containing steel punchings or barytes have been developed for reactor shielding.

The attenuation of gamma-rays is due to interactions between the gamma-rays and orbital electrons of atoms in the shield. The more electrons which can be put in the gamma-rays' path, the more rapidly will they be attenuated. This is achieved by the use of heavy elements such as lead or iron. In fact, the element responsible for inelastically scattering neutrons will also serve to attenuate gamma-rays. A detailed discussion of radiation shielding will be found in Ref. 5.

The absorption of radiation by the concrete shield produces heat within the shield which could cause high thermal stresses with resultant cracking of the concrete. In order to avoid this occurring, it is common practice to impose a so-called thermal shield between the pressure vessel and the biological shield. The thermal shield absorbs a large fraction of the slow neutrons and low energy gamma-rays which emerge from the reactor core, so preventing them from producing heat sources in the concrete shield.

Control of the neutron chain reaction in this reactor system is effected by rods of boron steel inserted into the reactor core. Part load operation may be achieved either by varying the mass flow of coolant, the coolant's temperature rise through the core or both. In order to minimize the deleterious effects of temperature variations on the fuel elements, the temperature rise is usually maintained constant and the mass flow varied.

The graphite moderated gas-cooled reactor has been adopted for electric power generation in the United Kingdom. The first generation of nuclear power stations is under construction, the design of their reactors being developed from those which exist at the Calder Hall power station. Data relating to these reactors is given in Table 1.3 whilst a cross-section through

TABLE 1.3. UNITED KINGDOM POWER REACTORS

	Calder Hall	Hunter-ston	Berkeley	Bradwell	Hinkley Point
Thermal output (MW)	182	535	550	530	980
Uranium loading (tonnes)	130	251	253	240	370
Specific power (MW tonne^{-1})	1·4	2·16	2·17	2·21	2·65
Core dimensions { Height (ft.)	21	23	24	26	25
Diameter (ft.)	31	44·5	42	40	49
Number of fuel channels	1695	3288	3275	2620	4500
Pressure vessel dimensions { Diameter (ft.)	37	70	50	67	67
Height (ft.)	70	(sphere)	80	(sphere)	(sphere)
Thickness (in.)	2	3	3	3	3
Coolant pressure (lb. in^{-2}) (gauge)	100	150	125	132	185
Coolant inlet temperature (°C)	141	204	160	180	179
Coolant outlet temperature (°C)	336	391	345	390	373

a reactor for the Hunterston power station, illustrating some of the features which have been discussed, is shown in Fig. 1.8.

The gas-cooled graphite moderated reactor employing natural uranium fuel and Magnox cans has been developed almost to its limit. For the combination of the phase change temperature in uranium metal and the

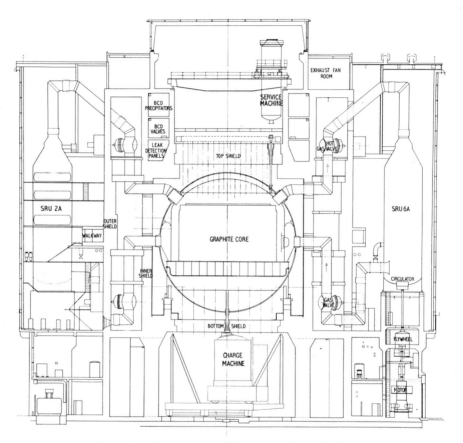

FIG. 1.8.   Cross-section of Hunterston Power Station.

relatively low temperature which Magnox can withstand causes the maximum attainable specific power and coolant temperature to be about 2·6 MW/tonne and 400° C, respectively (see Table 1.3). This results in the power generation from a reactor of a given size being limited, also the plant's thermal efficiency due to poor steam conditions. Any improvement in performance must result from overcoming the limiting fuel and can temperature. A reactor experiment having this as its object is the Advanced Gas-Cooled Reactor (A.G.R.)[6] being constructed for the United Kingdom Atomic Energy Authority. In this reactor it is proposed to use uranium dioxide sheathed in cans of beryllium or stainless steel. By using uranium dioxide the problem of the phase change temperature is eliminated, whilst beryllium or stainless steel can withstand much higher temperatures than Magnox. In this way it is expected to attain a specific power of 8·6 MW/tonne of uranium whilst the maximum coolant outlet temperature reached will be 575°C. The use of uranium dioxide has a further advantage in that it is less susceptible to neutron irradiation damage. Because of this it is expected to be able to irradiate the fuel elements to the extent of 10,000 MWD/tonne.

1.6. THE PRESSURIZED WATER REACTOR (P.W.R.)

This reactor uses light water to serve both as moderator and coolant. The water is maintained at a pressure of about 1500–2000 lb./in^2, the object of this being to prevent the water boiling and so make it possible to obtain the best possible steam conditions and plant efficiency. Because neutrons are slowed down from fission to thermal energies in a short distance in light water, a compact reactor core is obtained. Light water does, however, have the disadvantage that due to it having a relatively high neutron absorption cross-section, it is necessary to use enriched uranium fuel.

The fuel elements for this reactor are usually in the form of pellets of uranium dioxide clad in a zirconium alloy or stainless steel sheath. Uranium dioxide is chosen because of its compatibility with water and its resistance to irradiation damage.

The conditions under which the pressure vessel containing the reactor core has to operate are particularly arduous. For it has to withstand a high pressure as well as the corrosive action of water, which is extremely severe

TABLE 1.4. SHIPPINGPORT PRESSURIZED WATER REACTOR

Thermal output (MW)		231
Core dimensions	Height (ft.)	9
	Diameter (ft.)	8
Pressure vessel dimensions	Diameter (ft.)	10·5
	Height (ft.)	32·5
	Thickness (in.)	8·5
Coolant pressure (lb. in^{-2})		2000
Coolant inlet temperature (°C)		264
Coolant outlet temperature (°C)		281

when at high temperature and pressure. For this reason, the vessel is internally clad with a stainless steel lining.

The biological shield of a P.W.R. is usually provided by an iron–water shield.

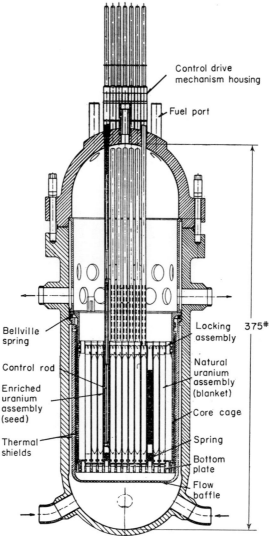

Fig. 1.9. Shipping port pressurized water reactor.

The P.W.R. has been largely developed in the U.S.A. for marine propulsion. It has, however, been adopted for that country's first nuclear power station at Shippingport in Pennsylvania. Features of the reactor for this power station are indicated in Table 1.4 and Fig. 1.9.

1.7. THE FAST REACTOR

In a thermal reactor, some neutrons are captured in $_{92}U^{238}$ causing the following nuclear reactions to proceed:

$$_{92}U^{238} + _0n^1 \rightarrow _{92}U^{239} + \gamma$$

$$_{92}U^{239} \rightarrow _{93}Np^{239} + _{-1}e^0$$

$$_{93}Np^{239} \rightarrow _{94}Pu^{239} + _{-1}e^0$$

The $_{94}Pu^{239}$ produced in this way is of vital importance since like $_{95}U^{235}$ it is capable of being fissioned by thermal neutrons and releasing neutrons. $_{94}Pu^{239}$ has so far been used principally for military purposes but it obviously has a possible use as a nuclear reactor fuel.

In a typical natural uranium thermal reactor, approximately 0.8 $_{94}Pu^{239}$ nuclei are produced for each $_{92}U^{235}$ nucleus destroyed. Now due to the change in the nuclear properties of uranium with neutron energy, at neutron energies of about 1–2 MeV, approximately 1.02 $_{94}Pu^{239}$ nuclei are produced per $_{92}U^{235}$ nucleus destroyed. Thus in a fast reactor employing enriched uranium it should be possible to produce more fissionable material than that which is consumed. If reactors working on this principle were to be built eventually all the available $_{92}U^{235}$ would be consumed. The reactors could then use the $_{94}Pu^{239}$ which had previously been produced together with the remaining supplies of $_{92}U^{238}$ and so simultaneously produce and consume $_{94}Pu^{239}$. Such a reactor is for obvious reasons called a fast power breeder reactor.

If the reactor is to be capable of breeding, it is essential that the neutron speed should be kept as high as possible. Hence all low mass number materials must be excluded from the core. Because of the absence of a moderator, a fast reactor core is very small compared to that of a thermal reactor. This calls for the use of a highly effective coolant. Liquid metal coolants such as sodium have to be employed because they are good heat transfer agents and yet satisfy the requirement of not being a good moderator. In order further to alleviate the heat transfer problem, the fuel must present a large surface area to the coolant. This is effected by using a large number of small diameter fuel rods. To illustrate these features, Fig. 1.10 shows the core of the fast reactor which has been built by the U.K.A.E.A. at Dounreay in North Scotland, the purpose of this being to test the concept of the fast power breeder reactor.

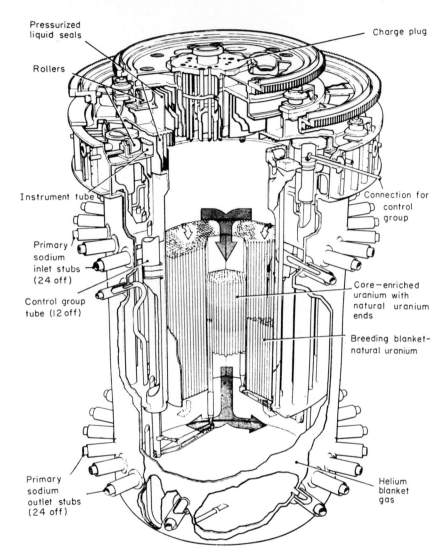

Pressurized
liquid seals

Charge plug

Rollers

Instrument tube

Connection for
control
group

Primary
sodium
inlet stubs
(24 off)

Core—enriched
uranium with
natural uranium
ends

Control group
tube (12 off)

Breeding blanket-
natural uranium

Primary
sodium
outlet stubs
(24 off)

Helium
blanket
gas

FIG. 1.10.   Dounreay fast reactor.

1.8.   NUCLEAR REACTOR SAFETY

In conclusion, a brief mention must be made of nuclear reactor safety, a
facet of reactor technology in which the structural engineer plays a major
part.

It has been seen that the process of nuclear fission results in the creation
of radioactive fission products. Due to their radioactivity these fission pro-

ducts are a severe health hazard. During normal reactor operation it is possible to ensure that the fission products are contained within the reactor. However, accident conditions may be envisaged which could lead to the release of most of the fission products to the atmosphere, so causing a major health hazard. It is one of the tasks of the reactor designer to assess whether particular accident conditions could occur or whether the likelihood of them occurring is extremely remote. Safety measures must then be incorporated in the reactor design to ensure that any credible accident does not lead to an unacceptably large release of fission products to the atmosphere. In the design of a new reactor system where there is no operational experience on which the designer may base his judgement, it may be necessary to safeguard against those accidents which appear to be only remotely possible.

All of the reactor systems which have been mentioned have two envelopes inherent in their design which serve to contain the fission products. The first of these envelopes is the fuel can whilst the second is the pressure vessel. For some reactor systems these are not sufficient to ensure safe operation under all conditions and it then becomes necessary to totally enclose the reactor and its pressure vessel within a containment vessel.

The accident which will be most likely to lead to the release of fission products is that in which the coolant flow fails due to rupture of the reactor pressure vessel. In this event the heating effect of the fission products may lead to melting of the fuel elements with the consequent release of fission products via the ruptured pressure vessel. The severity of this accident depends upon the reactor system. In the case of the graphite moderated gas-cooled reactor, although rupture of the pressure vessel would in itself be a catastrophe it would not lead to a major health hazard. For the graphite moderator has a large thermal capacity and so any coolant failure would result in a small temperature rise of the fuel which would not cause melting and the release of fission products. This situation does not exist in the case of the pressurized water reactor. The core does not have a large thermal capacity with the result that failure of the coolant flow would lead to melting of the fuel elements and the release of fission products. Because of this it is necessary to enclose a P.W.R. within a containment vessel. In some designs of P.W.R. it has been necessary to consider the effects of a violent nuclear energy release upon the containment vessel. Although the conditions required to attain this energy release are so abnormal as to be almost impossible, the designers have judged it to be necessary to design for such an accident. The effects of such a violent energy release are to produce shock waves and the possible detachment of components to produce high velocity missiles. The design of a containment vessel to withstand the effects of shock waves and missiles without rupturing is a difficult structural problem. This is due to the large degree of uncertainty in the magnitude of the loads produced by a violent energy release. Further, the plastic behaviour of structures under dynamic loads is a relatively unexplored field. For the interested reader, Ref. 7 illustrates the structural analysis of a particular containment problem whilst Ref. 8 illustrates a general approach to the structural aspects of the containment problem by the use of models.

REFERENCES

1. I. KAPLAN, *Nuclear Physics*. Addison-Wesley, Cambridge Mass. (1955).
2. S. GLASSTONE, *Principles of Nuclear Reactor Engineering*. Macmillan, London (1956).
3. W. B. HALL, *Reactor Heat Transfer*. Nuclear Engineering Monographs, Temple Press (1958).
4. *The Hazards to Man of Nuclear and Allied Radiations*. Cmd. 9780, H.M. Stationery Office, London (1956).
5. B. T. PRICE, C. C. HORTON, and K. T. SPINNEY, *Radiation Shielding*. Pergamon Press, London (1957).
6. Advanced gas cooled reactor at Windscale. *The Engineer* **209,** Nos. 5446 and 5447 (1960).
7. W. McGUIRE and G. P. FISHER, *Containment Studies of the Enrico Fermi Atomic Power Plant*. Symposium on Nuclear Reactor Containment Buildings and Pressure Vessels, Royal College of Science and Technology, Glasgow, May (1960).
8. W. E. BAKER, Scale model tests for evaluating outer containment structures for nuclear reactors. Paper 1028, *Second U.N. International Conference on the Peaceful Uses of Atomic Energy, Geneva, 1958*.

CHAPTER 2

MATERIALS IN NUCLEAR REACTOR CONSTRUCTION

G. H. BROOMFIELD

NOTATION

β^- = electron.

γ = gamma-ray.

δ = surface energy.

σ = stress.

σ_i = lattice friction stress (opposition to dislocation movement).

k_y = dislocation locking stress.

σ_y = yield stress (tension).

E = Young's modulus.

C = crack length.

DBTT = ductile–brittle transition temperature.

ϕ = integrated fast neutron dose in units of 10^{18} neutrons/cm^2.

nvt = integrated neutron dose, neutrons per cm^2 (n = neutrons per unit volume of incident beam, v = velocity, t = integrated time).

2.1. INTRODUCTION

ONE of the main concerns of an engineer considering materials for use in nuclear reactors is the damage that may be caused to the materials by nuclear radiations. Of these, neutrons damage materials in general; high energy fission products and alpha-particles damage fuels and, to a lesser extent, canning materials; beta- and gamma-rays heat metals but may damage the structure of inorganic compounds (thus affecting corrosion rates) and cause rapid deterioration of organic compounds, including polymers.

A great variety of materials, both non-metallic and metallic have been used in reactors, and to limit the scope of this chapter to reasonable proportions, it will be mainly confined to materials of major importance in natural uranium metal fuelled, gas-cooled, graphite moderated reactors.

Insufficient experimental results and theoretical derivations which are suitable for firm design data have been published to enable compilation of a useful reference work on the properties of materials under nuclear radiation.

The purpose of this chapter is to explain, in a simple manner, some of the currently acceptable mechanisms leading to changes in properties due to nuclear radiation, so that the value and portent of experimental data can be more readily appreciated by those unfamiliar with physical metallurgy.

The various points made have not been linked with particular items from the literature, but a list of references is appended, from which most of the information given was obtained, and in which will be found amplification of the theory of the various mechanisms of yield, fracture, creep, and also most of the data on irradiation damage which is available at present.

2.2. METALS IN PRESSURE VESSELS AND ASSOCIATED EQUIPMENT

Conventional metals are still used for the great proportion of reactor construction applications outside the core. The possible mechanisms and effects of neutron irradiation damage to these metals will be considered first.

Outside the core the effect of neutrons only need be considered. The increase in temperature due to electron and gamma-irradiation is relatively small and can be allowed for. High energy fission products and alpha-particles originating in the fuel do not penetrate fuel cans, nor do alpha-particles produced by neutron reactions with control rod materials leave the control rod cans.

Neutrons have two distinct effects; thermal neutrons may be captured, and cause transmutation, whilst fast neutrons damage metals by altering the basic atomic lattice structure. The first effect, that of transmutation, is important when elements of high thermal neutron capture cross-section are present, and when the elements resulting from transmutation are deleterious.

Cobalt has a capture cross-section of 37 barns and the reaction resulting from capture is

$$Co^{59} + n \rightarrow Co^{60} \xrightarrow{\beta^- + \gamma} Ni^{60}$$

The half life of Co^{60} is 5·2 years and the energy of the gamma-emissions is high, hence the principal disadvantage of cobalt in a steel is the high level of radioactivity that would result from its presence, although property changes may be important if it was originally an essential alloying element (e.g. in a cobalt bonded tungsten carbide).

The common alloying element with the next highest cross-section is manganese with 13·3 barns. The following reaction results from neutron capture:

$$Mn^{55} + n \rightarrow Mn^{56} \xrightarrow{\beta^- + \gamma} Fe^{56}$$

The half life of Mn^{56} is 2·58 hr and the cross-section of Fe^{56} is only 2·6 barns. After irradiation to a total dose of 5×10^{22} *nvt* thermal neutrons

0·7 per cent of the manganese present would be transmuted to iron. This change is negligible for most purposes and other transmutation effects are of no greater consequence.

Amongst welding steels, the molybdenum–boron types have become important, but they are not normally used for reactor construction. One of the reasons for this is that an isotope of natural boron has a cross-section of 4020 barns, and the reaction resulting from capture is

$$B^{10} + n \rightarrow Li^7 + He^4 + 2\cdot8 \, MeV$$

Natural boron contains only 18·8 per cent B^{10} and the loss of boron resulting from the reaction is unlikely to be important, but the evolution of trace amounts of low melting lithium together with the effects of the high energy alpha-particles may conceivably be deleterious.

In general, thermal neutron capture is of small importance in structural materials outside the core, except for the fact that it is neutron capture followed by radioactive decay which makes the materials inside the biological shield radioactive.

Thermal reactor cores are, of course, surrounded by a reflector consisting of a layer of moderating material, and, since all neutrons leaving the core pass through this layer, the large proportion of neutrons reaching structural members are thermal neutrons. There are, however, sufficient fast neutrons in the flux for the accumulated dose in a reactor pressure shell to be of significance.

Fast neutrons are generally considered to be those with energies in the range 0·5 to 2 MeV. Unlike other particulate irradiations they have no charge and hence affect atoms only by direct collision with the nucleus. Atomic nuclei are much smaller in terms of collision probabilities than total atomic radii; atom spacings in a metal are about 3×10^{-8} cm from centre to centre, whilst nucleus radii are, for this purpose, about 10^{-12} cm, and in most materials a neutron will pass through 10^8 or 10^9 atoms before colliding with a nucleus. The fast neutron dose received by a reactor pressure vessel in twenty years would probably be about $10^{18} nvt$, enough to collide with one atom in half a million.

Neutrons are much lighter than metal atoms and they only give up a small proportion of their energy at each collision, about 10^5 eV maximum in steels. This is, however, much greater than the level of about 25 eV required to move an atom from its lattice site, and a struck atom is accelerated at speed, away from its electron cloud, and becomes a high energy charged particle which interacts strongly with atoms in its path, dislodging them or raising their energy levels to high values. The result is a spike-shaped volume of a few hundred atoms which are raised to high energy levels and dislodged from their original lattice sites. Many of the displaced atoms, which find themselves in interstitial positions, are assumed to fall back quickly into vacant sites, but each high energy collision produces a shell of interstitials around a region containing vacancies. If the temperature of irradiation is high enough, residual point defects (i.e. interstitials and vacancies) may anneal out by migrating to positions such as surfaces or grain boundaries where they can be accommodated or moving until an interstitial meets a vacancy. In this way irradiation damage may be annealed out as fast as it occurs. It can also be annealed out by heating after irradiation.

Property changes due to the introduction of point defects may appear to be beneficial in some ways, however, the benefits are rarely of practical value whilst deleterious effects are of first importance. The following are brief descriptions of the effects on specific properties.

(i) *Tensile Properties*

First let us consider some of the factors governing deformation of metals. Two main criteria are said to govern yield and deformation in metals at ordinary temperatures, one the stress required for initial operation of dislocation sources, the other the stress required to overcome lattice frictional resistance to dislocation movement. These were linked for the case of body centred cubic metals (including alpha-iron) by Petch in this way;

$$\sigma_y = \sigma_i + k_y d^{-\frac{1}{2}}$$

(σ_y = yield stress, σ_i = lattice friction stress, k_y = dislocation locking stress, d = grain diameter.) Their significance in deformation is indicated

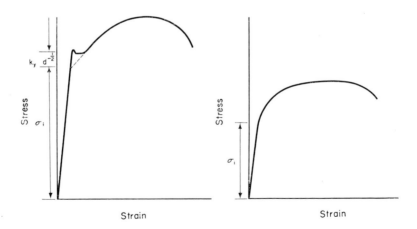

Fig. 2.1. (a) A nominal stress–strain curve for a mild steel, showing the significance of σ_i and k_y. (b) A nominal stress–strain curve for annealed iron in which k_y = zero.

in Fig. 2.1. Their relationship with grain diameter is obtained from the type of plot shown in Fig. 2.2.

Alloying metal atoms or defects dispersed through the lattice reduce its perfection, and this increases σ_i. Any effect which reduces the symmetry of a dislocation, or reduces its energy, tends to lock it in position, thus solute atoms, such as carbon or nitrogen which concentrate at dislocations, or vacancies which may make them serrated, tend to increase k_y.

The presence of point defects, due to irradiation, in a pure metal increases the frictional resistance to dislocation movement in a similar manner to atoms of alloying elements; also migration of point defects to dislocations has been shown to increase the stress required for initial dislocation movement in copper, until after a sufficient irradiation dose, it exceeds that

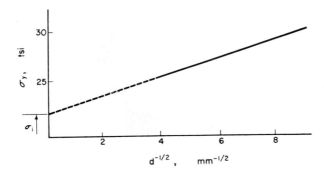

FIG. 2.2. The effect of grain size on σ_y. The slope $= k_y$.

required for continued movement. A form of dislocation locking is introduced similar to that brought about by carbon and nitrogen in mild steels. Other effects revealed by the tensile test are a reduction of work hardening rate after yield and a reduction of ductility.

Face centred cubic metals such as annealed copper and annealed stainless steel have indeterminate yield points (as distinct from proof stresses), because some dislocation movement occurs at low stresses. Irradiation introduced defects appear to prevent easy dislocation movement, until the yield point is increased several times, and finally a yield drop occurs, as shown in Fig. 2.3.

In mild steel, which normally shows a yield drop due to initial dislocation locking, the lattice friction effect is increased, until the difference between the stress to unlock dislocations, and the stress to cause subsequent slip, is small. The nominal stress strain curve changes with increased radiation dose as shown in Fig. 2.4.

Yield strengths increase as the cube root of the fast neutron dose up to dose levels of about 5×10^{18} neutrons per cm^2.

The level of hardening introduced by irradiation is lower than that which may be achieved by such methods as quenching and tempering of steel, or by cold working copper or bronze. One reason for this is that the intensity

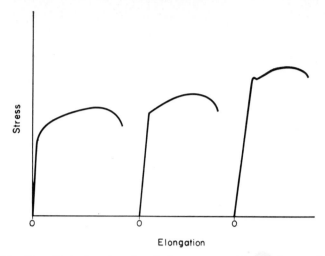

Fig. 2.3. The effect of neutron irradiation on austenitic stainless steel tensile properties. (a) Annealed. (b) Irradiated to 10^{19} neutrons/cm^2. (c) Irradiated to 10^{20} neutrons/cm^2.

of defect concentration is limited by annealing effects as vacancies and interstitials annihilate each other, and also by effects occurring as collision spikes overlap; it is interesting that irradiation of hard drawn wire has been shown to reduce its hardness.

Fig. 2.4. The effect of neutron irradiation on mild steel tensile properties. (a) Normalized. (b) Irradiated 10^{18} neutrons/cm^2 (fast neutrons). (c) Irradiated 10^{20} neutrons/cm^2 (fast neutrons).

Table 2.1 gives some results of tensile testing of metals before and after irradiation.

TABLE 2.1. THE EFFECT OF IRRADIATION ON TENSILE TEST RESULTS

Metal	Condition	Irr. dose (fast neutrons/ cm^2)	Yield stress (1000 lb/in^2)		U.T.S. (1000 lb/in^2)		Elongation (%)	
			Unirr.	Irr.	Unirr.	Irr.	Unirr.	Irr.
Carbon steel	Normalized	10^{19}	51	65·4	75	81·8	23	18
Carbon steel	Normalized	10^{20}	51	92	75	100	23	5
Austenitic stainless steel	Annealed	8×10^{19}	24	75	86	104	63	58
Copper	Annealed	5×10^{19}	8	30	27	34	42	28

(ii) *Notch Ductility*

The property of notch ductility may be defined as the ability of a metal to behave in a ductile manner under triaxial stress conditions, that is, under the stress conditions usually imposed at the base of a notch. It is not possible to impose and measure varying triaxial stresses in a convenient way, but a measure of notch ductility is obtained from tests such as the Charpy and Izod. Failure to behave in a notch ductile manner is to be considered under this heading, together with the principal modes of fracture, ductile and cleavage.

Deformation in a ductile material in tension proceeds by shear, under the influence of resolved shear stress. A very ductile metal will deform continuously until it necks to zero area (e.g. pure aluminium at high temperature). A less ductile material not under constraint will develop microscopic cracks as deformation proceeds, and these will link up to form a fracture in a shear plane (e.g. soft thin sheet). A similar material in the form of a round tensile test piece will have imposed upon it a triaxial stress system, in the middle of the necked region (due to the constraint on contraction by the outer material of the test piece) and in this region microscopic cracks formed in shear will link up with others in a plane normal to the stress axis; a microscopic crack is formed which grows outward until a region is reached in which shear movement is easy, and fracture then changes to a link-up of voids in 45° shear planes, producing the characteristic tensile test cup and cone.

In addition to a tendency to slip, some metals have a tendency to cleavage—a peeling apart of lattice planes with little or no plastic deformation—under stress normal to the plane in which it occurs. Metals which have shown cleavage failure are the body centre cubic, which include iron, chromium, tungsten and molybdenum; and some hexagonal types such as zinc. It is convenient to consider it as something which happens under rising stress, if slip does not occur first.

In steels at normal temperature the stress to initiate cleavage is higher than that for slip, so that fracture tests first produce a ductile crack.

A time element has been introduced here: the metal may cleave if slip does not occur first. The real importance of this lies in the fact that if sufficient shear stress is applied to a suitable lattice plane to overcome σ_i, the lattice friction and k_y the dislocation locking, dislocations start to move after a short but finite time, but if the stress increases to that required for cleavage during this time then a cleavage crack may result. This is a possibility when a strongly triaxial stress system reduces the resolved shear stress.

However, most brittle fractures start in a ductile manner. If a ductile crack has started, any triaxial stress system will be accentuated and a minimum (shear stress)/(direct stress) ratio will develop just beyond the crack tip. We may consider that a grain at the tip of the crack is able to deform, and by the mechanism of dislocation pile-up at the far boundary, exert a stress in the next grain. The rate of stress rise in this next grain will depend, amongst other things, on the rate at which the dislocations can be brought up to the boundary, which in turn is proportional to the number of dislocations in the deforming grain, that is to its size.

The shear stress in the grain just beyond the tip of the crack is reduced by triaxiallity and there is therefore a greater probability of the cleavage stress being reached before dislocations operate.

A further point is that the stress and time required to start dislocation movement are inversely proportional to temperature, whilst cleavage strength is only slightly increased as temperature falls.

Finally, if a cleavage crack does occur in this next grain, it will probably extend across the grain, and if the reduced Griffith–Orowan relation

$$\sigma = \sqrt{\left(\frac{E\delta A}{C}\right)}$$

(σ = stress, E = Young's modulus, δ = surface energy, C = crack length, A = a constant, approximately equal to 1000) is satisfied it will propagate.

Possibly due to the fact that cleavage in material near grain boundaries is more difficult, and also that cleavage cracks go through small angles in travelling from grain to grain (there may even be some shear at grain boundaries), continued propagation is less likely in fine-grained material than in coarse-grained; a lower temperature or more severe triaxiallity is needed.

The above discussion goes some way towards an explanation for the following observations:

(1) As temperature falls the fracture mode for a given steel fractured under a given set of conditions goes through a transition from ductile to brittle, as shown in Fig. 2.5(a) and (b).

(2) As the rate of load application is increased, the ductile–brittle transition temperature (DBTT) is increased (Fig. 2.5(c)).

(3) The DBTT increases with grain size.

(4) Increasing stress triaxiallity results in a decreasing DBTT. This gives rise to the size effect, and to the notch effect.

(5) Tensile tests show that neutron irradiation increases the shear stress required to initiate dislocation movement, and as might be expected an increased tendency to brittle fracture is observed, as shown in Fig. 2.6.

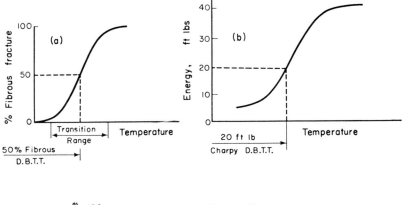

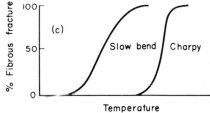

FIG. 2.5. Plots of the ductile–brittle transition, showing: (a) Determination of transition by fracture appearance. (b) By energy absorbed in Charpy tests. (c) The effect of rate of loading on the value obtained for the transition.

In this context, it is necessary to point out that although cleavage fracture of face centre cubic metals is virtually unknown, the fracture mode of such metals does change with triaxiallity of the stress system and with temperature. Plates which break in tension with a 45° angle shear fracture at one temperature may break with a fracture normal to the stress direction at a lower temperature, and the change in fracture mode results in a small reduction in the energy absorbed. This change may also be brought about by the increase in yield stress obtained by irradiation, or alternatively the temperature at which the change occurs is increased. This change in fracture mode has, perhaps unfortunately, been called a ductile–brittle transition and DBTT changes due to irradiation are quoted for some metals such as copper, nickel, aluminium alloys, and stainless steel. It should be appreciated that a change in fracture mode resulting in a large reduction of energy absorption in these metals is virtually unknown, and the possibility of sudden brittle failure of structures made with them is absent, *except*, of course, for those cases where failure occurs due to overstressing in steady or fatigue loading, or when components are made in such a way that they have very high residual stresses coupled with low ductility, or lastly in metals in which the possibility of inter-granular fracture exists due to incorrect manufacture or heat treatment.

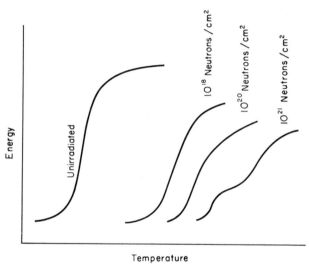

Fig. 2.6. The way in which the ductile–brittle transition is influenced by irradiation.

Now, to consider the effect of the ductile–brittle transition in design and manufacturing procedure for large pressure vessels.

In small pieces, stresses can often be readily calculated or measured, and notches can be eliminated in design and manufacture, but in large complex structures it is sometimes impossible to be sure that plastic deformation will not occur under design loads, and it is also impossible to ensure the removal of all notches produced in manufacture; that is such notches as are due to weld defects, plate edge cracks and so on. In addition the constraints on contraction normal to applied stresses in large structures lead to a consider-able degree of stress triaxiallity. Thus whilst cleavage crack initiation may be the factor limiting the failure of a small piece in a brittle manner, initiation of small cracks in a large structure is much more probable and brittle fracture propagation becomes the limiting factor.

Three conditions are necessary for brittle failure of a large structure:

(i) Brittle crack initiation in some notch, or other triaxially stressed region.
(ii) A temperature below the ductile–brittle transition of the material of the structure, under the stress system imposed.
(iii) An elastic energy storage in the structure high enough to maintain a stress level sufficient for crack propagation.

For safety it is desirable to avoid all three of these conditions as far as possible.

Although the first is not likely to be completely avoided, the possibility of crack initiation may be reduced by care in inspection for such items as large inclusions, cracks in plates and welds and other notches, by good design, and by measures avoiding stresses in excess of design stress. One of the most important factors in avoiding unexpectedly high stresses is adequate stress relief heat treatment after assembly by welding.

To avoid the second condition it is necessary to know that the material to be used has a sufficiently low ductile–brittle transition temperature.

As we have seen the DBTT is not a unique property of a metal, but it varies with the stress system and rate of application of load. Different results are also obtained for crack initiation and crack propagation. The Charpy test is essentially for brittle fracture initiation, whilst the problem here is one of crack propagation. The test which correlates best with known service failure data is the Robertson crack arrest test, but this involves the use of a very large sample, and is not a practical proposition for routine inspection. Charpy testing is therefore used and a correction made, to allow for observed difference in results of Charpy and Robertson tests. An addition to the 20 ft.lb. Charpy temperature of as much as 30°C may be desirable for thick plate. Some authorities have also recommended a correction of $+20°C$ for ageing effects which may occur during long service lives.

Neutron irradiation, as we have seen, increases the DBTT. Many of the experimental results obtained fit the relation

$$\Delta T = K\phi^{1/3}$$

in which ΔT = increase in DBTT, K = a constant, and ϕ = the fast neutron dose (as measured by nickel or sulphur monitoring) in units of 10^{18} neutrons per cm². There is evidence of wide departure from this, but not at the doses which a pressure vessel can be expected to receive.

A value of K given for coarse grained material is 30, and if it were assumed that this would allow for all irradiation effects in the vessel, the overall correction figure to be applied to the Charpy determined DBTT would be 85°C, for a sulphur dose of 5×10^{18} *nvt*. Since the Charpy determined DBTT for silicon killed steel is often about 0°C and, as we shall see, such steel may be used for a reactor shell because of the creep properties required, the temperature range in which brittle fracture is possible is up to 85°C. The inference of this is that after irradiation it is not permissible to reduce such a reactor shell to ambient temperature, at least whilst it is so stressed that condition (iii) is fulfilled.

This limitation has been accepted in principle, but because irradiation damage in steel anneals out continuously, at a rate which increases at higher temperature, the effect of a neutron dose of 5×10^{18} *nvt* (fast neutrons) received over a period of twenty years, by steel at 100°C and above, may be much less than that due to such a dose received in a few weeks in a research reactor. Both the United Kingdom Atomic Energy Authority's and the Central Electricity Generating Board's reactors are provided with test specimens which will be withdrawn at intervals to show the effect of a slowly accumulated dose, and these may well show that present estimates are pessimistic.

Condition (iii) is necessary for failure because a brittle crack can only propagate quickly, at about the speed of sound. In general only elastic energy stored in a structure can supply energy for crack propagation at a sufficient rate to maintain the necessary stress level. As the size of a pressure vessel increases the stress at which sufficient energy can be stored decreases, until in large vessels it appears that a stress barely above that required to propagate a brittle fracture will result in enough energy storage for the propagation stress to be maintained, in the face of stress relaxation due to passage of the crack. If condition (iii) is to be avoided in a large structure, the brittle fracture propagation stress becomes a limiting stress and this is about 10,000 lb./in². If normal safety factors are applied a very low design stress is obtained. Once again the necessity for stress relieving heat treatment is emphasized.

Lack of notch ductility together with poor design and fabrication practice has been responsible for a number of catastrophic brittle failures of large structures in ferritic steel. It is of first importance that such brittle failure of reactor components is avoided. Consequently, although it might be argued that some of the measures outlined above are very restricting, an even more pessimistic approach is justified if further doubts arise and information from truly representative experiment is not available.

(iii) *Creep Properties*

The form of a typical creep curve (Fig. 2.7), in which extension is plotted against time for a single stress at constant temperature, is well known.

A simple explanation of the processes of creep may be made if the curve is divided into three stages. The first stage shows a rate of extension which reduces with time; a phenomenon similar to work hardening occurs: dislocations are generated in slip planes, and move up to obstructions, such as grain boundaries, where they pile up until their density at the ends of the slip planes is such that they prevent generation of further dislocations. The significant difference between deformation in this stage of creep and that occurring in an ordinary tensile test is that dislocation movement occurs, under the influence of heat, at stresses below that required at room temperature and, if a steady second stage is to follow, at stresses below that required to overcome the influence of barriers such as grain boundaries, or small particles within the grains.

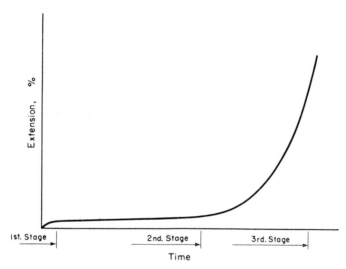

FIG. 2.7. A typical creep curve.

The second stage is usually believed to be controlled, not by dislocation generation and movement, but by vacancy migration. Vacancies present in the metal are able to diffuse, under the influence of increased temperature, at increased rates, and a favoured direction for diffusion is obviously toward possible vacancy sinks. The effect of vacancies on an edge dislocation is to allow the edge to climb as shown in Fig. 2.8.

When a dislocation has climbed out of a slip plane the pressure of dislocations (or lattice strain due to their presence) is relieved, and another one can be generated by the applied stress. A succession of such dislocation climbs and moves results in void formation at the end of the slip plane, and a micro-section of a material which has passed some way through the second stage shows voids along grain boundaries which are approximately normal to the direction of the applied stress. Grain boundary sites for voids are to be expected since the rate of vacancy diffusion along boundaries is several times that in the grains.

The third stage commences when the voids represent a sufficient cross-section area to cause an increase in stress such that the influence of grain boundary barriers is overcome, and strain occurs at an increasing rate, due to increase in the rate of void formation.

If this theory of creep is accepted, it can be appreciated that a structure with a few grain boundary barriers will have few sites for void formation, whilst a fine grain structure will deteriorate more rapidly due to a faster reduction in effective cross-section area, since the number of sites for void formation is increased. On the other hand a higher stress causes faster creep

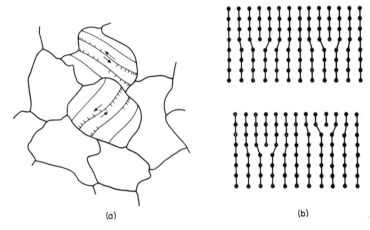

(a)   (b)

FIG. 2.8. Diagrammatic representations of dislocation movements: (a) Dislocations piled up at the ends of slip planes. (b) Dislocation climb, the depth of the " half plane " is reduced by vacancies.

mainly because of increased void formation, and the extension before fracture due to linking of many small voids is greater than when fracture is due to linking of a few large voids; creep ductility in accelerated tests is often higher than that observed in longer tests.

The curve shown in Fig. 2.7 is typical of many creep test results, and Fig. 2.9(a) shows the sort of results obtained by increasing the test temperature. Similar types of curve are obtained when the temperature is constant and the stress increased. An important feature of these curves is that they show good creep ductility, and if a member of a complex structure had such creep properties it could be expected to extend and relieve some of the imposed stress, if unwittingly overstressed. Some alloys, however, have creep curves of the type shown in Fig. 2.9(b), they have low creep ductility, and will accommodate only small deformations before failure. Stress rupture tests are often used to obtain information on creep ductility, but in general, only creep tests of full life duration can provide precise information.

When considering equipment designed for a life of twenty years most creep data available comes into the category of that derived from short-term tests, often creep tests do not extend much beyond a year. Fortunately there is a fairly reliable basis for extrapolation, in that log-log plots of both stress *v.*

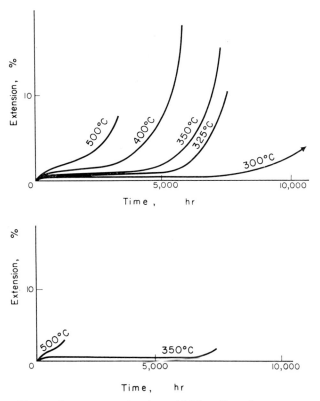

FIG. 2.9. Types of creep curve showing: (a) The effect of temperature on one material. (b) A material with poor creep ductility.

creep rate and stress *v.* time to a given extension give reasonably straight lines.

Neutron irradiation may be expected to increase the stress required to move dislocations, unless the temperature is such that continuous and complete annealing occurs. An increase in vacancy concentration is also to be expected although this will be small in comparison with normal vacancy concentrations at temperatures at which creep occurs.

From these two considerations a slight decrease or a slight increase in creep may be expected, and both have been reported, from results of relatively short-term tests.

The long-term effects of irradiation on creep cannot be precisely defined since there may be tendency to stress relaxation in the region of collision spikes, whilst other mechanisms may decrease or increase creep ductility. The use of extrapolation cannot, therefore, be considered as a firm basis for guaranteed performance, and, where actual full life data is absent, important structures must obviously be continuously monitored.

(iv) *Fatigue*

In common with much of the work on strength, most fatigue work on irradiated material has been done out-of-pile. Results have shown slight effects due to irradiation, with a tendency to a reduction of fatigue strength. It is not easy to predict the effect that long-term neutron irradiation may have on fatigue. Perhaps the best approach to the problem is that adopted in respect of other unpredictable fatigue effects, that is inspection at frequent intervals such that if a significant crack starts it will not progress to failure before detection.

2.3. REACTOR CORE MATERIALS

Non-conventional metals are found in the core, together with graphite. Some of the effects of irradiation on these materials are described below.

Power production reactors at present being built in Britain are designed to use rods of metallic natural uranium fuel, so that the changes that occur in the metal during burn-up are of first importance.

Burn-up effects are two-fold; the introduction of new atoms in the metal, and structural damage due to high energy fission products and neutrons. To these must be added the effects of temperature cycling.

It is convenient to consider temperature cycling first. Alpha-uranium has a marked anisotropy of thermal expansion, a single crystal contracts in one direction and expands in the other two on heating. Consequently in the normal polycrystalline material, thermal expansion in a grain may be opposed by contraction in one adjacent and local plastic deformation will occur. Cooling results in a tendency to reverse the stresses, but the material which has suffered plastic deformation on heating will perhaps be slightly work hardened, and deformation will occur in another region.

Repeated cycles of heating and cooling produce remarkable effects, a bar with preferred grain orientation will increase in length by 100 per cent after a sufficient number of cycles. A bar with a coarse grain structure shows surface wrinkling, and a fine randomly oriented structure is necessary if only surface slight roughening is to occur. This can be achieved, as indicated in Fig. 2.10, by a suitable casting technique.

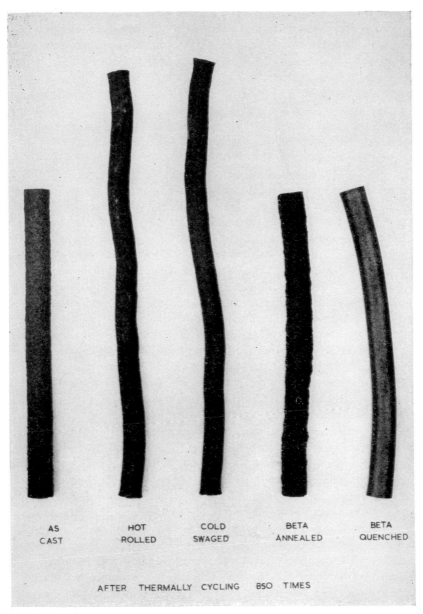

AS
CAST

HOT
ROLLED

COLD
SWAGED

BETA
ANNEALED

BETA
QUENCHED

AFTER THERMALLY CYCLING 850 TIMES

FIG. 2.10. The influence of production method and heat treatment on the response of uranium to thermal cycling.

One of the most important effects of irradiation on the properties of uranium is the effect on creep. The scale of irradiation damage in uranium fuel is immense, when compared with that in the pressure shell. Whilst one in a few hundred atoms of the steel of a pressure shell may be moved from its position in the course of its life, the effect of neutrons and high energy fission products in uranium fuel is to move each atom thousands of times in the life of the element. Any hardening effect of this is in practice masked by a combination of effects due to fast fission products and the anisotropic properties of alpha-uranium (e.g. thermal expansion coefficients: in the a crystallographic direction $= +36 \cdot 7 \times 10^{-6}$, in the b direction $= -9 \cdot 3 \times 10^{-6}$, in the c direction $+34 \cdot 2 \times 10^{-6}$ per °C).

The energy of fast fission products is measured in hundreds of MeV, but because they are ions and react strongly with atoms through whose electron clouds they pass, they rapidly lose their energy, which reappears as heat. Thus the energy of fission of a uranium atom is dissipated in a small volume of the metal, producing a " thermal spike ". Anisotropic expansion of the metal in the thermal spike gives rise to forces which promote a re-arrangement of atoms in such a way that the number of lattice planes in the b direction is increased at the expense of those in the a direction. It is considered that the presence of dislocations prevents the reaction reversing on cooling. After a certain irradiation dose, grains of a randomly oriented structure are all under an elastic stress close in magnitude to the yield due to the net growth in the b direction. A very low load on the whole will then induce a small degree of plastic strain, which will continue as thermal spikes recreate the stress system which first made the strain possible. This is the characteristic irradiation creep of uranium, which depends not only on the stress but also on the fission rate, and which is countered by bracing fuel elements to prevent bowing.

A further effect of fission thermal spikes in uranium is irradiation growth. This growth is analogous to that occurring on thermal cycling and depends on preferred orientation to a marked degree. Uranium bars with a fine random grain structure change in length by amounts varying from $-0 \cdot 3$ per cent to $+1$ per cent in long burn-up periods at temperatures below 350°C. It is probable that improved methods of manufacture will reduce the changes occurring, but the use of bars with a deliberately induced preferred orientation has helped to define the temperature range in which growth occurs.

Finally, as has been described in Chapter 1, uranium fuel becomes impregnated with gaseous fission products, and swelling occurs. Fissioned uranium atoms produce approximately twice their number of daughter atoms, hence some growth is bound to accompany burn-up, and if all daughter atoms remained in the uranium lattice about $0 \cdot 5$ per cent volume increase would occur for a burn-up of 3000 MWD/tonne. However, a large proportion of fission products are the inert gases xenon and krypton, which diffuse to lattice defects. The defects become enlarged to form minute bubbles, in which a high pressure is contained by metal surface tension. The small bubbles cause a volume increase of about 5 per cent in high burn-up elements. The volume of gas produced in a burn-up of 3000 MWD/tonne is approximately $2 cm^3$ per cm^3 uranium, and the pressure exerted in larger bubbles, at temperatures higher than 550°C can lead to " break-away " swelling in which surface tension forces are overcome and expansion is limited only by the creep strength of the metal.

The changes in natural uranium occurring under irradiation cause difficulties in reactor design and operation, and some method of reducing these has been sought from the outset. A remedy, which produces a marked improvement, is the addition of 10 to 14 per cent molybdenum, but this results in reduced fissile material if natural uranium is used, together with increased neutron capture. In other words enrichment of the fissile proportion of uranium would be necessary to achieve suitable reactivity, and this is not economically feasible in the U.K. at present.

A measure of success has been achieved with small additions of other elements, making it possible to ensure can integrity.

2.4. CANNING MATERIALS

Unalloyed uranium is not suitable for exposure to CO_2 coolant for long periods, because of its poor corrosion resistance. Further to this, radioactive fission products emitted from nuclear fuel would, if allowed to enter the coolant, cause severe difficulties in the way of contamination of ducting, heat exchangers, and pumps. Fuel rods are therefore canned in materials which will retain fission products and prevent corrosion, and which will not capture neutrons.

Magnox

A canning material used at present in the graphite moderated CO_2 cooled reactors is a magnesium alloy known as Magnox A12, which contains 0·5 to 1·0 per cent aluminium and 0·002 to 0·005 per cent beryllium. Magnesium unalloyed will burn in an atmosphere of CO_2, but one of the effects of the alloying elements is to make the metal non-combustible in air, even when molten. This apparent reduction of chemical activity is due to a coherent oxide film formed by the aluminium and beryllium, which serves to give the alloy good corrosion resistance in CO_2 coolant at maximum fuel element surface temperatures.

A further requirement of the canning material is that it should not combine or readily alloy with uranium. This requirement is met by magnesium, even above its melting point.

Since the range of temperature of operation of the fuel elements is wide and fuel element swelling has to be accommodated without can rupture, the creep properties of Magnox are of first importance. Table 2.2 shows some results which were published in 1958.

TABLE 2.2.   CREEP PROPERTIES OF HEAT TREATED MAGNOX A 12
(heated 4 hr. at 500°C)

Temp. (°C)	Stress (tons/in²)	Time to attain % creep strain: hr.								Test dura-tion (hr.)	% Strain at fracture
		0·1	0·2	0·5	1	2	5	10	20		
200	1·25	1	4	280	540	—	—	—	—	1170	1·65
200	1·5	—	—	20	73	256	770	—	—	775	6·0
200	1·75	—	1	3	14	29	145	286	—	286	10·0
400	0·1	11	20	62	133	252	539	880	—	1150	14·0
400	0·16	1	4	9	16	28	57	105	171	250	56·0
400	0·022	140	464	—	—	—	—	—	—	1110	0·29

It is readily apparent that the creep ductility at 200°C is generally less than at 400°C, but nevertheless at 400°C under certain conditions the creep ductility may still be low for practical purposes. Since the degree to which the can material needs to deform before rupture is largely controlled by fuel rod swelling, and this is small at 200°C but large at 400°C, an alloy with the performance shown in the table can usually accommodate the changes. There are, however, some failures of fuel cans and twelve out of the first 70,000 elements used in the Calder reactors showed defects which were probably due to void formation in third stage creep after a relatively high burn-up. Magnox grain size is of major importance, since a fine-grain material shows a greater creep ductility.

Canning materials which have been used or proposed for other fuel elements are aluminium alloys, stainless steel, zirconium alloys and graphite. Each will be briefly discussed.

Aluminium Alloys

These alloys have been used in water cooled and boiling water reactors. The necessary corrosion and creep resistance is provided by aluminium–nickel–iron, and aluminium–silicon–iron alloys. These are alloys with a strongly cathodic second phase. Their thermal neutron capture cross-section is higher than magnesium alloys.

Stainless Steel

This material has probably been used for a wider range of reactor types than any other; these reactor types include water cooled, boiling water, gas cooled and sodium cooled fast types. One of the most interesting projected uses is in the advanced gas cooled reactor, where cans with a wall thickness of less than 0·020 in. will be used to contain UO_2. Thin cans are necessary to reduce the mass of neutron capturing material in the reactor core. Their production and use introduces interesting problems in steel cleanliness and integrity, and in the nature of can inner wall damage due to fast fission products and knocked-on uranium atoms. The best composition for corrosion resistance, welding properties, and resistance to deterioration under temperature and irradiation conditions is a further problem.

Zirconium

This metal has good physical properties at temperatures up to 450°C, and also has a low neutron capture cross-section when freed from hafnium. It is highly reactive chemically, forming strong hydrides, nitrides and oxides, the latter forming coherent impervious films under suitable conditions. Corrosion resistance of the metal in high pressure high temperature water depends on the integrity of the oxide film and this varies depending on the original nitrogen and hydrogen content, and the manner in which hydrogen, formed in the corrosion process, enters the metal. A fine dispersion of hydride coincides with good corrosion resistance, whilst grain boundary hydride concentration is associated with poor corrosion resistance. Very pure zirconium has excellent corrosion resistance, and the principal function of alloying additions is to render harmless the impurities normally found in commercial material. " Zircaloys ", the most widely used alloys contain up to 1·5 per cent Sn with smaller amounts of Fe, Cr and Ni, whilst the Russian " Ozhennites " contain up to 1·5 per cent total of similar alloying elements, with the addition of niobium.

2.5. GRAPHITE

Many materials have been used as moderators, but most important in power producing reactors is graphite. Whilst its neutron moderating properties may not be as good as heavy water, for instance, the fact that it can be used as a material for supporting a lattice of fuel elements at high temperature enhances its value.

It is similar to metals in that only neutrons affect its structure. (Although gamma-radiation affects its rate of reaction with carbon monoxide.) Its purpose is, of course, to reduce the energy of fission neutrons to thermal energy, that is, to reduce neutron energies from 2 MeV to about 0·025 eV. In the process graphite atoms are knocked from their lattice positions and become lodged in interstitial spaces, usually between the hexagonal planes shown in Fig. 2.11.

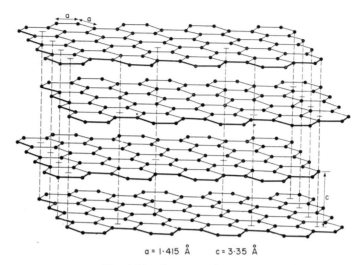

$a = 1.415 \ \text{Å} \qquad c = 3.35 \ \text{Å}$

FIG. 2.11.   Structure of graphite.

The presence of atoms between the planes distorts the lattice and the c dimension increases. The a dimension is decreased at high doses. The first observed effect of irradiation is an increase in volume, due to crystal growth in the c direction, so that graphite produced by extrusion and having preferred orientation grows in the direction normal to the extrusion direction.

At temperatures in excess of 300°C radiation growth may be exceeded by another effect which appears to be a reduction of crystallite size, accompanied by increased efficiency of packing—pore radii decrease. The net result is a general contraction of the mass.

Thus a graphite moderator assembly must be so designed that initial graphite expansion, and possibly later contraction, is allowed for.

The amount of irradiation damage which accumulates, in the form of interstitial atoms, depends on the temperature. At temperatures in excess of 150°C atom mobility is sufficient for many of the interstitials to find their way back to normal lattice sites as fast as they are produced; a relatively small concentration of displaced atoms accumulates. At lower temperatures, concentrations of interstitials can be higher, and at 30°C interstitial atoms present after a saturation dose represent stored energy of over 600 cal.g. This energy, known as Wigner energy, can be released on heating to about 150°C, and under adiabatic conditions a large temperature rise will take place. Wigner energy in reactors which operate at low temperature is an embarrassment, and very careful heating to allow release is necessary, at intervals which are sufficiently close to prevent danger of uncontrolled release starting at reactor operating temperature. However, because saturation Wigner energy is lower at higher temperatures the problem is not expected to arise in power producing reactors.

2.6. LIQUID METAL COOLANTS AND CONTAINER MATERIALS

Liquid metals are the only coolants which are capable of extracting heat at a sufficient rate from a fast neutron reactor core without complication in terms of high pressure and high core temperature. Of liquid metal coolants sodium is certainly the cheapest and usually the more suitable, although its more expensive alloys with potassium are sometimes used because they can be liquid at room temperature. In addition to its use in fast reactors, sodium has a sufficiently low thermal neutron cross-section to allow its use as a thermal neutron reactor coolant. An American experimental reactor, the Sodium Reactor Experiment, has been built and operated.

The most common material for container and fuel cans in sodium cooled fast reactors is stainless steel. Iron, and the alloying elements in stainless steel, have very low solubilities in sodium up to 550°C, but difficulties are encountered due to oxygen, with which sodium is normally contaminated. Chromium, the principal alloying element of stainless steel, can combine with sodium oxide in the liquid, possibly forming a chromate. This disrupts the normal oxide film and penetrates the grain boundaries, weakening them and allowing whole grains to be removed by the flowing liquid metal. A liquid metal oxygen content of less than 25 ppm is necessary to prevent intergranular oxidation, and this is normally achieved by cooling a proportion of the sodium stream until dissolved Na_2O is precipitated, it is then filtered off. This process is known as cold-trapping.

Niobium and vanadium have also been used as canning materials, in the sodium cooled Dounreay reactor in Scotland. Whilst these metals can be held in contact with metallic uranium, without danger of alloying, at a higher temperature than stainless steel, they introduce a complication due to the possibility of corrosion by an unusual mechanism. Like chromium they combine with sodium oxide, and the resulting compound is soluble in sodium, the solubility being small but increasing with temperature. It is therefore possible for the metal to be corroded, and the corrosion product dissolved in sodium as it forms, to be precipitated in heat exchangers, as saturation is reached when the sodium cools. Corrosion by oxidation and mass transfer is prevented when the oxygen content of the sodium is reduced to below 1 ppm. This low oxygen concentration can be reached by cold-trapping in a suitably constructed system, but more easily by hot-trapping with zirconium or titanium held at about 650°C.

2.7. MISCELLANEOUS MATERIALS

Plastics and rubbers are not normally used inside reactor cores or pressure vessels, since they deteriorate rapidly under the influence of gamma, beta and neutron irradiation. However, they will be briefly discussed since they are necessary for electrical machinery which may be installed inside the biological shield, and are sometimes used as neutron energy attenuating materials.

The structure of polymers is due to a relatively delicate balance of ionic bonds, which can be changed and broken by the energy imparted to atoms via electron excitation by gamma-rays. The higher energies imparted by neutrons are, of course, even more damaging.

The following is a list of observed effects of irradiation of some polymers:
Hydrogen evolution.
Evolution of low molecular weight hydrocarbons.
Evolution of hydrogen chloride from polyvinylchloride.
Hardening.
Embrittlement.
Oxidation of free surfaces.

In general thermoplastic resins are damaged most quickly, whilst mineral-filled phenolics have shown relatively good resistance. However, a sufficient radiation dose would be received in from 1 to 100 hr. in a power reactor core to ruin all plastics, even if temperature conditions were suitable.

Pure alumina and magnesia, sintered or in powder form have been found adequate for electrical insulation purposes in reactor cores. Their conductivity is increased by several orders of magnitude, due to increased vacancy populations, but this is normally insignificant.

Concrete, used for shielding, shows a slow but steady loss of water under irradiation, and some loss of strength is to be expected. However, an accelerated neutron dose to the maximum that concrete shielding is likely to receive (i.e. 10^{18} neutron/cm^2) does not result in crushing strength measurements which are outside the normal scatter of pre-irradiation results.

2.8. FUTURE DEVELOPMENTS

Elucidation of the long-term effects of pressure shell irradiation may provide possible justification for relaxation of the present requirements for maintenance of shell temperature well above the original DBTT. Data on creep under irradiation is sparse partly because determination of effects is experimentally difficult, but some stress relaxation work has been reported, and actual creep data can be expected in the future. The present conflicting requirements imposed by operating conditions on steels at present available—fine grain for low DBTT, coarse grain for creep resistance but fine grain for high rupture ductility—has stimulated investigations of alternative steels to provide a formula combining fine grain and creep resistance without the penalty of low creep ductility incurred by some low alloy steels.

Progress toward reactors of higher rating and smaller core sizes may in time be such that hardened and tempered alloy steels can economically replace the present normalized mild steels. This should reduce the possibility of brittle fracture, unless the effects of long-term irradiation prove to be even worse than the present deliberately pessimistic forecasts. Unfortunately, elimination of both brittle fracture and creep problems by the use of austenitic steel pressure shells is not likely to be an economic possibility for gas cooled reactors as at present envisaged.

A magnesium zirconium canning alloy known as ZA may well find a place alongside Magnox, under the low temperature conditions where Magnox creep ductility is low.

In power reactors for the distant future it appears that metals will play a secondary role in the core, the pattern of the high temperature gas cooled reactor is one of graphite containers for a ceramic or cermet fuel, with metals used only for base supports and other smaller details.

REFERENCES

Stress Systems

M. GENSAMER, *Strength of Metals under Combined Stress.* American Society for Metals (1958) (reprint).

Deformation of Metals

N. F. MOTT, *Atomic Structure and the Strength of Metals.* Pergamon Press, London (1958).
A. H. COTTRELL, *Dislocations and Plastic Flow in Crystals.* Clarendon Press, Oxford (1953).
A. H. COTTRELL, *Theoretical Structural Metallurgy.* Edward Arnold.
B. CHALMERS, *Physical Metallurgy.* John Wiley and Chapman & Hall (1959).

Creep and High Temperature Effects

G. V. SMITH, *Properties of Metals at Elevated Temperatures.* McGraw-Hill, New York (1950).
R. F. HILLS and D. R. HARRIES, Sigma phase in austenitic stainless steels. *Chem. Process Engng.* **41,** No. 9 (1960).

Fracture

B. L. AVERBACK et al., Fracture. *Proceedings of an International Conference on the Atomic Mechanisms of Fracture*, held in Swampscott, Massachusetts, 12th–16th April, 1959. Technology Press of M.I.T. and John Wiley, New York (1959).
A. A. WELLS, The mechanics of notch brittle fracture. *Welding Res.* **7,** No. 1 (1953).

Radiation Effects

M. J. HILLIER, Thermal stresses due to gamma irradiation. *Nucl. Technol.* **5,** No. 46 (1960).
A. H. COTTRELL, The effects of neutron irradiation on metals and alloys. *Metall. Rev.* **1,** No. 4, 479–522 (1956).
A. H. COTTRELL, The effects of nuclear irradiation on structural materials. *Chart. Mech. Engng.* **7,** No. 3 (1960).

D. R. HARRIES, *A Survey of the Effects of Neutron Irradiation on the Properties of Iron and steels*. U.K.A.E.A. publication, A.E.R.E. M/TN. 54 (1958).

R. G. BERGGREN *et al.*, Tensile and stress rupture properties of irradiated stainless steels and inconel. *Proceedings of the A.E.C. Welding Forum, Chicago, Illinois.* October (1959).

L. GRAINGER, *The Behaviour of Reactor Components under Irradiation.* International Atomic Energy Agency, Vienna (1960).

S. F. PUGH, *Swelling in Alpha Uranium due to Irradiation.* U.K.A.E.A. publication, A.E.R.E.–R. 3458 (1960).

J. W. JOSEPH, *Stress Relaxation in Stainless Steel under Irradiation.* A.E.C. Research and Development Report. DP. 369. June (1959).

S. F. PUGH, Damage occurring in uranium during burn-up. *Proceedings of the International Conference on the Peaceful Uses of Atomic Energy 1955*, **7**, 44, P/443.

R. E. BOWMAN, How radiation affects engineering materials. *Materials in Design Engineering*, 119–34 (1960).

The Iron and Steel Institute, *Symposium on Steels for Reactor Pressure Circuits*, London, 30th November–2nd December (1960).

Irradiation Effects on Graphite

R. E. NIGHTINGALE *et al.*, Damage to graphite irradiated up to 1000°C. *Proceedings of the Second U.N. International Conference on Peaceful Uses of Atomic Energy 1958*, **7**, 295, P/614.

U.S./U.K. Graphite Conference, held at St Giles Court, London, 16th–18th Dec. (1957), U.S. Atomic Energy Commission TID.7565 (1959).

Liquid Metals

R. N. LYON, *Liquid Metals Handbook.* United States Atomic Energy Commission, NAVEXOS p. 733 (Rev.) (1952); *Liquid Metals Handbook*—Sodium—Na K Supplement. United States Atomic Energy Commission, TID.5277 (1955).

Canning Materials

D. E. THOMAS, Aqueous corrosion of zirconium and its alloys at elevated temperatures. *Proceedings of the International Conference on the Peaceful Uses of Atomic Energy, 1955*, **9**, 407–13, P/537.

G. M. ADAMSON *et al.*, Metallurgy of zirconium and titanium alloys. *Proceedings of the Second U.N. International Conference on Peaceful Uses of Atomic Energy, 1958*, **5**, 3, P/1993.

T. J. HEAL, The mechanical and physical properties of magnesium and zirconium canning materials. *Proceedings of the Second U.N. International Conference on Peaceful Uses of Atomic Energy, 1958*, **5**, 208, P/49.

CHAPTER 3

THE CONSTRUCTION OF PRESSURE VESSELS IN MILD STEEL

D. F. T. ROBERTS

3.1. INTRODUCTION

THE health hazard of radioactive contamination is such that the uncontrolled release of radioactive material cannot be accepted as a risk, so that any failure of nuclear reactor vessels must be prevented. In any economic design for a commercial power plant reactor the reactor vessel must be irradiated by neutrons, since internal shielding of the entire container would be prohibitively expensive. This means that the vessel will be affected by neutron irradiation, and will, if containing any elements liable to activation, itself become radioactive and hazardous to the health of the operators.

It is thus necessary to design for a given useful life without maintenance of any kind.[1] In practice, a complete inspection cannot be made after the reactor has been operating owing to the high level of the activity, so that the design must be completely safe for the operating life of the reactor, usually taken to be twenty years.

The fuel element cans, the fuel, and the maximum steel thicknesses weldable for the desired vessel size, are limiting factors deciding the temperature and pressure of the heat transfer medium. Present (1958) designs have working pressures of CO_2 gas coolant of 120–170 lb./in^2 minimum temperature 200°C (392°F) approximately, maximum temperature 425°C approximately (800°F). The thickness of the vessels varies from 4 in. to $1\frac{1}{2}$ in. depending on size and shape. Fig. 1.8 is a diagrammatic view of the Hunterston design (400°F to 800°F coolant, 3 in. thick reactor vessel, 150 lb./in^2 (gauge) working pressure). The reactor vessel will be exposed to these conditions plus the neutron flux escaping from the reactor core, and the remaining vessels, such as ducting and heat exchangers, will be exposed to any activity carried by the heat transfer medium including dust from the reactor.

Any failure of a vessel in the coolant circuit will be hazardous during operation, but if the reactor were shut down the non-neutron irradiated vessels (ducting, heat exchangers, auxiliary CO_2 equipment) could be repaired and examined quite thoroughly in the normal way. The reactor vessel and some relatively small parts of the charge or servicing machines will be so active as to require remote examination and repair. Normal maintenance and even normal inspection of the reactor vessel is therefore not possible at present due to access difficulties. There are thus three classes of reactor pressure vessel: those neutron irradiated at full working conditions, those not neutron irradiated at full working conditions, and those few vessels such as charge and servicing machines which are only lightly and intermittently irradiated.

Present designs are based on the use of concrete or cast iron for the neutron shield and a conventional pressure vessel as the heat and pressure container. Whilst the material of the pressure vessel may be well known, the design requirements have unusual features. A nuclear reactor vessel must have openings through which to load and unload fuel elements in the core channels. A civil power reactor has about two hundred such openings and three thousand channels. Mechanically operated control rods and shut-down rods must also be operated through nozzles in the shell, and inlet and outlet coolant nozzles provided. A power plant reactor is also unusual in that the reactor vessel is very large, 70 ft. diameter (over $170,000 \text{ft}^3$ capacity) being a common size. The vessels may be spherical or cylindrical, a sphere being normally chosen for 275MW reactors.

The successful design and manufacture of such a vessel is bedevilled by the tolerances essential to all the mechanical connections to and operations within the vessel.

The use of a single container working at the coolant maximum temperature and pressure is not feasible at present as creep can only be limited by the use of more expensive alloy steels. The advantages of increased strength inherent in these steels cannot be fully used when design is based on British codes of practice, so that it is cheaper to use a mild steel vessel operating below the creep limits of stress and temperature. This may be done by thermal insulation or by double-shell " re-entrant " design in which the pressure container is cooled by the minimum-temperature coolant.

3.2. NEUTRON IRRADIATION OF STEELS

The neutron irradiation of steels has embrittling effects. Neutrons collide or interact with the atoms of the iron crystal lattice, displacing them and causing defects in the lattice structure. These nuclear collisions do not have any close equivalent in their effects to non-nuclear damage such as work hardening or fatigue. This makes impossible the reproduction of the damage by existing techniques without neutron irradiation.[2] The damage is temperature-dependent as rapid annealing and self-healing commences above 350°C, so that the cumulative damage diminishes quite quickly above this temperature.[2] As all study of effects on creep and mechanical properties must be by actual irradiation, data are sparse, but acceleration of creep has been established in some steels so that avoidance of cumulative damage by high-temperature operation may be at the expense of more rapid creep.[2]

At lower temperatures, at which creep is insignificant, cumulative damage causes some loss of ductility and increase of tensile strength.[3] This change is not serious, but the change in the impact transition temperature, to which the brittle fracture transition temperature is related, is relatively great. The cumulative effect has been estimated to be an increase of 100°C in twenty years' service in a power reactor shell.[4] The selection and fabrication of a reactor vessel material must thus be based on the avoidance of brittle fracture (see below) by all possible means. The brittle fracture temperature of available thick mild steel plates varies between $-40°C$ and $+50°C$ depending on the type of steel and its condition. If the irradiation effect were simply additive in all cases, the worst case would be a vessel liable to brittle fracture at 150°C, a temperature only about 50°C below a normal minimum coolant temperature. The cumulative effects of irradiation are believed to be greatest during irradiation at about 200°C, the normal minimum coolant temperature, and the rise in the impact transition temperature decreases as the irradiation temperature is lowered. It is not economic to cool the vessel shell below the minimum coolant temperature.

3.3. BRITTLE FRACTURE

Brittle fracture has been found to occur in mild steel structures under normal working stresses at ambient or sub-ambient temperatures. The fracture is of the cleavage type when brittle fracture occurs, and is propagated at very high speeds. Welded monolithic structures are liable to catastrophic failure in this way, there being no discontinuities to arrest the fracture as in a riveted structure. The factors affecting the liability to brittle fracture are:

(1) The brittle fracture transition or arrest temperature of the material. Fracture is normally ductile in mono- or bi-axial loading above this temperature in steel.

(2) A concentration of stress due to a notch, which may be accidental in the form of a crack or flaw in the metal or weld, or a design detail such as a square corner.

(3) A residual tensile stress in the region of the notch, very likely of yield-point magnitude. Welding residual stresses are a common source of such stress.[5]

(4) The availability of a power source to propagate the fracture, that is, to provide the necessary mechanical work to separate the crack surfaces.

Existing loads may be adequate, and stored elastic energy is known to be a power source in the absence of loading.[6]

Accordingly, the design and manufacture of the vessel must be such as to avoid notches or stress concentrations. The vessel must be stress-relieved before testing to remove residual stresses, and the material chosen must be of a low brittle fracture arrest temperature. The fabrication methods must not unduly affect these properties or give rise to notches or flaws.

The propagation and arrest phenomena in brittle fracture are measured by the Robertson test.[7] As the specimens are large and the test rig expensive, the Charpy V-notch impact test is used as a material acceptance and check test. The correlation between these two tests is only fair but adequate for defined materials and conditions, the V-notch test specification being the attainment of a minimum energy absorption at, usually, $-10°C$, rather than fracture appearance.

3.4. CONVENTIONAL DESIGN REQUIREMENTS

The considerations above are additional to the normal design requirements, such as dimensional accuracy and adequate stability. Stability here refers to the retention of all properties in service, not only dimensions, such as strength, ductility and impact transition temperature. Corrosion allowances must be made, so that corrosion in CO_2 must be assessed.[8] If the reactor shell is to be used in the creep range of stress and temperature, even if only under fault conditions the stress-rupture and creep properties of the chosen steel must be examined. The heat-affected zone of the plate next to the weld must be tested as well as the chosen weld metal. The stability of these two materials must also be checked. Fatigue is not of importance except in the bellows and certain tubular parts of the pressure circuit.

The avoidance of stress-raisers and the certain attainment of a twenty-year repair-free service life can only be aimed for by the perfection of the manufacture. For instance, all fillets must be smooth so that assumptions necessary to design formulae are realized. In general, an adaption of the British Standard 1500 Code of practice is used, and Lloyds Register have published a Provisional Code for nuclear vessels.[9]

3.5. NUCLEAR AND FUEL CANNING FACTORS

The operation of the reactor itself depends on the attainment of design neutron fluxes, so that materials working within the core must be free of neutron absorbers or materials which become very radioactive. This requirement affects the use of materials which are mechanically part of the pressure vessel shell, because scale from, or broken pieces of such material could enter the core and cause localized heating or neutron absorption. For instance, the coolant gas valve seatings must be made of material free of boron or cobalt. Alternative materials to those normally containing these elements must be proven under the working conditions required.

The use of a wide variety of materials is prohibited by the requirements of fuel canning material compatibility.[10] Quite small particles of numerous metals and oxides can react with or form low-melting alloys with the magnesium alloy and, melting at maximum operating temperatures, would result in punctures of the can wall, allowing the coolant CO_2 to react with the uranium metal fuel inside. Fortunately, iron and iron oxide are compatible, but many normal metals and their oxides are not. Copper is particularly dangerous, so that the use of copper brazes or even temporary weld backing bars must be avoided unless copper pick-up can be absolutely prevented.

The final requirement is the highest possible gas-tightness of the entire coolant circuit, owing to radioactive contamination by fission products and induced activity. For this reason bolted joints, which are avoided whenever possible, must be seal-welded.

3.6. SELECTION OF MILD STEEL SUPPLY

The steel chosen must have:

(1) Known and reliable properties in the required thicknesses.

(2) Satisfactory brittle fracture quality.

(3) Good fabrication and welding quality.

(4) Established manufacturing potential and supply in the desired form, for example, large plates or thick bars, free of defects.

Most of these properties are established by prior use in the construction of Class I pressure vessels, none of which should have developed faults due to the material in, say, five years of service. Factor 3 need not necessarily be proven in this way as smaller vessels can be manipulated with higher preheat temperatures than are possible for site construction.

The use of forgings is necessary for a good design as the inlet and outlet gas nozzles and other nozzles cannot be fabricated to the same quality and properties from plate. A forging material corresponding as closely as possible to the plate material must be found. Castings are not normally specified for use in the pressure shell.

Both the plate and forging material must be available in a sound state, free from defects such as laminations, cracks or surface defects and with good thickness tolerances.

The soundness of the prime plate and forgings is proved by ultrasonic inspection, and all exposed edges are examined by magnetic particle methods for cracks or laminar defects. Visual examination is essential. Where necessary, the surfaces to be examined must be prepared, and flame cleaning or grinding is widely used.

The properties of the steel must be consistent through the thickness of the sections employed, and this must be verified at all stages of fabrication. The maximum section for the Hunterston design is about 6 in.

The properties of the steel as delivered from the mills or forge must be checked before fabrication. As it is not easy to guarantee that simulated heat-treatment of small test coupons will reproduce well enough the response to such treatment of a large piece, it is better to have the steel delivered in bulk in a definite condition of heat treatment, usually normalized. Test coupons can then be considered representative of a plate or forging with little error, and the response to further treatment more readily assessed.

Two types of steel have been chosen to meet all the requirements listed above. A normal silicon-killed boiler plate of high manganese to carbon ratio, heat-treated to give a fine grain size and good impact properties can be used, or an aluminium-treated notch-ductile steel equivalent to British Standard 2672ND IV. The former has reasonable creep resistance whilst having a better brittle fracture propagation temperature than normal boiler plate, whilst the latter has lower creep resistance so that the shell must be below 350°C working temperature, but has a very good brittle fractive propagation temperature.

Forgings can now be obtained in closely similar steels, but the attainment of the ND IV grade impact specification consistently has proved difficult and forgings in this steel only became in free supply in 1959.

3.7. EFFECTS OF FORMING AND WELDING ON PLATE PROPERTIES

The selection of the steel for the vessels is a compromise between the control of fabrication effects on plate properties and the resistance of the steel to such effects. Mild steels are generally resistant to fabrication damage, and it might be thought that only gross bad practice could cause a deterioration in the desired quality. The effects of fabrication processes on the impact energy transition temperature as shown by the Charpy V-notch energy results can be quite unfavourable. There are the effects of hot work such as hot pressing, cold work such as cold rectification and cold setting to shape by warwicks or pressing or dogging, heat treatment such as normalizing or stress relieving and thermal and stress cycles imposed by flame-cutting and welding.

(i) *Hot Pressing and Normalizing*

Thick plate (over $2\frac{1}{2}$ in.) is most conveniently worked into shape for a spherical shell by pressing hot. Normalizing, that is heating to about

900° C and cooling in air, refines the ferrite grain size of the steel and improves the impact properties without impairing the ductility. By hot pressing in the normalizing temperature range the two operations are combined. The dangers, which are well understood, are, (a) overheating or oversoaking the plate which can cause an increased prior austenite grain size and poor impact V-notch properties, and (b) pressing at too low a temperature so that a poor metallurgical structure, residual stresses and possibly strain damage are caused. The fine-grain aluminium-treated steels which give the lower brittle fracture propagation temperatures are more liable to grain growth, but are less likely to sustain residual stress or strain damage than the normal silicon-killed steels. These latter are more resistant to creep due to their free nitrogen content which also can cause strain ageing. In either case careful control and specification of soaking temperature and time, the pressing time and minimum temperature, and cooling in free still air will ensure the correct properties. As the steel is better purchased in the normalized condition, the reactor shell is thus double-normalized. The impact properties are tested after hot pressing to prove the operation successful.

(ii) *Cold Rectification*

The normal degree of fabrication cold working has no great effect on aluminium-modified notch-ductile steels, and no severe effect on the silicon killed steels. However, it is very easy to exceed this normal degree if reasonable dimensional tolerances are not achieved, and cold rectification must be limited by specifying maximum bending and straightening tolerances. These correspond to less than 0·05 per cent permanent strain. The steam-raising unit plates are cold rolled to shape before welding, but these are not required to meet any impact energy specification.

(iii) *Stress Relief Heat Treatment*

This is used to reduce residual stresses due to forming and welding, and is considered good practice. No correctly designed, fabricated and stress-relieved vessel has, thus far, ever failed by brittle fracture. It is nonetheless found that the heat treatment necessary can lower the impact properties of the plate, whether aluminium modified or normal silicon-killed steel.[11] The heat treatment time must therefore be chosen to be the minimum for effective relaxation of the stresses at the temperature attained. In heating such large vessels as reactor spheres the control of the temperature is difficult and it is not possible to jig or support the vessel, so that the penalty of over-treament may be a misshapen vessel, as well as failure to get a low brittle fracture propagation temperature. A further difficulty can arise as over-relieving can cause the U.T.S. of the steel to fall below that specified for the design.

It is known from work on the Wells[12] test that under-relieving is dangerous, so that relaxation of stresses to about one ton per square inch is necessary. Residual stresses over 4 tons/in^2 can aid the initiation of brittle fracture. As working stresses are from 5 to 7 tons/in^2, residual stresses much over 2 tons/in^2 could cause overstress at points of stress concentration. If relaxation to under $\frac{1}{2}$ ton/in^2 were desired, the dead-weight stress could cause buckling at points which were over-relieved, so that the relaxation temperature and time must be correctly judged.

The variation of temperature from point to point in the structure must be controlled during the thermal treatment of these large vessels, as a steep temperature gradient causes residual stresses and even local distortion.

In some cases local stress relief of individual welds must be carried out. The work of Kennedy and others has shown the danger of brittle fracture due to residual stress actually induced by uncontrolled local heating, again due to too steep a temperature gradient. Accordingly, safe gradients are specified and adhered to when local stress relieving is necessary.

(iv) *Flame Cutting and Gouging, Welding*

These operations raise the temperature of a layer of the steel to its melting point very rapidly, the ensuing cooling rate being much more rapid than oil-quenching in the case of thick steel sections. The resulting heat-affected zone has a different metallurgical structure from the original steel and the severe temperature gradient causes a residual yield-point tensile stress in the weld and adjacent plate balanced by a more diffuse compression in the remainder of the plate.[13] The changes in mechanical properties in the heat-affected zone are acceptable with mild steels, but the ductility and impact energy values are lowered. Preheating during the welding operations helps to reduce the cooling rate if too small an electrode gauge or current has to be used and thus prevents unwanted hardening of the heat-affected zone and weld metal. The high manganese content of the notch-ductile steels used increases the tendency to hardening, but to secure these good impact properties the carbon content must be lower than that of normal boiler plate, so that the hardening is not severe with a reasonable preheat.[14] Construction would become much more difficult due to operator discomfort if a preheat greater than about 150°C were necessary, and a preheat of 100–120°C is generally used. Preheating is controlled by temperature-indicating crayons or surface pyrometers, the heat source being propane burners or electric resistance heaters. The preheat temperature depends on the thickness of metal being welded, and no preheat is required for normal welding operations on plate under $1\frac{1}{2}$ in. thick in these qualities of steel within the welding current ranges permitted.

The severe thermal gradients caused by these processes cause plastic deformation and distortion of shape in the parts being joined, hence the yield-point residual stresses. Extreme residual stress, causing cracking, can result from large volumes of weld metal in small areas, so that whenever possible weld seams are designed not to cross or overlap, and any repair welds necessary must be planned to avoid local concentrations of welding. In some cases the removal of an entire plate may be the only acceptable solution to a repair problem. Cracking due to severe residual stresses can occur during stress relief, which is very serious since repair welds subsequent to stress relief must be stress-relieved again. The dangers of local stress-relief of this type are such that a very expensive installation or even a complete re-relieving might be required.

3.8. SELECTION OF WELD METAL

(i) *Mechanical Properties*

The mechanical properties of the weld metal must be equivalent to those of the steels used, or better. The thick plate used causes unusually rapid cooling of the weld as deposited, and as most of the welding is positional, this effect cannot be countered by using large-gauge electrodes with a greater heat imput. The preheat used partly prevents undue hardening, which would cause loss of ductility, and also prevents fissuring. Fissuring is the formation of multiple microscopic cracks in each weld bead due primarily to hydrogen dissolved in the weld metal.[15] The hydrogen is derived from moisture in the coating or flux constituents and hydrogen gas present dissolved in the metal powders in the electrode coating. To give the greatest assurance of freedom from fissures, low-hydrogen electrodes are always used, although these types are not always the easiest to use. The mechanical properties of low-hydrogen (class 6) weld metal are good, but great difficulty is experienced in obtaining consistent V-notch impact values.[16]

Weld metal is, in a multi-run welded joint, a composite structure composed of layers or stringers of fine-grained refined weld metal interspersed in the original weld beads (Figs. 3.1(a) and (b)). The fine-grained layers are roughly equivalent to normalized steel, the temperature rise due to the superimposed weld layer being sufficient to give this effect in part of each weld bead. Both of these prime materials give scattered V-notch impact values, and the proportion of these two in an impact test specimen can vary as the weld layers are thinner than a Charpy specimen thickness. The variation in results makes it very difficult to guarantee a minimum impact energy absorption at the chosen test temperature. Improved electrodes are still being developed to overcome this difficulty (Fig. 3.2).

This requirement for minimum V-notch impact values restricts the use of automatic welding processes, since these are only of value when thick weld layers are deposited at high currents. Some advantage in speed is gained by using automatic welding in making two-plate panels which can be manipulated in a welding shop, but the current used, and thus the welding speed,

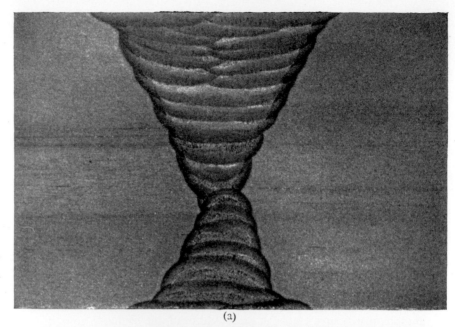

(a)

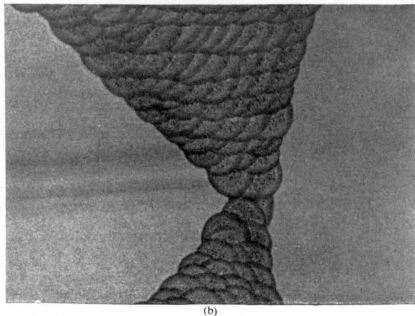

(b)

FIG. 3.1.   Cross-section of butt welds 3-in. reactor plates. (a) Semi-vertical/semi-overhead position. (b) Horizontal/vertical position. Note: the dark zones round each weld bead are refined weld metal. The light " grainy " areas are unrefined. The grain size is *not* apparent in the photograph, being much smaller,

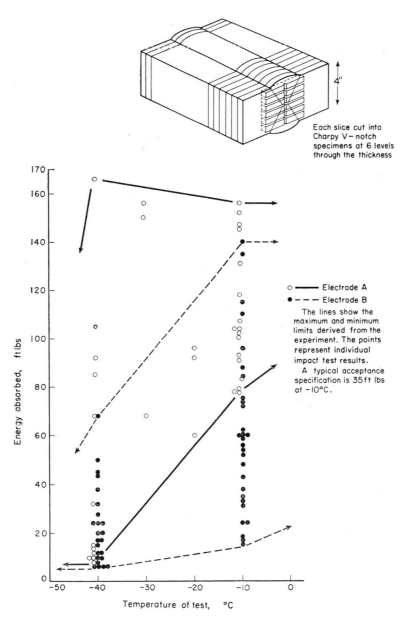

FIG. 3.2. Comparison of scatter of impact values at temperatures in the transition region. Weld metals A and B, semi-vertical weave welds in 4-in. plate. Charpy V-notch specimens cut as in inset figure above, notch orientation as shown.

is restricted.[17] If thick weld layers were used, the impact properties would fail to meet the impact–energy requirements (Fig. 3.3).

The non-irradiated vessels, such as steam-raising units, much of the ducting, and lightly irradiated vessels such as the charge machine vessel and servicing vessel, are not subject to such severe impact–energy requirements and various automatic welding processes can be used in their manufacture. These vessels, about 15 to 19ft. in diameter and 40 to 60ft. long, can be manipulated so that most welding is downhand.

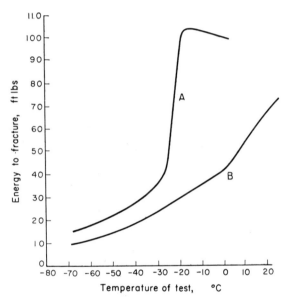

FIG. 3.3. Minimum Charpy V-notch impact energy plotted against test temperature. Automatic welding in 3-in.-thick plate, process A compared with process B. Welding currents similar values in both cases.

(ii) Special Welds

(a) Clean conditions welding. The nuclear and compatibility requirements mentioned before forbid the use of normal manual metal-arc electrodes after the vessel is cleaned for graphite core stacking because of contamination by manganese, sodium and fluorine in particular. As some welds on the pressure vessel internals must be made after stress relief, techniques avoiding the use of these electrodes have to be used. The manual Argonarc and CO_2-shielded consumable-electrode processes are used in this case. The latter is fully usable in all positions using the correct welding power source, whereas the argonarc process, and the argon or argon/1 per cent oxygen consumable-electrode process are not usable overhead or vertically.

(b) *Dissimilar metal welding.* Some parts of the coolant circuit may be made of stainless steel for corrosion resistance or flexibility. Examples are the burst cartridge detection tubes or ducting bellows. The joining of austenitic stainless steel to mild steel is difficult since the differential expansion causes high stresses, and the mixed metals in the weld can be hardenable and subject to carbon migration on prolonged heating above 300°C, either of which can cause failure.[18] Two solutions are feasible, the avoidance of austenitic or high-chromium alloys altogether, or the use of special alloys to make the necessary welds, these alloys being of intermediate expansion coefficient, and resistant to carbon migration embrittlement. The latter is convenient for service below 300°C, the former providing complete security, if adequate corrosion allowances be made for service over 300°C.

(iii) *Welding Technique*

The final consideration in the choice of welding electrodes is their effective use in construction. As the large spherical reactor vessel cannot be manipulated, even if prefabricated in parts, positional welding is necessary. This restricts the electrode gauge and current to be used. The radiographic soundness of the welded seams must be perfect, and a very high standard of radiographic inspection and welding are necessary. This applies to all the welding in the coolant circuit, because freedom from repairs is most likely to be achieved by perfect welding. The reactor vessel must be free of flaws that could initiate brittle fracture, and, as the limiting size of an initiating flaw is unknown, all possible precautions are taken to avoid any flaw. The radiographic inspection standard is thus the limit of detection achieved in a reasonable time with the best technique available. Penetrameter sensitivities of $1\frac{1}{2}$ per cent of the specimen thickness are normally achieved, and flaws, pores or slag particles, of this size are located, cut out, and repaired by re-welding to achieve a flaw-free weld to this standard. This means that particles 0·045 in. in diameter or more are removed in 3 in. plate seams.

This degree of perfection can only be achieved by selecting an electrode which gives good radiographic soundness in all welding positions. The technique of deposition must be carefully chosen and the welders selected by making test plates to the necessary standard. Any falling-off in the quality of seams by any welder is checked and the welder re-qualified if necessary. A welding school is provided on the construction site.

All important welds in the vessels must be made by a proved procedure. This is essential because, firstly, no vessel weld can ever be tested mechanically, and secondly certain vital weld joints cannot be examined by radiography. Alternative non-destructive inspection methods such as ultrasonic testing are not yet accepted by the Inspecting Authorities because entirely reproducible and satisfactory results have not yet been shown. Magnetic and penetrant methods of crack detection are accepted and much used, but the indications from these are confined to a zone within $\frac{1}{8}$ in. from the surface. In consequence, the only way to establish the quality and soundness of such non-radiographed seams is to make an identical test piece in the same thicknesses of the same steels by a definite welding procedure, and examine this destructively. As mechanical tests are destructive, the same consideration applies to the test plates which are continuous with every seam or every 100 ft. length of welding seam if the seams be too short and numerous. The tensile and impact results on the test plate only prove the quality of the weld in the test plate itself unless complete uniformity of the vessel and test plate welds be secured. The maintenance of the procedure for each type of weld seam helps the radiographic standard to be kept, and ensures that mistakes which might cause defective welds are avoided. The procedure includes distortion control data and the mode of preheating, since these are important to the success of the weld. Nozzles are preheated internally which reduces the stresses set up by welding and thus prevents cracking.

It is necessary to avoid the use of more than one type of electrode on the construction site, otherwise errors could easily arise. The electrode coatings in use at present are hygroscopic, and the electrodes must be dried before use to prevent hydrogen being introduced in the weld by absorbed water in the electrode. The electrodes are stored in a warmed storeroom, baked immediately before use, and kept in heated " quivers ", which are occasionally warmed by connecting a special heater in the quiver to the welding current supply. The issue of too many electrodes which may be carelessly used is thus avoided, and the arrangement is practical for welders working on the curved surfaces of a sphere. The welding plant used is also carefully specified to suit the electrodes and the work done.

The design of the weld joints, both mechanically and for fabrication, is important. Any unwelded part of a joint is a virtual notch, and it is good practice in irradiated vessels to avoid any non-penetration welds. As far as possible forged nozzles with welding flanges are used, but small nozzles must be let into the vessel shell by full-penetration welds, which cannot be radiographed. Techniques for the ultrasonic examination of these welds are being developed urgently as these welds are numerous and relatively highly rated. The use of full-penetration welds can be difficult when access to one side of the plates is not possible, and numerous methods have been developed for doing these. Welds in small-bore piping (under 1 ft. 6 in. diameter) are good examples, but others occur in clean-condition welding. The use of removable copper backing bars to control the first weld run is feasible if the weld can be ground to remove any copper transferred during welding, but a non-removable backing bar causes a virtual notch because it can rarely be completely fused. The E.B. insert (argonarc process) can be completely fused, and it is much used. Welding flux (submerged-arc flux) can be used as a backing which is flexible and " pours ". A skilled pipe welder can make a full-penetration weld, given the correct welding preparation, by control of the electrode and molten weld metal, and can do this in any position. The use of argonarc or oxyacetylene welding is resorted to in very difficult cases.

Stud welding for the attachment of thermal insulation to the outside of the vessels is essential, and this process is very carefully controlled, as the weld is prone to flaws if wrongly made, and the stud is inevitably a stress concentrator.[19]

Normal butt welds must be ground flush and to even thickness to aid high-sensitivity radiography. Other welds must be ground smooth to improve crack detection by magnetic methods, which is necessary for all non-radiographed welds and many radiographed seams.

The correct welding preparation has been referred to previously and this is an essential part of a successful weld. The position of the weld decides the form of the preparation, since the technique of deposition is varied to avoid trapping welding slag (flux), (Fig. 3.4). Access for back-gouging and the correct disposition of the welds to allow " balancing " is secured by correct preparation also. Typical examples are shown in the diagrams. All welds, whenever possible, are back-gouged to remove any unsound metal in the first welding pass.

The weld preparations also affect the residual stress and welding strains, by the method of deposition and quantity of weld metal required to join them. Both U and V type preparations are possible but flame-cut V pre-parations are invariably used as the machining required for U preparations would be expensive for curved surfaces. Dressing by hand grinding is often required to secure a perfect, clean preparation with the correct gaps and form, which is inspected before welding. The prepared seam edges are examined and magnetically inspected for any small laminar defects which may cause small flaws, and these are ground out and repaired by welding when necessary.

The disposition of the weld vees is also affected by welding access, and must be decided at the design stage to ensure the following:

(1) Access for assembly and clamping of the pieces.

(2) Access for the welder.

(3) Access for the welding electrode.

(4) " Visual " access, that is, the correct relation of the electrode, preparation and welder's line of sight. This can be faulty even when (2) and (3) are apparently satisfactory.

(5) Access for back-gouging: grinding may be necessary if a flame gouging torch cannot be manipulated.

(6) Access for inspection, surface grinding, and radiography.

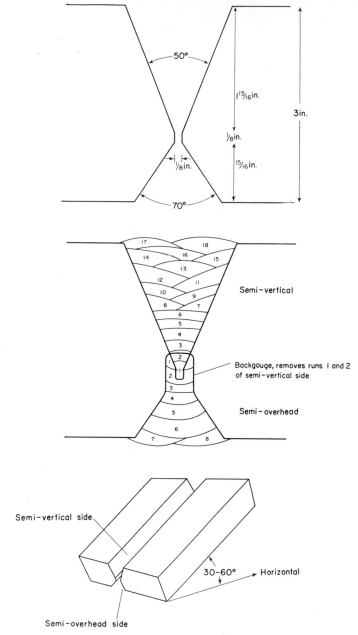

FIG. 3.4(a). Typical weld preparation and sequence of weld runs semi-vertical.

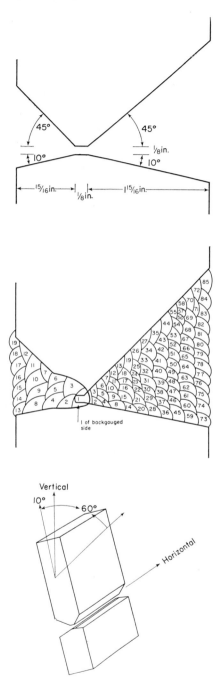

FIG. 3.4(b). Typical 3-in. plate horizontal–vertical weld preparation and sequence. N.B. the 10° tilt towards the large Vee is rarely used.

3.9. INSPECTION

The need for an adequately staffed inspection department and sufficient welding supervisors is evident. The methods of inspection at each stage have been described already.

The ultimate inspection of the finished vessels is the pneumatic or hydraulic proving test, when all operations are completed, but inspection using crack-detecting equipment is necessary after stress relief to ensure that no deformation or cracking has occurred during stress relief. The mechanical properties of the materials and welds are established by testing the production test plates and cut-outs made during fabrication, which are stress-relieved with the vessel. In the case of the reactor vessel, Robertson crack-arrest tests are included on selected materials.

The irradiation effects will be continuously assessed by monitoring specimens placed in various positions in the reactor during operation and taken out at regular intervals during the working life. Some specimens will be situated in positions with a very high neutron flux to give an accelerated test which will provide a close estimate of the ultimate rise in the crack-arrest or safety temperature.

3.10. CONSTRUCTION OF THE REACTOR, COOLANT CIRCUIT AND STEAM-RAISING UNITS

The methods of construction used depend upon the manipulation equipment chosen. Vessels may be built " plate small ", that is by welding together the individual plates in position, or partly prefabricated and erected by a crane and welded in position in units, or completely prefabricated and transported to the site for erection. Various advantages and disadvantages accrue from each method, and complete prefabrication is obviously impossible for large vessels. A typical nuclear power station has a 50 to 70 ft. diameter spherical or cylindrical reactor vessel $2\frac{1}{2}$ to 4 in. thick, ducting for the coolant circuit 3 to 6 ft. in diameter $\frac{1}{2}$ to $1\frac{1}{4}$ in. thick, and steam-raising units 15 to 20 ft. diameter and 40 to 60 ft. high, $1\frac{1}{4}$ to 3 in. thick.

The steam-raising units depicted in Fig. 3.5, of 150 tons weight are shop welded on manipulator rollers by automatic welding (Fig. 3.6) and have hand-welded end closures (Fig. 3.7). The plates for the main cylinder, which vary in thickness owing to the thermal sleeve tube plates being pierced with many holes, are welded together after the edges of the plates have been planed to the correct welding preparation and the curvature formed by cold rolling. The plates are held together by spiders, and welded into short cylindrical tiers which are then butt-welded circumferentially end to end to form the final cylinder. All this welding is carried out using heavy-current (800 A) submerged melt automatic welding, the units being manipulated so

Fig. 3.5.   Hunterston steam-raising units after erection.

that all welding is in the flat or downhand position. This process in any case requires absolutely clean weld preparations with very close butting tolerances ($\pm 1/64$ in.) so that edge planing is essential. The thermal sleeve holes are jig-drilled and the thermal sleeves manually welded with fillet welds.

The erection of these large steam-raising units at site requires a crane or derrick lift, and therefore a large crane must be available. If not, pre-

6

FIG. 3.6. View of site welding shop—manufacture of steam-raising unit barrels.

fabrication may be in tiers and the circumferentials welded *in situ*. A number of automatic fluxed processes may be used, adapted from those developed for storage-tank erection. These processes are in practice only applicable to circumferential (horizontal–vertical welding) seams, and no vertical seams have yet been welded automatically for nuclear work, rather than tankage. If small lifting gear only be available, the reactor itself must be built plate small, either of the largest plates available or of two-, three- or even four-plate panels prefabricated from these large plates. Three-inch-thick plates 15 ft. by 10 ft. weighing about seven to eight tons are currently available, so that a four-plate panel could weigh some thirty-two tons.

The alternative method is to use a Goliath crane (Fig. 3.8) of 250–400 tons capacity so that whole tiers may be lifted. This method is expensive in capital equipment but more rapid, as units can be prefabricated simultaneously. The method also has advantages in distortion control, since angular distortion and shrinkage are inevitable transverse to all weld seams. Building in tiers allows all the plates to be clamped and tacked together on a jig before welding, so that local distortion is more easily controlled and a cumulative distortion prevented. Even without jigs, it is easier to prevent cumulative errors. A further desirable feature is that it is possible to change

FIG. 3.7.   Transformer cone of steam-raising unit after welding.

the handing of the weld preparation within each prefabricated unit. Most welding preparations must be relatively unequal to begin with as back-gouging or chipping out the first weld passes is essential for sound welds. This removes some weld and plate material, so that if equal vee depths from

FIG. 3.8.   Hunterston Goliath crane lifting a tier.

each side are to be obtained, or rather, vee depths allowing for flame gouging distortion which will still be slightly unequal, the original preparation may have vees proportioned 2/3 : 1/3 in depth. This arrangement balances the contraction across the seam about the neutral axis so that the residual distortion is a pure shrinkage. " Balancing " is carried out during welding using templates, which aid measurement of the peaking in or out of the joint. In practice, welding is commenced on one vee and continued until peaking reaches a safe limit (5/16 in. maximum, normally 3/16 in. on 3 in. plate), when the seam is backgouged and welding carried out in the gouged side until counter-peaking of about $\frac{1}{8}$ in. is obtained. Welding is then carried out on each vee so as to produce diminishing peaking and finish to a close tolerance. If the original preparation be wrong, balancing is impossible and strongbacks across the joint must be used.

As the contraction stress of the $1\frac{1}{2}$ in. deep welds in 3 in. plate is a large fraction of the plate strength, thick strongbacks welded with $\frac{3}{4}$ in. fillets are the only solution, involving extra welding and plate wastage, as well as repair and inspection, including radiography, where possible, of the scarred surfaces after removing the strongbacks. As might be expected, the angular distortion per run depends on the thickness of weld metal or plate underneath it, the distortion being roughly equivalent to the bending associated with a surface strain of 0·5 per cent, well above the normal yield point strain. This bending is sharply localized in the plane of the weld bead. Hence the thicker the weld, the less the possibility of removing peaking. The vee included angle affects angular and shrinkage distortion, but the use of small vees makes welding and slag removal difficult so that in practice only 50° included angle or larger vees may be used to produce sound welds unless the root gap be enlarged.

The root gap cannot be large as the weld metal is prone to cracking when " bridging " a large gap. Cracking, even in the root run, which is gouged out later, must be avoided. The advantage in a root gap is twofold. Firstly, the quantity of waste metal is reduced since porosity or slag-trapping is localized into the narrow gap rather than a wider vee. Secondly, if the root gap be filled and the root faces be completely penetrated, the first run is more or less of square cross-section. This produces a pure shrinkage with no angular distortion, so that the lever effect of the next run is reduced.

TABLE 3.1. SHRINKAGE OF WELD SEAMS

(allowed for in prime plate size)

Thickness (in.)	No. of weld runs, approx.	Shrinkage (in.) across seam
1	8	1/16
2	15	1/8
3	30	1/5
4	55	3/16

The shrinkage also induces more complex distortion. Even were balancing perfect, a sphere containing a weld seam could only distort uniformly if the

Fig. 3.9.   Reactor shell tiers, skirt and inner shell tier in site welding tanks with
covers removed.

seam was a great circle. A seam removed from a great circle must produce
buckling. As it is impossible to weld on great circles without uneconomic
wastage of plate, the tier method is an excellent way of minimizing such
effects.

The tiers are set up in " dustbins " (Fig. 3.9), circular tanks with removable covers to give protection from the weather. Fig. 3.10 is of a bottom cap
set up and clamped together, the cap being partly composed of prefabricated
two-plate panels. The clamps are clearly visible, and these must be such as
to allow close adjustment of the weld gaps, which must be $\frac{1}{8}$ in. to 3/16 in.
Radial steel girders set in the concrete floor provide a good surface for
setting-up to the required dimensions. Fig. 3.8 shows a tier being lifted
into the reactor biological (neutron) shield, after the required trimming to
size and preparation of the circumferential weld edges, which are differently
angled because of the position change.

The biological shield is equipped with a temporary roof to exclude rain,
and the tiers are assembled inside. These are dogged together to draw out
local irregularities, which is a good method of avoiding cumulative distortion.
The weld preparations must coincide closely, a displacement of $\frac{1}{8}$ in. laterally
being the maximum permissible, 1/16 in. normally being achieved. This

FIG. 3.10. Bottom cap clamped for welding.

requires good metrology and correct tolerances in each item at a 35ft. radius. The top and bottom caps are welded in jigs as these are not self-sustaining like the tiers.

The welding shrinkage, and the avoidance of slag-trapping, makes essential standard welding practice at T-seam connections (X-seam connections are avoided by design). The " vertical " seam of the T is always made first, the edge having run-off plates so that the weld may be trimmed to a clean smooth prepared edge. The " cross " seam is then welded as a plain seam. In plate-small construction the tiers have to be propped as far apart as possible to permit this. Repair welds involving patches or replacement plates are very troublesome to handle in consequence and T-connections are made artificially by gouging out beyond the patch if the corners cannot be rounded.

The reactor sphere plates are pressed hot in a 2000-ton press to secure the correct shape, using mild steel dies. The weld preparations are then flame-cut on the curved plates (Fig. 3.11). This task becomes very complex when the knuckle plates of cylinders are being made owing to the small and varying radii, because of the accurate positioning of the nose of the preparation

FIG. 3.11.   Flame cutting welding preparations on 3-in. reactor plate.

required.[20] In the design illustrated, only the relatively thin dished end and transformer piece of the S.R.U.s are of this type, but a thick cylindrical reactor shell requires careful design of the plate-cutting gear. Spherical reactor shells are not so difficult, and the curvature and angulation of the plate edges can be produced by simple templates of hardboard or thin sheet steel.

Flame-cutting causes a very slight distortion owing to the spreading of the heat as the cut progresses. The tensile residual stress due to the upsetting and shrinkage along the cut edge causes very little distortion. In both flame-cutting and welding the longitudinal shrinkage is just over elastic strain limits (0·2 per cent) and is non-cumulative. The longitudinal shrinkage in a 15 ft. weld seam in 3 in. plate is 1/8 to 5/16 in.

The longitudinal shrinkage can cause distortion in some flame-cutting or welding operations. The radial shrinkage of circumferential seams and cut edges is almost negligible (1/32 in.) in 19 ft. diameter vessels, but the radial sag in a spherical plate of 35 ft. diameter when numerous nozzle holes are cut in it is found to be 3/8 in. (Fig. 3.12). Welding the nozzles causes a further 3/8 in. decrease. This flattening is believed to be due to the residual

FIG. 3.12. Special flame-cutting machine boring opening in Hunterston reactor vessel bottom head.

stress around the hole edges. A 1½ ft. square plate 3 in. thick, welded into an immovable surround would become nearly 1/32 in. thinner due to the weld transverse shrinkage, and in welding nozzles the same stresses tend to reduce the sphere radius. In this case, then, the transverse shrinkage can apply to augment the longitudinal strain, but in the case of the flame-cut holes the effect on the sag must be by the longitudinal stress only.

These distortions must be allowed for in the construction of the sphere, as " balancing " can only partly prevent them. Really, unbalance is used to cause the seam to peak out, but this requires great care and cannot prevent all flattening.

3.11. CONCLUSION

It has not been possible in this short article to do more than indicate some of the metallurgical and dimensional controls required in some parts of the reactor pressure circuit of a nuclear power station. In general, it will be seen that the construction involves only the scrupulous observance of the best codes of practice, and that no really new requirements or methods are involved. Even the danger of leakage or rupture, and the inability to carry out repairs, are only extensions of the difficulties experienced with, say, vessels used for toxic materials or super-high pressures in the chemical industry.

REFERENCES

1. SIR L. OWEN, Welding and the nuclear power programme. *Brit. Weld. J.* **6**, No. 5, 197–204 (1959).
2. A. H. COTTRELL, Effects of neutron irradiation on metals and alloys. *Met. Rev.* **1** pt. 4, 479–522 (1956).
3. D. R. HARRIES, The effects of neutron irradiation on the properties of iron and steels. *J. Iron Steel Inst.* **194**, (3), 289–304 (1960).
4. D. R. HARRIES, R. W. NICHOLS and C. JUDGE, The effect of neutron irradiation on the ductile–brittle transition temperature of steels and the relevance to reactor pressure vessels. *Iron and Steel Institute Symposium on Steels for Reactor Pressure Circuits, Nov.–Dec. 1960.*
5. A. A. WELLS, P. H. R. LANE and G. COATES, Experiments on the arrest of brittle cracks in 36-in.-wide steel plates. *Brit. Weld. J.* **3**, No. 12, 554–70 (1956).
6. W. G. WARREN and H. G. VAUGHAN, The initiation of brittle fracture at welded joints in steel structures. *Trans. Inst. Weld.* **16**, No. 5, 127–35 (1958).
7. T. S. ROBERTSON, Propagation of brittle fracture in steel. *J. Iron Steel Inst.* **175**, 361 (1953).
8. T. PAINE and C. E. MOORE, The oxidation of reactor steels in carbon dioxide. *Iron and Steel Institute Symposium on Steels for Reactor Pressure Circuits 1960.*
9. *Survey of Pressure Components for Land Based Nuclear Installations: Provisional Requirements 1960;* and Supplement No. 1, *CO_2 Cooled Graphite Moderated Reactor System 1960.* Lloyds Register of Shipping, Land Division.
10. A. B. McINTOSH and T. J. HEAL, *Materials for Nuclear Engineers*, 243, § 7.7. Temple Press (1960).
11. J. H. GROSS and R. D. STOUT, The performance of high strength pressure-vessel steels. *Weld. J.* **35**, 115s–119s (1956).
12. R. KENNEDY, The influence of stress-relieving on the initiation of brittle fracture in welded plate specimens. *Brit. Weld. J.* **4**, No. 11, 529–34 (1957).
13. R. GUNNERT, *Residual Welding Stresses.* Almquist Wiksell, Stockholm (1955).
14. L. REEVE, Weldability of ND steels. *Brit. Weld. J.* **4**, No. 9, 425–32 (1957).
15. H. G. VAUGHAN and H. E. DE MORTON, *Brit. Weld. J.* **4**, No. 1 40–61 (1957).
16. F. WATKINSON, Notch ductility of mild steel weld metal. *Brit. Weld. J.* **6**, No. 4, 162–74 (1959).
17. J. A. LUCEY, A. H. B. SWAN and P. F. WILKS, Some welding development applicable to the fabrication of heavy pressure vessels for nuclear power stations. *Brit. Weld. J.* **4**, No. 10, 449–57 (1957).
18. R. J. CRISTOFFEL and R. M. CURRAN, Carbon migration in welded joints at elevated temperatures. *Weld. J.* **35**, 9, 457s–468s (1956).
19. F. KOENIGSBERGER and Z. GORCIA-MARTIN, Investigation into the fatigue strength of steel welds as compared with normal screwed studs. *Trans. Inst. Weld.* **16**, No. 2, 36–44 (1953).
20. J. W. GETHIN, Flame cutting and jigging for nuclear power stations. *Brit. Weld. J.* **5**, No. 9, 400–7 (1958).

CHAPTER 4

THE LINEAR ELASTIC ANALYSIS OF STATICALLY INDETERMINATE STRUCTURES

P. B. MORICE

NOTATION

Scalars

$A_{()}$ = area at a section.

a to j = section labels.

ds = infinitesimal element of length on structures.

E = elastic modulus.

h = interval between sections.

$I_{()}$ = second unit of area at a section.

l = total number of Simpson coefficients.

$m_{i,j()}$ = moment distribution value at a section.

n = statical indeterminacy.

$n_{i,j()}$ = direct force distribution value at a section.

r = number of Simpson coefficients for each stress resultant.

s = shear force distribution.

t = number of deflexions.

w = number of loading cases.

α = dummy suffix for current section.

$\gamma_{()}$ = Simpson's Rule coefficient.

Matrices

$\mathbf{F}$ = flexibility distribution of the structure.

$\mathbf{H}$ = stress resultant distribution due to unit values of the indeterminates at the releases.

$\mathbf{u}$ = displacements.

$\mathbf{k}_1$ = diagonal matrix of structural stiffness at sections.

$\mathbf{k}_2$ = diagonal matrix of intervals.

$\mathbf{k}_3$ = diagonal matrix of Simpson coefficients.

$\bar{\mathbf{x}}_t$ = stress resultant distributions in statically indeterminate structures.

$\bar{\mathbf{x}}^0$ = stress resultant distributions in released structures due to loads.

$\bar{x}_\delta$ = stress resultant distributions in released structures due to unit loads at deflexion points.

Δ = deflexion values.

I = the unit matrix.

4.1. INTRODUCTION

THIS chapter is concerned with one of the two fundamental methods for the linear elastic analysis of statically indeterminate structures, that is structures in which the deflexions are directly proportional to the loads causing them or resulting from them. Essentially, the requirement is that the principle of superposition and the reciprocal theorem are applicable.

Whilst the method described is of general application to plates, shells and thin walled rods as well as frames of all types, I shall restrict myself here to this latter type of structure. These structures are usually described as one-dimensional (1D), or as skeletal frames, since the analysis is carried out by representing the structure as a mathematical model consisting of elastic centre lines possessing the appropriate elastic properties of flexural, torsional, extensional, etc., flexibility. Clearly a single coordinate along the centre-line is sufficient to specify a position on a member—hence 1D.

The two fundamental methods of structural analysis may be shown to follow from the two complementary principles of stationary potential energy.[1] A wide variety of techniques may be employed for structural analysis, but in the particular formulations with which we are at present concerned the methods are either (1) based upon displacements as unknowns, whereby equations of equilibrium are set up, the solution of which evaluates the displacements, or (2) based upon forces as unknowns, whereby equations of compatibility are set up, the solution of which determines the forces. In either case the complete solution for forces and displacements then follows directly.

The first method is often called the stiffness method and the second the flexibility method. These can be compared as follows:

Stiffness	Flexibility
Unknown displacements, u	Unknown forces, x
Stiffness matrix, S	Flexibility matrix, F
Hence forces due to u are Su	Hence displacements due to x are Fx
Forces due to load, p	Displacements due to load, u
For equilibrium, $Su + p = 0$	For compatibility, $Fx + u = 0$
Solve for u	Solve for x

We must note that, in the above comparison, whilst the overall solution to the structural problem of forces and displacements is the same by any exact method of analysis, the solutions to the equations of the two methods may not be numerically the inverse of each other. In the case of a structure of the type of Fig. 4.1(a), the stiffness method would involve up to six unknowns, whilst the flexibility method would involve twenty-four unknowns. For the

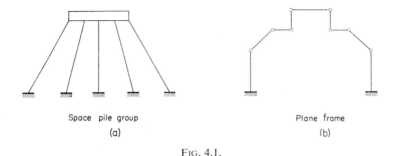

Space pile group

(a)

Plane frame

(b)

FIG. 4.1.

structure of Fig. 4.1(b) a stiffness method might involve twenty-four unknowns, whilst the flexibility method requires three.

The number of unknowns depends upon the kinematical or statical indeterminacy of the structure.[1,2]

For the purpose of this lecture I shall restrict myself to the flexibility method.

4.2. SOME DEFINITIONS

It is convenient to define the meanings of some terms as follows:

(1) Stress resultant. The six possible stress integrals or stress moment integrals on the cross-section of a member, e.g. bending moment M, shear force S, direct force N, torsion T (Fig. 4.2).

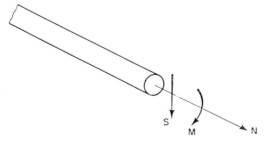

FIG. 4.2.

(2) Release system. The chosen arrangement of releases (cuts, hinges,

slides, etc.) which is used to change the statically indeterminate structure into a statically determinate structure (Fig. 4.3).

(3) *Statical indeterminacy.* The number of releases of stress resultant which have to be inserted into a structure to make it statically determinate, e.g. a single hinge releases one bending moment.

(4) *Particular solution.* The distribution of stress resultants due to the action of the applied loads on the released or statically determinate structure. These will be denoted m_0, s_0, n_0, t_0, etc. The particular solution displacements may result from temperature strains when the equivalent values of

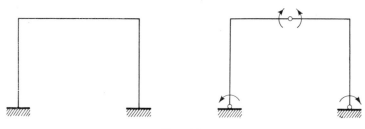

FIG. 4.3.

m_0, n_0, etc., may be used in the evaluation of the indeterminate forces provided they are not included in the final solution (4.1) below, since the particular solution temperature displacements are stress free.

(5) *Unit stress resultant diagrams.* The distribution of stress resultants on the released (statically determinate) structure due to the individual action of unit values of the indeterminate forces x_1, x_2, etc. These will be denoted m_1, s_1, n_1, etc., due to $x_1 = 1$, m_2, s_2, etc., due to $x_2 = 1$, etc.

It is to be noted that whilst the particular solution is usually that of the statically determinate structure, this is not necessary, and known solutions to structures of a lower degree of indeterminacy may be used as a starting point for the analysis. (Special care has to be taken if this is the case in temperature distortion calculations.)

4.3.   PRINCIPLE OF SUPERPOSITION

Since the analysis we are concerned with is that of the linear elastic behaviour of a structure, we can find the effects of several loads and forces acting together upon a structure by adding the effects of these loads and forces acting separately. Thus the actual stress resultant distributions, M, S, N, etc., in a loaded statically indeterminate structure can be found by forming the released (statically determinate) structure and adding together the separate effects upon it of the loads and the indeterminate forces x_1, x_2, x_3, etc.

$$M = m_0 + m_1 x_1 + m_2 x_2 + \ldots$$
$$S = s_0 + s_1 x_1 + s_2 x_2 + \ldots$$

$$(4.1)$$

etc.

The values of x_1, x_2, x_3, etc., being found so that continuity may be re-established at the releases (cuts, hinges, slides, etc.), i.e. by satisfying compatability equations.

4.4. MATRICES

It is convenient to use matrix notation for the analysis since one equation can express the relationship between quantities irrespective of the number of degrees of indeterminacy or the number of stress resultants involved in the problem. The barest essentials of matrix algebra are given below.

(1) Definition. A matrix is a rectangular array of numbers, or linear operators

$$\mathbf{A} = \begin{bmatrix} a_{11} & a_{12} & a_{13} & a_{14} \\ a_{21} & a_{22} & a_{23} & a_{24} \\ a_{31} & a_{32} & a_{33} & a_{34} \end{bmatrix}$$

Matrices may be added or subtracted when the number of rows and of columns in each is the same. The addition or subtraction is performed piecewise upon each of the corresponding elements of the matrix.

(2) Multiplication. Matrix multiplication is performed by multiplying each element of the rows in the left-hand matrix by the corresponding element in the column of the right-hand matrix and adding the result, e.g.

$$\mathbf{AB} = \mathbf{A} \times \mathbf{B} = \begin{bmatrix} a_{11} & a_{12} \\ a_{21} & a_{22} \end{bmatrix} \times \begin{bmatrix} b_{11} \\ b_{21} \end{bmatrix} = \begin{bmatrix} (a_{11}b_{11} + a_{12}b_{21}) \\ (a_{21}b_{11} + a_{22}b_{21}) \end{bmatrix}$$

Consequently, only matrices with the number of columns in the first equal to the number of rows in the second may be multiplied together. It will be noted that, if we describe the matrix $\mathbf{A}$ as a 2×2, i.e. two rows and two columns, and the matrix $\mathbf{B}$ as a 2×1, the product $(2 \times 2) \times (2 \times 1)$ gives a resulting matrix which is (2×1). The order of the matrices in a product is seen to be of vital importance.

(3) Transposition. A matrix is said to be transposed when the elements a_{ij} are replaced by the elements a_{ji}, e.g. if

$$\mathbf{A} = \begin{bmatrix} a_{11} & a_{12} & a_{13} \\ a_{21} & a_{22} & a_{23} \end{bmatrix}$$

the transpose is

$$A' = \begin{vmatrix} a_{11} & a_{21} \\ a_{12} & a_{22} \\ a_{13} & a_{23} \end{vmatrix}$$

It will be seen that if we transpose the product of two matrices, this is equivalent to the reversed product of the individual transposed matrices, i.e.

$$(\mathbf{AB})' = \mathbf{B}'\mathbf{A}'$$

(4) Inversion. Some square matrices have inverses denoted $\mathbf{A}^{-1}$ such that a matrix multiplied by its inverse gives a unit matrix, e.g.

$$\mathbf{A} \times \mathbf{A}^{-1} = \begin{vmatrix} 1 & 0 & 0 \\ 0 & 1 & 0 \\ 0 & 0 & 1 \end{vmatrix} = \mathbf{I} = \text{the unit matrix}$$

Such matrices have to be square and the determinant of the coefficients of the matrix $\mathbf{A}$, $|A|$, must not equal zero.

4.5. ANALYSIS

We shall start by re-writing equations (4.1) in an equivalent matrix form

$$\bar{\mathbf{x}}_t = \bar{\mathbf{x}}_0 + \bar{\mathbf{x}}$$

or

$$\bar{\mathbf{x}}_t = \bar{\mathbf{x}}_0 + \mathbf{H}\mathbf{x} \qquad (4.2)$$

Here

$$\bar{\mathbf{x}}_t = \begin{vmatrix} M \\ S \\ \cdot \\ \cdot \end{vmatrix} \begin{array}{l} \text{moment,} \\ \text{shear,} \\ \text{etc.} \end{array}$$

represents the total stress resultant state of the loaded indeterminate structure at every point and each element of $\bar{\mathbf{x}}_t$ is therefore a function of the positional co-ordinate s. The number of elements in $\bar{\mathbf{x}}_t$ depends upon the type of problem, e.g. one for a pin-jointed frame, three for a plane frame, six for a general space frame.

The matrix
$$\bar{\mathbf{x}}_0 = \begin{bmatrix} m_0 \\ s_0 \\ \cdot \\ \cdot \end{bmatrix} \begin{matrix} \text{moment,} \\ \text{shear,} \\ \text{etc.,} \end{matrix}$$

represents the particular solution which is the stress resultant state, due to a single load system at every point in the released structure, and is also a function of *s*.

The matrix
$$\mathbf{H} = \begin{bmatrix} m_1 & m_2 & \cdot & \cdot & \cdot \\ s_1 & s_2 & \cdot & \cdot & \cdot \\ \cdot & \cdot & \cdot & \cdot & \cdot \end{bmatrix} \begin{matrix} \text{moment,} \\ \text{shear,} \\ \text{etc.} \end{matrix}$$

represents the stress resultant state of the released structure due to unit values of each of the arbitrary constants (unknown forces) *x*, and is also a function of *s*.

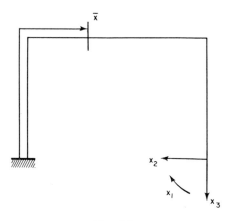

FIG. 4.4.

Let us consider the stress resultants due to the arbitrary constants at some current point *s* in the structure (Fig. 4.4)

$$\bar{\mathbf{x}} = \mathbf{H}\mathbf{x} \tag{4.3}$$

Suppose that at the point *s* we allow a set of infinitesimal deformations $d\bar{\mathbf{u}}$ to occur over a length d*s*, where $d\bar{\mathbf{u}}$ is a column matrix, the elements of which are the displacements in the sense of the stress resultants $\bar{\mathbf{x}}$. The

7

virtual work done by the stress resultants $\bar{x}$ acting over the deformations $d\bar{u}$ may be written as the matrix product

$$W_1 = d\bar{u}' \, \bar{x}$$

where $d\bar{u}'$ is the transpose of $d\bar{u}$. The column matrix $d\bar{u}$ has to be transposed so as to be conformable for multiplication with $\bar{x}$ to form the inner product which is the work.

The deformations $d\bar{u}$ at the point s in the structure will cause displacements $d\underline{u}$ at the releases in the directions of the arbitrary constant stress resultants x (Fig. 4.5). The virtual work done at the releases by the arbitrary constants x acting through these displacements is

$$W_2 = d\underline{u}' \, x$$

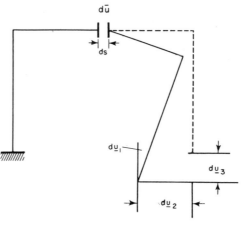

Fig. 4.5.

If, for the time being, the structure is assumed to be rigid except for the length ds, where the local deformations $d\bar{u}$ occur, then the work done at the releases must equal the work done at the current point s since no strain energy can be stored in a rigid body.

Therefore $W_1 = W_2$

whence $d\bar{u}' \, \bar{x} = d\underline{u}' \, x$

and using (3) we may write $d\bar{u}' \, Hx = d\underline{u}' \, x$

therefore $d\bar{u}' \, H = d\underline{u}'$ (see footnote*)

* In general we cannot " divide through " by $\bar{x}$ since it is a column matrix and has no inverse. The operation is only possible because the equation has to be true for all x.

or by the rules of the transpose of a product

$$d\underline{u} = \mathbf{H}' \, d\bar{\underline{u}} \qquad (4.4)$$

The relationship between equations (4.3) and (4.4) is described as a contragredient one, and we can say that stress resultant and displacement transform contragrediently. Where contragredience exists there is always a related invarient. In this case it is work.

The total displacement $\underline{u}$ at a release due to the arbitrary constants x is evidently the integral throughout the structure of the elementary contributions $d\underline{u}$ from each elementary length ds in the structure

$$\underline{u} = \int d\underline{u}$$

which from (4.4) gives

$$\underline{u} = \int \mathbf{H}' \, d\bar{\underline{u}} \qquad (4.5)$$

where it is to be remembered that $\mathbf{H}'$ is a functional matrix in s.

We must now investigate the relations between the deformation $d\bar{\underline{u}}$ and the stress resultants $\bar{\mathbf{x}}$ at the point s in the structure. These are the flexibilities of the section of the member, i.e. $1/EI$, k/CA, $1/EA$, etc., when the stress resultants and displacements are defined in coordinates colinear with the principal axes of the sections of the members of the frame.

We can evidently write an elastic relation between displacements of the element ds and the stress resultants in the form

$$
\begin{bmatrix} d\bar{u}_1 \\ d\bar{u}_2 \\ d\bar{u}_3 \\ \cdot \\ \cdot \end{bmatrix}
=
\begin{bmatrix} \dfrac{ds}{EI} & \cdot & \cdot & \cdot \\ \cdot & \dfrac{k\,ds}{CA} & \cdot & \cdot \\ \cdot & \cdot & \dfrac{ds}{EA} & \cdot \\ \cdot & \cdot & \cdot & \cdot \end{bmatrix}
\begin{bmatrix} \bar{x}_1 \\ \bar{x}_2 \\ \bar{x}_3 \\ \cdot \end{bmatrix}
$$

which may be written

$$d\bar{\underline{u}} = \tilde{\mathbf{F}} \, \bar{\mathbf{x}} \, ds \qquad (4.6)$$

where $\tilde{\mathbf{F}}$ is the flexibility matrix of an element of length of a member; in this case with respect to the principal axes. Clearly $\tilde{\mathbf{F}}$ may also be a function of the position s. Had we considered the flexibility with respect to axes other than the principal axes, the matrix would have included non-zero elements not on the leading diagonal. The displacements (4.5) can now be written

$$\underline{u} = \int \mathbf{H}' \, \tilde{\mathbf{F}} \, \mathbf{x} \, ds \qquad (4.7)$$

and (4.3) can be substituted into (4.7) to obtain

$$\underline{u} = \int H' \tilde{F} H \, ds \, x$$

If we write

$$F = \int H' \tilde{F} H \, ds \tag{4.8}$$

then

$$\underline{u} = Fx \tag{4.9}$$

This is the relation between the arbitrary constants x and their correspond-ing displacements $\underline{u}$ at the releases in the structure which has been made statically determinate. In the analysis of the statically indeterminate structure the structure was made continuous by ensuring that the displacements $\underline{u}$ were equal and opposite to the displacement $\mathbf{u}$ due to the applied load.

In the case of a single applied load system the stress resultants at any point in the released structure due to the load are given by $\bar{x}_0$ so that analogously to (4.7) we may write

$$-\underline{u} = \mathbf{u} = \int H' \tilde{F} \bar{x}_0 \, ds \tag{4.10}$$

or from (4.9)

$$Fx = -\mathbf{u} \tag{4.11}$$

Equation (4.11) can be written in the form

$$x = -F^{-1} \mathbf{u} \tag{4.12}$$

and (4.12) can be substituted back into (4.3) to give

$$\bar{x}_t = \bar{x}_0 - H F^{-1} \mathbf{u} \tag{4.13}$$

This equation itself can be written in terms of (4.8) and (4.10) to obtain finally

$$\bar{x}_t = \bar{x}_0 - H \left(\int H' \tilde{F} H \, ds \right)^{-1} \int H' \tilde{F} \bar{x}_0 \, ds \tag{4.14}$$

which enables the solution to the structural problem $\bar{x}_t$ to be expressed in terms of the effects on the released structure of the applied loading $\bar{x}_0$, the unit indeterminates H and the distribution of structural flexibility $\tilde{F}$.

4.6. ANALYTICAL CHECKS

Although sophisticated checks of the analysis may be carried out, these are lengthy particularly if the statics of the released system solutions are to be included. There is, however, one simple check which can assist in show-ing up arithmetical errors. This is best performed by feeding back as a new particular solution $\bar{x}_0$ the final solution to the problem $\bar{x}_t$. The arith-metic is then different from that of the original analysis, since each of the calculations $\mathbf{u}_1 = \int H' \tilde{F} \bar{x}_t \, ds$ and $x_1 = -F^{-1} \mathbf{u}_1$ uses different values. Indeed, each of the above quantities should be zero in this case and the complete application of equation (4.14) with $\bar{\mathbf{x}}_t$ substituted for $\bar{\mathbf{x}}_0$ should present the same solution $\bar{\mathbf{x}}_t$ if the arithmetic is correct.

4.7. DEFLEXIONS

It is also seen from the above analysis or by a direct appeal to the principle of virtual forces that the deflexion at any point in a structure is given by the expression

$$\delta = \int \bar{\mathbf{x}}_\delta{}' \, \tilde{\mathbf{F}} \, \bar{\mathbf{x}}_t \, ds \tag{4.15}$$

where $\bar{\mathbf{x}}_\delta$ is the distribution of stress resultants due to a unit force acting on the released structure at the position and in the direction of the required deflexion δ.

4.8. COMPUTATION

The computation of equation (4.14) involves integrations which will rarely be carried out analytically in practice, and numerical procedures will normally be adopted.

A typical form of the expression

$$\int \mathbf{H}' \, \tilde{\mathbf{F}} \, \mathbf{H} \, ds$$

in the case of flexural energy only will be

$$\int m_i \frac{1}{EI} \, m_j \, ds \tag{4.16}$$

where m_i and m_j are the unit moment distributions and $1/EI$ is the bending flexibility distribution.

For numerical integration each of these functions will be specified at convenient points on the structure and, if we use Simpson's Rule, we shall have an even number of strips and consequently an odd number of sections (Fig. 4.6). The integration (4.16) is then replaced by a summation, since

$$\int m_i \frac{1}{EI} \, m_j \, ds \simeq \sum_{\alpha=1}^{\gamma} m_{i(\alpha)} \frac{1}{EI_{(\alpha)}} \frac{h}{3} \gamma(\alpha) \, m_{j(\alpha)} \tag{4.17}$$

where the symbol α refers to the current section over the range of sections 1 to r, which may count some sections twice if the interval lengths change, h is the interval length and γ is the Simpson coefficient 1, 2 or 4. In using this numerical integration expression two points may be remembered. Firstly, Simpson's Rule is a two-strip formula and each of the functions m_i, m_j and $1/EI$ must be continuous over each pair of intervals, and secondly, the interval lengths h may vary from pair to pair, provided, of course, the Simpson coefficients are included correctly.

For practical computational purposes the expression (4.17) can be written as a matrix product. [2,3]

$$\sum_{\alpha=1}^{\gamma} m_{i(\alpha)} \frac{1}{EI_{(\alpha)}} \frac{h}{3} \gamma(\alpha)\, m_{j(\alpha)} = \mathbf{H}' \mathbf{k}_1^{-1} \mathbf{k}_2\, \mathbf{k}_3\, \mathbf{H} \qquad (4.18)$$

where $\mathbf{k}_1$ is a diagonal matrix of values of $EI_{(\alpha)}$, $\mathbf{k}_2$ is a diagonal matrix of intervals $h/3$ and $\mathbf{k}_3$ is a diagonal matrix of Simpson coefficients $\gamma_{(\alpha)}$.

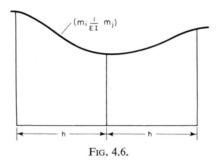

FIG. 4.6.

For example, a twice times statically indeterminate structure with bending flexibility only and sections 1 to r will have matrices of the form

$$\mathbf{H}' \mathbf{k}^{-1} \mathbf{k}_2\, \mathbf{k}_3\, \mathbf{H} = \begin{bmatrix} m_{1(1)} & m_{1(2)} \cdots m_{1(r)} \\ m_{2(1)} & m_{2(2)} \cdots m_{2(r)} \end{bmatrix} \begin{bmatrix} EI_{(1)} & & & \\ & EI_{(2)} & & \\ & & \cdot & \\ & & & EI_{(r)} \end{bmatrix}^{-1}$$

$$\times \begin{bmatrix} h/3 & & & \\ & h/3 & & \\ & & \cdot & \\ & & & h/3 \end{bmatrix} \begin{bmatrix} 1 & & & \\ & 4 & & \\ & & \cdot & \\ & & & 1 \end{bmatrix} \begin{bmatrix} m_{1(1)} & m_{2(1)} \\ m_{1(2)} & m_{2(2)} \\ \cdot & \cdot \\ m_{1(r)} & m_{2(r)} \end{bmatrix} \qquad (4.19)$$

This same technique can be applied to the whole of equation (4.14) giving

$$\overline{\mathbf{x}}^t = (\mathbf{I} - \mathbf{H}(\mathbf{H}' \mathbf{k}_1^{-1} \mathbf{k}_2\, \mathbf{k}_3\, \mathbf{H})^{-1} \mathbf{H}' \mathbf{k}_1^{-1} \mathbf{k}_2\, \mathbf{k}_3)\overline{\mathbf{x}}_0 \qquad (4.20)$$

where it is to be noted that the matrix $\overline{\mathbf{x}}_0$ need not be restricted to $(r \times 1)$ but may include as many load conditions, ω, as required, i.e. $(r \times \omega)$.

The equation (4.15) can similarly be integrated numerically as

$$\delta = \bar{\mathbf{x}}'_\delta \mathbf{k}_1^{-1} \mathbf{k}_2 \mathbf{k}_3 \bar{\mathbf{x}}_t \tag{4.21}$$

Again in (4.21) the stress resultants $\bar{\mathbf{x}}_\delta$ for unit loads at the deflexion points may apply for as many deflexion points t as required so that $\bar{\mathbf{x}}_\delta$ will be $(r \times t)$.

So far we have considered the computation for the case of one stress resultant, m. The method may also be used for computations involving several stress resultants when the ordinates of the stress resultants m will be followed by those of the others n, s, etc., resulting in l values given by $l = r$, $l = 2r$, $l = 3r$, etc., dependent upon the number of stress resultants included.

The form of the matrix products becomes

$$\begin{bmatrix} m_{1(1)}, m_{1(2)} \ldots m_{1(r)}, n_{1(1)}, n_{1(2)} \ldots n_{1(r)} \\ m_{2(1)}, m_{2(2)} \ldots m_{2(r)}, n_{2(1)}, n_{2(2)} \ldots n_{2(r)} \end{bmatrix} \begin{bmatrix} EI_{(1)} & & & & \\ & EI_{(2)} & & & \\ & & \cdot & & \\ & & & \cdot & \\ & & & & EA_{(1)} \\ & & & & & EA_{(2)} \end{bmatrix}$$

etc.

4.9. MACHINE PROGRAMME

Using the Ferranti Pegasus Computer Matrix Interpretive Scheme[4] in its Preset Parameter form, we can write a general programme as follows which will compute stress resultants, a check and deflexions.

In a particular problem in which we know the values of l, n, w and t it is possible to compress the working into less storage space than is shown in the general programme. This is of importance when large problems are being dealt with and storage space is at a premium.

D
N
Linear skeletal frame analysis
J 64·0

$(0,241 \times 242) \to 1$	Input **H**
$(0,241/) \to 5001$	Input $\mathbf{k}_1$
$(0,241/) \to 5002$	Input $\mathbf{k}_2$
$(0,241/) \to 5003$	Input $\mathbf{k}_3$
$(5001, 241/), (1,241 \times 242) \to 5004$	Form $\mathbf{k}_1^{-1}\mathbf{H}$

$(5002, 241/) \times (5004, 241 \times 242) \to 5005$	Form $k_2 \, k_1^{-1} \, H$
$(5003, 241/) \times (5005, 241 \times 242) \to 5004$	Form $k_3 \, k_2 \, k_1^{-1} \, H$
$(5004, 241 \times 242) \, * \to 5005$	Form $H' \, k_1^{-1} \, k_2 \, k_3$
$(5005, 242 \times 241) \times (1, 241 \times 242) \to 5006$	Form $F = H' \, k_1^{-1} \, k_2 \, k_3 \, H$
$(5006, 242 \times 242) \to 5007$	Copy F
$(0, 241 \times 243) \to 5008$	Input $\bar{x}_0$
$(5005, 242 \times 241) \times (5008, 241 \times 243) \to 5009$	Form $u = H' \, k_1^{-1} \, k_2 \, k_3 \, \bar{x}_0$
$(5006, 242 \times 242), (5009, 242 \times 243) \to 5010$	Form $-x = F^{-1} \, u$
$(1, 241 \times 242) \times (5010, 242 \times 243) \to 5011$	Form $-\bar{x} = -Hx$
$(5008, 241 \times 243) - (5011, 241 \times 243) \to 5011$	Form $\bar{x}_t = \bar{x}_0 + \bar{x}$
$(5011, 241 \times 243) \to 0$	Output $\bar{x}_t$
$(5005, 242 \times 241) \times (5011, 241 \times 243) \to 5009$	Form $u_1 = H' \, k_1^{-1} \, k_2 \, k_3 \, \bar{x}^t$
$(5007, 242 \times 242), (5009, 242 \times 243) \to 5010$	Form $-x_1 = F^{-1} \, u_1$
$(1, 241 \times 242) \times (5010, 242 \times 243) \to 5012$	Form $-\bar{x}_1 = -Hx_1$
$(5011, 241 \times 243) - (5012, 241 \times 243) \to 5012$	Form $\bar{x}_1^t = \bar{x}^t + \bar{x}_1$
$(5012, 241 \times 243) \to 0$	Output $\bar{x}_1^t$
$(0, 241 \times 244) \to 5013$	Input $\bar{x}_\delta$
$(5001, 241/) \times (5013, 241 \times 244) \to 5014$	Form $k_1^{-1} \, \bar{x}_\delta$
$(5002, 241/) \times (5014, 241 \times 244) \to 5013$	Form $k_2 \, k_1^{-1} \, \bar{x}_\delta$
$(5003, 241/) \times (5013, 241 \times 244) \to 5014$	Form $k_3 \, k_2 \, k_1^{-1} \, \bar{x}_\delta$
$(5014, 241 \times 244) \, * \to 5013$	Form $\bar{x}_\delta' \, k_1^{-1} \, k_2 \, k_3$
$(5013, 244 \times 241) \times (5011, 241 \times 243) \to 5015$	Form $\Delta = \bar{x}' \, k_1^{-1} \, k_2 \, k_3 \, \bar{x}_t$
$(5015, 244 \times 243) \to 0$	Output Δ
*	

I

Z

In order to run this programme two sets of data are required. The first is a "scaling" set called the preset parameters, which adjusts the general programme as written above to suit the particular structural problem. For this we must give numerical values to enable the machine itself to replace the parameters 241, 242, 243 and 244 and 5001 to 5015 by their required numbers.

Here the significance is as follows:

$241 = l = 1, 2, 3$, etc., r, according to the number of stress resultants
$242 = n$ the statical indeterminacy
$243 = w$ number of loading cases
$244 = t$ number of deflexions
$5001 = l \times n + 1$
$5002 = l(n+1) + 1$
$5003 = l(n+2) + 1$
$5004 = l(n+3) + 1$
$5005 = l(2n+3) + 1$

$5006 = l(3n+3)+1$
$5007 = l(3n+3)+n^2+1$
$5008 = l(3n+3)+2n^2+1$
$5009 = l(3n+w+3)+2n^2+1$
$5010 = l(3n+w+3)+n(2n+w)+1$
$5011 = l(3n+w+3)+n(2n+2w)+1$
$5012 = l(3n+2w+3)+n(2n+2w)+1$
$5013 = l(3n+3w+3)+n(2n+2w)+1$
$5014 = l(3n+3w+t+3)+2n(n+w)+1$
$5015 = l(3n+3w+2t+3)+2n(n+w)+1$
Total space $= l(3n+3w+2t+3)+2n(n+w)+wt$

The second set of data is that relating to the actual structure to be computed and will consist of:

H The $(l \times n)$ matrix of the stress resultant values for unit values of each indeterminate, including repeated values if made necessary by unequal pairs of intervals.

$\mathbf{k_1}$ The (diag l) matrix of the section stiffness values—including repeated values if necessary.

$\mathbf{k_2}$ The (diag l) matrix of intervals.

$\mathbf{k_3}$ The (diag l) matrix of Simpson coefficients.

$\overline{\mathbf{x}}_0$ The $(l \times w)$ matrix of stress resultant values due to the loadings, including repeated values if required.

$\overline{\mathbf{x}}_\delta$ The $(l \times t)$ matrix of stress resultants due to visit forces at the deflexion points.

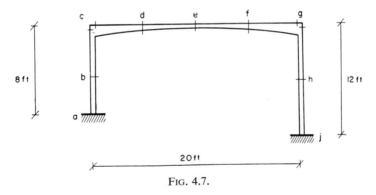

FIG. 4.7.

4.10. EXAMPLE

As an example we shall consider an unsymmetrical fixed foot portal frame in which we include flexural and direct energy (Fig. 4.7). We note that each pair of leg intervals is different, but the transom values are all equal. The load conditions will be as shown in Fig. 4.8, whilst we will call for the side sways at g and the mid span deflexions.

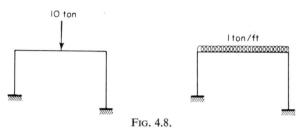

FIG. 4.8.

Forming the released structure by cutting the foot at j (Fig. 4.9) we obtain the stress resultant distributions shown in Fig. 4.10.

The tabular layout of data which is convenient for this problem is shown in Table 4.1, dividing by E. This involves considerable savings in input digits.

TABLE 4.1.

		H			k_1	k_2	k_3	$\bar{x}^0$		$\bar{x}\delta$	
		1	2	3				1st	2nd	1st	2nd
a		+1	+4	+20	+1	+1·33	+1	+100	+200	+8	+10
b		+1	+8	+20	+1·5	+1·33	+4	+100	+200	+4	+10
c		+1	+12	+20	+2	+1·33	+1	+100	+200	+0	+10
c		+1	+12	+20	+2·5	+1·67	+1	+100	+200	+0	+10
d		+1	+12	+15	+1·5	+1·67	+4	+50	+112·5	+0	+5
e	m	+1	+12	+10	+1	+1·67	+2	+0	+50	+0	+0
f		+1	+12	+5	+1·5	+1·67	+4	+0	+12·5	+0	+0
g		+1	+12	+0	+2·5	+1·67	+1	+0	+0	+0	+0
g		+1	+12	+0	+2	+2	+1	+0	+0	+0	+0
h		+1	+6	+0	+2	+2	+4	+0	+0	+0	+0
j		+1	+0	+0	+2	+2	+1	+0	+0	+0	+0
a		+0	+0	−1	+0·5	+1·33	+1	−10	−20	+0	−1
b		+0	+0	−1	+0·75	+1·33	+4	−10	−20	+0	−1
c		+0	+0	−1	+1·0	+1·33	+1	−10	−20	+0	−1
c		+0	−1	+0	+1·2	+1·67	+1	+0	+0	−1	+0
d		+0	−1	+0	+0·8	+1·67	+4	+0	+0	−1	+0
e	n	+0	−1	+0	+0·4	+1·67	+2	+0	+0	−1	+0
f		+0	−1	+0	+0·8	+1·67	+4	+0	+0	−1	+0
g		+0	−1	+0	+1·2	+1·67	+1	+0	+0	−1	+0
g		+0	+0	+1	+1·0	+2	+1	+0	+0	+0	+0
h		+0	+0	+1	+1·0	+2	+4	+0	+0	+0	+0
j		+0	+0	+1	+1·0	+2	+1	+0	+0	+0	+0
Sums		+11	+97	+110	+29·15	+36·68	+48	+420	+915	+7	+42

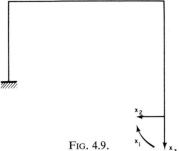

FIG. 4.9.

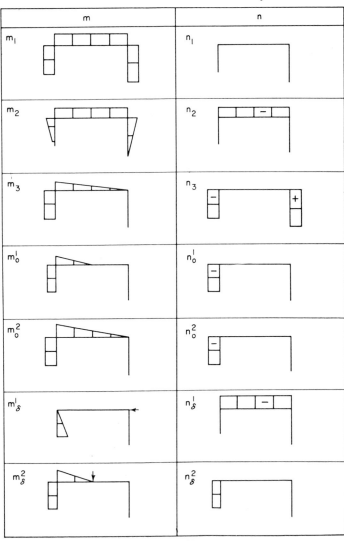

FIG. 4.10.

The preset parameter tape for this example will be prepared as follows:

T 1600
$+22$ (*l*)
$+3$ (*n*)
$+2$ (*w*)
$+2$ (*t*)

T 2000
$+67$ (5001)
$+89$ (5002)
$+111$ (5003)
$+133$ (5004)
$+199$ (5005)
$+265$ (5006)
$+274$ (5007)
$+283$ (5008)
$+327$ (5009)
$+333$ (5010)
$+339$ (5011)
$+383$ (5012)
$+427$ (5013)
$+471$ (5014)
$+515$ (5015)
J. 40·0

N.B. The total space required is 518 locations.
The output of results will appear as shown in Table 4.2.

TABLE 4.2.

17/3/60———32

Linear skeletal frame analysis

$\rightarrow$
15
$n+1$

0
$-0·32843451$
$+0·90702915$
$+2·14249278$
$+2·14249278$
$-0·28079052$
$-2·70407380$
$-0·12735708$
$+2·44935966$

+2·44935966
+0·59616418
−1·25793129
−0·48465665
−0·48465665
−0·48465665
−0·30886591
−0·30886591
−0·30886591
−0·30886591
−0·30886591
−0·51534335
−0·51534335
−0·51534335

$$= +1·44488153$$

1

−0·41965627
+1·16851397
+2·75668412
+2·75668412
−0·89577141
−2·04822684
−0·70068234
+3·14686221
+3·14686221
+0·76460693
−1·61764835
−0·98049108
−0·98049108
−0·98049108
−0·39704254
−0·39704254
−0·39704254
−0·39704254
−0·39704254
−1·01950891
−1·01950891
−1·01950891

$$= +0·07301568$$

*

→
20
$n+1$

0

−0·32843420
+0·90702949
+2·14249315
+2·14249315

$$-0 \cdot 28079010$$
$$-2 \cdot 70407333$$
$$-0 \cdot 12735656$$
$$+2 \cdot 44936023$$
$$+2 \cdot 44936023$$
$$+0 \cdot 59616470$$
$$-1 \cdot 25703081$$
$$-0 \cdot 48465664$$
$$-0 \cdot 48465664$$
$$-0 \cdot 48465664$$
$$-0 \cdot 30886592$$
$$-0 \cdot 30886592$$
$$-0 \cdot 30886592$$
$$-0 \cdot 30886592$$
$$-0 \cdot 30886592$$
$$-0 \cdot 51534336$$
$$-0 \cdot 51534336$$
$$-0 \cdot 51534336$$

$$= \; +1 \cdot 44488639$$

1

$$-0 \cdot 41965558$$
$$+1 \cdot 16851478$$
$$+2 \cdot 75668504$$
$$+2 \cdot 75668504$$
$$-0 \cdot 89577040$$
$$-2 \cdot 04822574$$
$$-0 \cdot 70068114$$
$$+3 \cdot 14686351$$
$$+3 \cdot 14686351$$
$$+0 \cdot 76460805$$
$$-1 \cdot 61764741$$
$$-0 \cdot 98049106$$
$$-0 \cdot 98049106$$
$$-0 \cdot 98049106$$
$$-0 \cdot 39704257$$
$$-0 \cdot 39704257$$
$$-0 \cdot 39704257$$
$$-0 \cdot 39704257$$
$$-0 \cdot 39704257$$
$$-1 \cdot 01950892$$
$$-1 \cdot 01950892$$
$$-1 \cdot 01950892$$

$$= \; +0 \cdot 07302684$$
*

$\rightarrow$
27
$n+2$

0

+1·79699451
+5·54798933

$= +7·34498385$

1

+2·31631932
+6·35297331

$= +8·66929262$
*

REFERENCES

1. J. C. DE C. HENDERSON and P. B. MORICE, *The Analysis of Engineering Structures.*
   Institution of Structural Engineers Fiftieth Anniversary Volume, 189–95 (1958).
2. P. B. MORICE, *Linear Structural Analysis.* Thames & Hudson (1959).
3. J. C. DE C. HENDERSON, A. D. EDWARDS and J. MUNRO, *An Application of an Electronic
   Digital Computer to the Linear Analysis of Skeletal Structures.* Imperial College.
   Con. Tech. Report No. 1, April (1959).
4. FERRANTI Ltd., Matrix Interpretive Scheme.

CHAPTER 5

THE USE OF COMPUTERS
IN STRUCTURAL PROBLEMS

E. A. RICHARDS

5.1. INTRODUCTION

THE two basic types of aids to computing are: firstly, analogues, in which quantities occurring in the calculation are represented by physical variables which are continuously variable, such as lengths, angles, voltages, currents, and time; and secondly digital equipment, in which numbers occurring are represented by physical objects which may assume a few discrete states, such as counting wheels which click into one of ten positions, switches which may be open or closed, and the presence or absence of holes in a tape.

5.2. ANALOGUE COMPUTERS

A slide rule provides a common example of an analogue computer. The accuracy attainable is a function of its size and precision of manufacture. Analogous remarks apply to all analogue equipment.

Another well-known device, the speedometer of a car, is supplied with data in the form of a rotation which is proportional to the distance travelled, which is differentiated with respect to time to indicate speed.

Rotating shafts are a convenient analogue, because the degree of rotation is not limited by the size of the machine. Differential analysers were built in the 1930s and 40s (notably by Bush) to solve differential equations. In fact these are regarded as integral equations, and the principal components are integrators based on the wheel and disc principle, in which a large disc drives a small wheel by friction. The distance x of the wheel from the centre of the disc is variable. The rotation is proportional to the product $x\theta$. Hence the mechanism is a multiplier. By varying x as the disc turns, the machine performs integration, for

$$\alpha \text{ is proportional to} \int x \, d\theta$$

Gearwheel systems are used for addition and subtraction in differential analysers. The usual necessity to amplify the small torque available from the driven wheel, and to counteract backlash and the difficulty of changing equations, is disadvantageous.

Many contemporary differential analysers use very stable d.c. voltage amplifiers in conjunction with resistance networks to add and subtract, and with capacitors to integrate (the voltage across being proportional to the total current fed in); a.c. voltages are also used. The performance of the amplifiers is often such that the overall accuracy is limited by the tolerances of the plug-in components used to provide the numerical constants in the simulated equations.

The development of digital computers in the last decade has overtaken that of general purpose analogue machines. Special analogue machines are extremely useful for simulating complex systems. Amazingly realistic aircraft simulators, for example, consist of a cockpit indistinguishable from that of the simulated plane, backed by computers which determine the configuration of all the indicating devices, including noise, vibration, and the feel of the controls, from the effects of the pilot's actions plus such changes in weather and failures of equipment as the instructor may decide. Similarly reactor simulators have been built for the purposes of research and training.

5.3. EARLY DIGITAL COMPUTERS

Examples of digital equipments are: digits (still used for counting), revolution counters, and cash registers. Unlike analogue devices, they are all capable of unlimited accuracy, within the capacity of the equipment, which can be arbitrarily increased.

The first modern calculating machine was built by Charles Babbage in about 1830, which was used for performing polynomial interpolation. He proposed a larger machine, called a " Difference Engine ", which would fit up to seventh-order polynomials and print the results. Although he obtained government support, the project was never completed. He also planned a much superior " Analytical Engine ". This would have resembled modern computers (which did not materialize until a century later) in every significant way except for its mechanical operation. The analytical engine was to read operating instructions from equipment similar to large punched cards. It had storage facilities for both instructions and numbers. The possibility was envisaged of the course of action of the machine being influenced by the nature of the result obtained so far, such as whether or not a number is negative. (In long division, for example, a trial divisor is rejected or accepted according to the remainder found at any stage.) The flow of information within a computer is shown in Fig. 5.2. The ideas of subroutine of instructions, and of introducing numbers for counting operations, were familiar to Babbage. But only small parts of the analytical

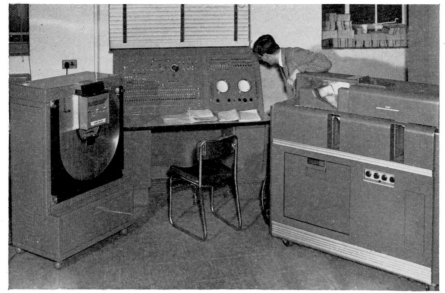

FIG. 5.1. Control Console, paper tape reader, card reader and punch—Deuce Mark IIa.

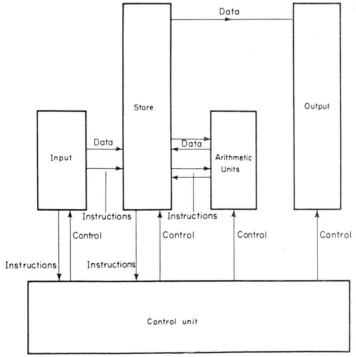

FIG. 5.2. Flow of information within a computer.

engine were built. The principles were rediscovered and applied in America during the Second World War.

The first automatic computer to be completed was the Harvard "Mark I" (1944) which resembled Babbage's machine inasmuch as it used wheels for number storage. These were, however, actuated by electric relays. Punched cards were used as input.

The first electronic machine was the Pennsylvania "ENIAC" (1946), which compiled extensive ballistic tables. The storage device was electronic valves, which could be retained in either a conducting or non-conducting state. Eighteen thousand valves were used—considerably more than later computers.

A typical first-generation computer is shown in Fig. 5.1.

5.4. BINARY NOTATION

In order to use conducting valves and other two-state recording media efficiently it is customary to express numbers in binary, or scale of two, notation rather than decimal, or scale of ten, notation.

In common decimal notation the power of 10 by which any integer, ranging from 0 to 9, is to be considered multiplied is indicated by its position, with the more significant digits on the left, e.g.

$$387 \cdot 4 = 3 \times 10^2 + 8 \times 10^1 + 7 \times 10^0 + 4 \times 10^{-1}$$

Similarly, in binary notation the power of 2 by which any integer, ranging only from 0 to 1, is to be considered multiplied is indicated by its position, the more significant digits may again be on the left, or on the right.

The latter case is illustrated here. The convention derives from the practice of regarding graphs as increasing to the right, and is called "Chinese" binary, e.g.

$$1011 = 1 \times 2^0 + 0 \times 2^1 + 1 \times 2^2 + 1 \times 2^3$$

(Chinese binary)   (decimal)

$$= 1 \quad + 0 \quad + 4 \quad + 8$$

$$= 13$$

Again,

$$1 \cdot 101 = 1 \times 2^{-1} + 1 \times 2^0 + 0 \times 2^1 + 1 \times 2^2 \text{ (decimal)}$$

(Chinese binary) $= 5\frac{1}{2}$

5.5. STORAGE DEVICES

Present-day computers are distinguished amongst other things by their storage capacity and type. Information in binary may be transmitted as a series of electrical impulses. The presence of a pulse indicates a 1 and its absence a 0. Such a sequence can be stored indefinitely as an acoustic wave in a tube of mercury, called a " delay line ". The impulses are created by applying the voltage to a piezoelectric crystal—as used in crystal microphones—in contact with the mercury, and received a little later by a similar crystal at the far end. The received signal is amplified, reshaped, and returned to the first crystal.

Delay lines can also be constructed from nickel wire.

Magnetic recording, using the principle of the tape recorder, is widespread. As well as tape, magnetic drums and discs are used. These contain a large number of short circular tracks, more quickly accessible than a corresponding length of tape.

The persistent glow on a cathode-ray tube has been used to store large numbers of dots.

Magnetic cores are widely used, in which each tiny blob of magnetic material can exist in two states, and be switched by a network of wires. A lot of individual cores is needed, but all the information is quickly accessible. The use of conducting valves has been mentioned. For large stores the cost is prohibitive.

As well as their use as input and output media, punched paper tape and cards can be used as auxiliary stores.

Generally speaking, the more rapidly information can be transferred to and from a store, and hence the more its utility, the greater its cost per digit. Therefore, most computers contain fast stores of limited capacity backed by large but relatively slow stores.

5.6. DESCRIPTION OF A COMPUTER

The central feature of any computer is its control section (Fig. 5.2). When a new instruction is transferred to control, its separate digits are used to control switches which ensure that the desired action occurs. The instruction generally contains a reference to one or more addresses within the machine. To take a hypothetical example the binary digits:

$$| \, 0010 \, | \, 1110 \, | \, 1000 \, | \, 1010 \, | \, 1011 \, |$$

entering control may be split into five groups as indicated, denoting the numbers 4, 7, 1, 5, 12.

This could mean " Perform operation type 4 (multiplication, say) on the numbers stored in addresses 7 and 1, store the result in address 5, and proceed to obey the instruction stored in address 12 ". The types of instruction commonly available to programmers include:

Reading data and instructions into the machine.
Output of results.
Transference of information between storage positions.

Elementary arithmetic operations.

Comparisons of numbers.

Choice of alternative procedures according to, for example, the sign of a number, or its magnitude.

Single instructions which, used repeatedly, will fetch (or store) data from consecutive addresses.

Visible (or audible) signals to indicate the course of the program to the operator.

It is not usual for functions such as **sin** and **log** to be generated by hardware. Instead, subroutines are written which evaluate these functions as required.

5.7. PROGRAMMING FACILITIES

The user of a computer is likely to be provided, by the manufacturer or others, with not only subroutines for producing commonly occuring functions but a library of complete programmes for standard operations such as the solution of linear equations, many ordinary and partial differential equations, etc., which enable much computing work to be performed by engineers and others who are not computer specialists.

Many master programmes have been written which enable operations to be controlled without reference to the basic instruction code.

Instead, the user employs " instructions " which are easier to handle than the basic instructions, and which may include such powerful examples as the multiplication of matrices or the numerical integration of a function. These user " instructions " are unscrambled by the master programme which then causes the appropriate subroutines to be fetched and obeyed.

In order to establish compatibility between different computers, an internationally agreed language, ALGOL, has been devised. This follows closely the usual algebraic notation, and includes some words of English. It is intended that a programme written in ALGOL shall be capable of translation into the machine code of any computer. The process of translation will of course be performed by a computer.

5.8. AN APPLICATION TO THE ANALYSIS OF RIGID FRAMEWORKS

Notation

A = area.

α = inclination of end 2 of a member relative to end 1, measured anticlockwise from the positive x-direction.

c, d = constants of integration.

$\mathbf{D}$ = displacement vector.

$\mathbf{D}_r$ = displacement vector of joint r.

E = Young's modulus.

$\mathbf{F}$ = force vector.

$\mathbf{F}^r$ = force vector at joint r.

$\mathbf{F}^r{}_{(k)}$ = force on member k at joint r.

I = second moment of area.

L = length of a beam.

M = applied couple.

$\mathbf{R}$ = rotation transformation matrix.

x, y = co-ordinate directions, variables in basic differential equation.

$x_i, y_i, \theta_i \ (i = 1,2)$ = small displacements at end i of a beam.

$X_i, Y_i, M_i \ (i = 1,2)$ = forces at end i of a beam.

$\mathbf{Y}$ = a stiffness matrix, having the property $\mathbf{YD} = \mathbf{F}$.

$\mathbf{Y}_{ij} \ (i,j = 1,2)$ = stiffness matrix relating force at beam end i to displacement at end j.

$\mathbf{Y}_{ij(k)}$ = $\mathbf{Y}_{ij}$ of beam k.

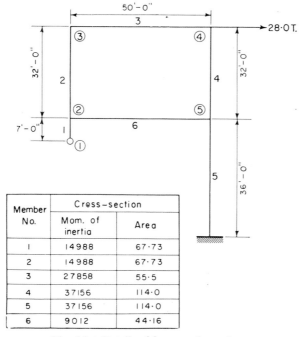

Member	Cross–section	
No.	Mom. of inertia	Area
1	14988	67·73
2	14988	67·73
3	27858	55·5
4	37156	114·0
5	37156	114·0
6	9012	44·16

Fig. 5.3. Details of frame and members.

Fig. 5.3 shows a two-dimensional rigid frame, subject to a number of loads, including a twenty-eight ton horizontal force at joint 4. Figs. 5.4 and 5.5 show the forces and deflexions corresponding to this loading case,

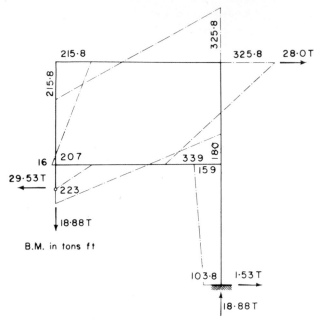

FIG. 5.4. Wind and crane surge b.m. diagram.

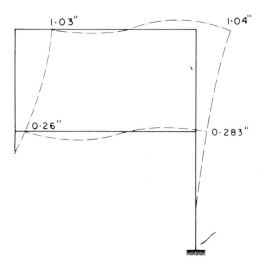

FIG. 5.5. Wind and crane surge deflexion diagram.

and there follows a description of how these results were obtained by the use of a digital computer.

The input data sheets (Figs. 5.6 and 5.7) show the form in which the problem was given to the computer installation. Lengths, areas, and inertias

SCHEME 2.
TITLE :- MECH. ANNEXE FRAME (SUBMITTED BY SOUTHALL)

INPUT DATA FOR BUILDING FRAMEWORKS. DEUCE PROGRAMME 78004

Job no: A/3102/01/973   78004/092   Date: 26.9.60

Members		No. of members used:-						
Member No:	Length (ft)	A(in²)	I (in⁴)	cos ∝	sin ∝	joint at end 1	joint at end 2	

Punching instruction	Bristol Tab Buff	Yellow tip	Yellow stripe	Pink tip	Pink stripe	G.I.P code cards a	b	Row
1	7	67.73	14988	0	1	1	2	2
2	32	67.73	14988	0	1	2	3	3
3	50	55.5	27858	1	0	3	4	4
4	32	114	37156	0	1	5	4	5
5	36	114	37156	0	1	0	5	6
6	50	44.16	9012	1	0	2	5	7
7								8
8								9
9								Y
10								X
11								O
12								1
13								2
14								3
15								4
16								5
17								6
18								7
19								8
20								9
21								Y
22								X
23								O
24								1
25								2
26								3
27								4
28								5

Finish triad with blanks

Joints		5	No. of joints in framework :-			Punch in b column of row 9 of purple data card	
Joint No:	Connected to rigid foundations by member No.			Punch P	Joint No	State if pinned or roller supported	
1				Y	1	PINNED	
2				X	2		
3				O	3		
4				1	4		
5	5			2	5		
6				3	6		
7				4	7		
8				5	8		
9				6	9		
10				7	10		

FIG. 5.6.

APPLIED LOADS AT JOINTS

No. of cases: 5   Job no: A/3102/01/973

Units: Forces in tons : Moments in ton–100 inches

Case			A	B	C	D	E	F	G	H	I
Punching instructions			* Punch each case as a separate 10,4,4, matrix (LKO8/1) on buff. 1st parameter card: Y row 1 × P17 X row (3 × no. of joints) × P17 O row no. of decimal places × P1 I row P₃–11 2 row 5 × P17 2nd parameter card: copy of largest element. (not row sum)								
Joint	X	1	0								
1	Y	2	0								
	M	3	0								
	X	4	0								
2	Y	5	−45								
	M	6	−45.0								
	X	7	0								
3	Y	8	−80								
	M	9	−80								
	X	10	0	−28.0	+28.0	0	0				
4	Y	11	−80	0	0	−263.5	−100.2				
	M	12	+80	0	0	− 17.42	+ 7.05				
	X	13	0								
5	Y	14	−45								
	M	15	+45								
	X	16									
6	Y	17									
	M	18									
	X	19									
7	Y	20									
	M	21									
	X	22									
8	Y	23									
	M	24									
	X	25									
9	Y	26									
	M	27									
	X	28									
10	Y	29									
	M	30									
Total	Column number :3×no. of points+1										
Number of decimal places: make total no. of places up to 9			−250.0	−28.0	+28.0	−280.92	−93.15				

FIG. 5.7.

and inclinations were given for each member. (Originally the inclination was specified as an angle, the apparently retrograde step of requiring a sine and a cosine is more convenient in the common case of an all rectangular structure.) Lists are also given of the joints occurring at the ends of the members and of foundation details. Any number of loading cases can then be specified, according to a sign convention printed at the top of the data sheet.

This data is processed, and the output for each loading case consists of:

(a) a list of joint deflections; and

(b) a list of the forces acting on the ends of each member.

For the loading in Fig. 5.4 these deflexions and forces are given in Table 5.4 and Fig. 5.9.

(i) *Method of Analysis*

A displacement method of analysis is employed, in which the main steps are:

(1) Prepare a matrix of stiffness coefficients for each standard member, which relates the components of displacement and rotation at the member ends to the forces and couples applied there by the equation.

$$\begin{bmatrix} \text{stiffness} \\ \text{of member} \end{bmatrix} \begin{bmatrix} \text{end} \\ \text{displacements} \end{bmatrix} = \begin{bmatrix} \text{applied} \\ \text{end forces} \end{bmatrix}$$

(2) Introduce compatibility conditions, by identifying the movements of member ends with the movements of corresponding framework joints.

(3) Introduce equilibrium conditions, by adding all applied forces to those member ends meeting at any joint and equating the total to the force applied at that joint.

(4) Collect all the equilibrium equations into a simple matrix equation:

$$\begin{bmatrix} \text{stiffness of} \\ \text{structure} \end{bmatrix} \begin{bmatrix} \text{joint} \\ \text{displacements} \end{bmatrix} = \begin{bmatrix} \text{applied loads} \\ \text{at joints} \end{bmatrix}$$

By the manner of its formation the structural stiffness matrix will be assembled from parts of the member stiffness matrices.

(5) Provided that sufficient fixity has been introduced (by clamping one of the member ends, say) it will be possible to solve the equation for the joint displacements, which is the first set of results to be printed.

(6) The now known displacements of the member ends are substituted into the equations in paragraph (1) above, so determining the applied forces which must exist at the ends of the separate members. These results are printed, one set for each loading case. From them it is a straightforward matter to draw bending movement diagrams.

A DEUCE programme employing this method has been used over one hundred times, with an average of about ten loading cases each time.

A few modifications have been made to the original version. A change in the basic unit of length employed gives more accurate results in certain awkward cases. The last part of the programme determining the internal forces was intolerably slow. The assembly and inversion of a stiffness matrix corresponding to ten joints took about twenty-five minutes, followed by about six minutes per loading case.

The effect of these several times six minutes had been underestimated, and the last part of the programme was then written in the basic machine code, reducing its time to one minute per loading case. It would be possible considerably to speed the programme by replacing the master control programme with basic instructions of similar effect. But in this case the instructions have been modified to a considerable extent and the replacement would not be an easy matter. The programming effort is in fact being applied to writing an entirely new version of the programme, with refinements which could not now be included in the original.

(ii) *Derivation of the Stiffness Matrix of a Horizontal Beam in Two Dimensions*

The possible displacements to be considered are extension and bending. The possible displacements of end 1, when end 2 is rigidly held, are (see Fig. 5.8):

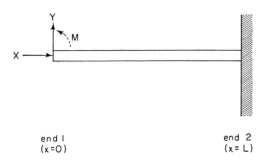

end 1   end 2
(x=0)   (x= L)

Fig. 5.8.

(a) Extension.
Hooke's law gives

$$x_1 = \frac{L}{EA} X_1$$

(b) Bending due to a couple.
Applying a couple M_1 at end 1 gives

$$\frac{d^2 y}{dx^2} = \frac{-M_1}{EI}$$

Integrating twice gives

$$\frac{dy}{dx} = \frac{-M_1}{EI}x + c$$

$$y = \frac{-M_1 x^2}{EI \; 2} + cx + d$$

and using the condition that $dy/dx = y = 0$ when $x = L$ we find that

$$c = \frac{M_1 L}{EI}$$

$$d = \frac{-M_1 L^2}{2EI}$$

and therefore when $x = 0$,

$$y_1 = \frac{-L^2}{2EI} M_1$$

and

$$\theta_1 = \frac{dy}{dx} = \frac{L}{EI} M_1$$

(c) Bending due to a force.
Applying a force Y_1 gives

$$\frac{d^2 y}{dx^2} = \frac{Y_1 x}{EI}$$

Integrating as before:

$$\theta_1 = \frac{dy}{dx} = \frac{Y_1 x^2}{EI \; 2} + c'$$

$$y_1 = \frac{Y_1 x^3}{EI \; 6} + c'x + d'$$

and using the end conditions gives that at end 1, where $x = 0$,

$$y_1 = \frac{L^3}{3EI} Y_1$$

$$\theta_1 = \frac{L^2}{2EI} Y_1$$

Collecting together the results, the principle of superposition enables the following flexibility matrix to be constructed, relating forces and moments at end 1.

$$
\begin{bmatrix}
\dfrac{L}{EA} & 0 & 0 \\[2mm]
0 & \dfrac{L^3}{3EI} & \dfrac{-L^2}{2EI} \\[2mm]
0 & \dfrac{-L^2}{2EI} & \dfrac{L}{EI}
\end{bmatrix}
\begin{bmatrix}
X_1 \\[2mm] Y_1 \\[2mm] M_1
\end{bmatrix}
=
\begin{bmatrix}
x_1 \\[2mm] y_1 \\[2mm] \theta_1
\end{bmatrix}
$$

(flexibility matrix)　　(force vector)　(displacement vector)

The matrix is easily inverted, giving a stiffness matrix with the required property:

$$
\begin{bmatrix}
\dfrac{EA}{L} & 0 & 0 \\[2mm]
0 & \dfrac{12EI}{L^3} & \dfrac{6EI}{L} \\[2mm]
0 & \dfrac{6EI}{L} & \dfrac{4EI}{L}
\end{bmatrix}
\begin{bmatrix}
x_1 \\[2mm] y_1 \\[2mm] \theta_1
\end{bmatrix}
=
\begin{bmatrix}
X_1 \\[2mm] Y_1 \\[2mm] M_1
\end{bmatrix}
$$

(stiffness matrix)　(displacement vector)　(force vector)

(iii) *The Transfer Matrix, and* Y_{21}

The stiffness matrix found above will henceforth be denoted by Y_{11} (Kron's notation), where the first suffix 1 refers to the end displaced and the second to the end at which the forces act.

The stiffness matrix giving the reactions at end 2 due to the displacement of end 1, denoted by Y_{21}, is found by considering the equilibrium of the member. The equilibrium conditions are:

$$X_2 = -X_1$$
$$Y_2 = -Y_1$$
$$M_2 = LY_1 - M_1$$

or in matrix form

$$
\begin{bmatrix}
X_2 \\[2mm] Y_2 \\[2mm] M_2
\end{bmatrix}
=
\begin{bmatrix}
-1 & 0 & 0 \\[2mm]
0 & -1 & 0 \\[2mm]
0 & L & -1
\end{bmatrix}
\begin{bmatrix}
X_1 \\[2mm] Y_1 \\[2mm] M_1
\end{bmatrix}
$$

Substituting for the displacement at end 1

$$
\begin{bmatrix} X_2 \\ Y_2 \\ M_2 \end{bmatrix} = \begin{bmatrix} -1 & & \\ & -1 & \\ L & & -1 \end{bmatrix} \begin{bmatrix} \mathbf{Y}_{11} \end{bmatrix} \begin{bmatrix} x_1 \\ y_1 \\ \theta_1 \end{bmatrix}
$$

$$
= \begin{bmatrix} -\dfrac{EA}{L} & 0 & 0 \\[2mm] 0 & -\dfrac{12EI}{L^3} & -\dfrac{6EI}{L^2} \\[2mm] 0 & \dfrac{6EI}{L^2} & \dfrac{2EI}{L} \end{bmatrix} \begin{bmatrix} x_1 \\ y_1 \\ \theta_1 \end{bmatrix}
$$

$$
= \begin{bmatrix} & & \\ & \mathbf{Y}_{21} & \\ & & \end{bmatrix} \begin{bmatrix} x_1 \\ y_1 \\ \theta_1 \end{bmatrix}
$$

(iv) $\mathbf{Y}_{22}$ *and* $\mathbf{Y}_{12}$ *Matrices*

These matrices give the forces induced at ends 2 and 1 by displacing end 2 while end 1 is held. $\mathbf{Y}_{22}$ could be found by an analysis similar to that which determined $\mathbf{Y}_{11}$, and then $\mathbf{Y}_{12}$ found by considering equilibrium. A neater way is to note that by the reciprocal theorem

$$
\mathbf{Y}_{12} = \mathbf{Y}_{21} \text{ transposed}
$$

and then, by equilibrium,

$$
\mathbf{Y}_{22} = \begin{bmatrix} -1 & \cdot & \cdot \\ \cdot & -1 & \cdot \\ \cdot & L & -1 \end{bmatrix} \mathbf{Y}_{21}
$$

Using either approach it is found that

$$
\mathbf{Y}_{12} = \begin{bmatrix} -\dfrac{EA}{L} & 0 & 0 \\[2mm] 0 & -\dfrac{12EI}{L^3} & \dfrac{6EI}{L^2} \\[2mm] 0 & -\dfrac{6EI}{L^2} & \dfrac{2EI}{L} \end{bmatrix}
$$

and
$$\mathbf{Y}_{22} = \begin{bmatrix} \dfrac{EA}{L} & 0 & 0 \\[2mm] 0 & \dfrac{12EI}{L^3} & \dfrac{-6EI}{L^2} \\[2mm] 0 & \dfrac{-6EI}{L^2} & \dfrac{4EI}{L} \end{bmatrix}$$

Now collecting all the stiffness matrix results so far obtained, and using the principle of superposition, there results the complete stiffness equation for a single member:

$$\left[\begin{array}{c:c} \mathbf{Y}_{11} & \mathbf{Y}_{12} \\ \hdashline \mathbf{Y}_{21} & \mathbf{Y}_{22} \end{array}\right] \begin{bmatrix} \text{displacements} \\ \text{(end 1)} \\ \hdashline \text{displacements} \\ \text{(end 2)} \end{bmatrix} = \begin{bmatrix} \text{forces} \\ \text{(end 1)} \\ \hdashline \text{forces} \\ \text{(end 2)} \end{bmatrix}$$

Thus if the displacements at both ends are known it is possible to determine the end reactions. It is not possible to solve these equations to find the displacements in terms of the forces, for the relations between the coefficients induced by the transfer matrices make the whole matrix singular. A physical interpretation of this is that, while knowledge of end displacements implies determinate forces, knowledge of the forces is insufficient to determine the location of any member.

(v) *Beams in Other Directions*

In this section primed quantities refer to a frame of reference fixed in space, and unprimed quantities refer as before to axes local to a beam, such that the axis of x is parallel to the length of the beam.

A transformation between the systems can be expressed as:

$$\begin{bmatrix} x \\ y \\ \theta \end{bmatrix} = \begin{bmatrix} \cos\alpha & \sin\alpha & 0 \\ -\sin\alpha & \cos\alpha & 0 \\ 0 & 0 & 1 \end{bmatrix} \begin{bmatrix} x' \\ y' \\ \theta' \end{bmatrix}$$

$$\begin{bmatrix} X \\ Y \\ M \end{bmatrix} = \begin{bmatrix} \cos\alpha & \sin\alpha & 0 \\ -\sin\alpha & \cos\alpha & 0 \\ 0 & 0 & 1 \end{bmatrix} \begin{bmatrix} X' \\ Y' \\ M' \end{bmatrix}$$

or
$$D = RD'$$
$$F = RF'$$

The original equation
$$YD = F$$

thus implies
$$Y\overline{R}D' = RF'$$

and since
$$R^{-1} = \overline{R}$$

$$(\overline{R}YR)D' = F'$$

Thus the stiffness matrix of an oriented beam is given by $\overline{R}YR$.

In the particular case of $\alpha = \pi/2$, the four submatrices become

$$
\begin{vmatrix}
Y'_{11} & Y'_{12} \\
\cdots & \cdots \\
Y'_{21} & Y'_{22}
\end{vmatrix}
=
\begin{vmatrix}
\dfrac{12EI}{L^3} & 0 & \dfrac{-6EI}{L^2} & \dfrac{-12EI}{L^3} & 0 & \dfrac{-6EI}{L^2} \\[2mm]
0 & \dfrac{EA}{L} & 0 & 0 & \dfrac{-EA}{L} & 0 \\[2mm]
\dfrac{-6EI}{L^2} & 0 & \dfrac{4EI}{L} & \dfrac{6EI}{L^2} & 0 & \dfrac{2EI}{L} \\[2mm]
\dfrac{-12EI}{L^3} & 0 & \dfrac{6EI}{L^2} & \dfrac{12EI}{L^3} & 0 & \dfrac{6EI}{L^2} \\[2mm]
0 & \dfrac{-EA}{L} & 0 & 0 & \dfrac{EA}{L} & 0 \\[2mm]
\dfrac{-6EI}{L^2} & 0 & \dfrac{2EI}{L} & \dfrac{6EI}{L^2} & 0 & \dfrac{4EI}{L}
\end{vmatrix}
$$

In the general case no terms are zero and trigonometric factors are evident (see references by Livesley), but the manipulation of these more complicated matrices is exactly the same as in our illustrative example.

The primes will henceforth be dropped, it being understood that a rotation transformation has been performed on Y if necessary.

Table 5.1 gives the Y_{11} matrices of the six beams in the illustrative example.

(vi) *Compatibility Conditions*

We now identify the end displacements of the several members with the displacements of the joints of the structure. The numbering of the members and joints is shown in Fig. 5.3. All horizontal members are taken to have

9

their own end 1 to the left and all vertical members are taken to have their own end 1 at the lower end. A suffix in brackets will distinguish a member; a superfix, a joint.

TABLE 5.1. Y_{11} MATRICES OF THE SIX BEAMS WHICH COMPRISE
THE STRUCTURE

(Unit of length = 100 in.)

(1)	(2)	(3)
$\begin{bmatrix} 394485 & 0 & -165683 \\ 0 & 1048202 & 0 \\ -165683 & 0 & 92782 \end{bmatrix}$	$\begin{bmatrix} 4129 & 0 & -7928 \\ 0 & 229294 & 0 \\ -7928 & 0 & 20296 \end{bmatrix}$	$\begin{bmatrix} 120250 & 0 & 0 \\ 0 & 2012 & 6035 \\ 0 & 6035 & 24142 \end{bmatrix}$

(4)	(5)	(6)
$\begin{bmatrix} 10236 & 0 & -19654 \\ 0 & 385937 & 0 \\ -19654 & 0 & 50314 \end{bmatrix}$	$\begin{bmatrix} 7189 & 0 & -15529 \\ 0 & 343055 & 0 \\ -15529 & 0 & 44724 \end{bmatrix}$	$\begin{bmatrix} 95680 & 0 & 0 \\ 0 & 650 & 1952 \\ 0 & 1952 & 7810 \end{bmatrix}$

For the forces on member 1 in terms of the displacements of joints 1 and 2 we have

$$\mathbf{Y}_{11(1)}\mathbf{D}^1 + \mathbf{Y}_{12(1)}\mathbf{D}^2 = \mathbf{F}^1_{(1)}$$
$$\mathbf{Y}_{21(1)}\mathbf{D}^1 + \mathbf{Y}_{22(1)}\mathbf{D}^2 = \mathbf{F}^2_{(1)}$$

Similarly for the other members in turn:

$$\mathbf{Y}_{11(2)}\mathbf{D}^2 + \mathbf{Y}_{12(2)}\mathbf{D}^3 = \mathbf{F}^2_{(2)}$$
$$\mathbf{Y}_{21(2)}\mathbf{D}^2 + \mathbf{Y}_{22(2)}\mathbf{D}^3 = \mathbf{F}^3_{(2)}$$
$$\mathbf{Y}_{11(3)}\mathbf{D}^3 + \mathbf{Y}_{12(3)}\mathbf{D}^4 = \mathbf{F}^3_{(3)}$$
$$\mathbf{Y}_{21(3)}\mathbf{D}^3 + \mathbf{Y}_{22(3)}\mathbf{D}^4 = \mathbf{F}^4_{(3)}$$
$$\mathbf{Y}_{11(4)}\mathbf{D}^4 + \mathbf{Y}_{12(4)}\mathbf{D}^5 = \mathbf{F}^4_{(4)}$$
$$\mathbf{Y}_{21(4)}\mathbf{D}^4 + \mathbf{Y}_{22(4)}\mathbf{D}^5 = \mathbf{F}^5_{(4)}$$
$$\mathbf{Y}_{11(5)}\mathbf{D}^0 + \mathbf{Y}_{12(5)}\mathbf{D}^5 = \mathbf{F}^0_{(5)}$$
$$\mathbf{Y}_{21(5)}\mathbf{D}^0 + \mathbf{Y}_{22(5)}\mathbf{D}^5 = \mathbf{F}^5_{(5)}$$
$$\mathbf{Y}_{11(6)}\mathbf{D}^2 + \mathbf{Y}_{12(6)}\mathbf{D}^5 = \mathbf{F}^2_{(6)}$$
$$\mathbf{Y}_{21(6)}\mathbf{D}^2 + \mathbf{Y}_{22(6)}\mathbf{D}^5 = \mathbf{F}^5_{(6)}$$

In the equations for member 5, the displacement of the lower end has been denoted by $\mathbf{D}^0$. Since all components of this vector are zero the terms including $\mathbf{D}^0$ can be omitted.

(vii) *Equilibrium Conditions*

Let the applied force at joint r be $\mathbf{F}^r$. This must equal the total of the forces acting on the members meeting at r.

Therefore

$$\mathbf{F}^1_{(1)} = \mathbf{F}^1$$
$$\mathbf{F}^2_{(1)} + \mathbf{F}^2_{(2)} + \mathbf{F}^2_{(6)} = \mathbf{F}^2$$
$$\mathbf{F}^3_{(2)} + \mathbf{F}^3_{(3)} = \mathbf{F}^3$$
$$\mathbf{F}^4_{(4)} + \mathbf{F}^4_{(3)} = \mathbf{F}^4$$
$$\mathbf{F}^5_{(4)} + \mathbf{F}^5_{(5)} + \mathbf{F}^5_{(6)} = \mathbf{F}^5$$

By substituting the previous expressions for $\mathbf{F}$'s with suffixes into the second of these last equations (the first is not typical), there results for $\mathbf{F}^2$:

$$\mathbf{Y}_{21(1)}\,\mathbf{D}^1 + [\mathbf{Y}_{22(1)} + \mathbf{Y}_{11(2)} + \mathbf{Y}_{11(6)}]\,\mathbf{D}^2 + \mathbf{Y}_{12(2)}\,\mathbf{D}^3 + \mathbf{Y}_{12(6)}\,\mathbf{D}^5 = \mathbf{F}^2$$

Similar results hold for the other joints.

(viii) *The Stiffness Equation of the Whole Structure*

All these expressions for the applied loads at joints can be assembled to form the following single matrix equation:

$$
\begin{bmatrix}
\mathbf{Y}_{11(1)} & \mathbf{Y}_{12(1)} & 0 & 0 & 0 \\
\mathbf{Y}_{21(1)} & [\mathbf{Y}_{22(1)}+\mathbf{Y}_{11(2)}+\mathbf{Y}_{11(6)}] & \mathbf{Y}_{12(2)} & 0 & \mathbf{Y}_{12(6)} \\
0 & \mathbf{Y}_{21(2)} & [\mathbf{Y}_{22(2)}+\mathbf{Y}_{11(3)}] & \mathbf{Y}_{12(3)} & 0 \\
0 & 0 & \mathbf{Y}_{21(3)} & [\mathbf{Y}_{22(3)}+\mathbf{Y}_{22(4)}] & \mathbf{Y}_{21(4)} \\
0 & \mathbf{Y}_{12(6)} & 0 & \mathbf{Y}_{12(4)} & [\mathbf{Y}_{11(4)}+\mathbf{Y}_{22(5)}+\mathbf{Y}_{22(6)}]
\end{bmatrix}
\begin{bmatrix}
\mathbf{D}^1 \\ \mathbf{D}^2 \\ \mathbf{D}^3 \\ \mathbf{D}^4 \\ \mathbf{D}^5
\end{bmatrix}
=
\begin{bmatrix}
\mathbf{F}^1 \\ \mathbf{F}^2 \\ \mathbf{F}^3 \\ \mathbf{F}^4 \\ \mathbf{F}^5
\end{bmatrix}
$$

which is the stiffness matrix of the whole structure, multiplied by the displacements of the structure, giving the load on the structure.

Ignoring for the moment that joint 1 is constrained in two directions, the presence of a rigid support to member 5 is already sufficient to make the

TABLE 5.2.　STIFFNESS MATRIX OF THE ENTIRE STRUCTURE

	Joint 1			Joint 2			Joint 3			Joint 4			Joint 5		
	x	y	θ	x	y	θ	x	y	θ	x	y	θ	x	y	θ
Joint 1 x	512	0	−165683	−394485	0	−165683	0	0	0	0	0	0	−95680	0	0
y	0	512	0	0	−1048202	0	0	0	0	0	0	0	0	−650	1952
θ	−165683	0	2782	16583	0	6391	0	0	0	0	0	0	0	−1952	3905
Joint 2 x	−394485	0	16583	494294	0	107755	−4129	0	7928	0	0	0	0	0	0
y	0	−1048202	0	0	1278146	1952	0	−229294	0	0	0	0	0	0	0
θ	−165683	0	6391	157755	1952	100889	−7928	0	148	0	0	0	0	0	0
Joint 3 x	0	0	0	−4129	0	−7928	124379	0	7928	−120250	0	0	0	0	0
y	0	0	0	0	−229294	0	0	231306	6035	0	−2012	6035	0	0	0
θ	0	0	0	7928	0	148	7928	6035	4439	0	−6035	12071	0	0	0
Joint 4 x	0	0	0	0	0	0	−120250	0	0	130486	0	19654	−10236	0	19654
y	0	0	0	0	0	0	0	−2012	−6035	0	387949	−6035	0	−385937	0
θ	0	0	0	0	0	0	0	6035	12071	19654	−6035	74459	−19654	0	25157
Joint 5 x	−95680	0	0	0	0	0	0	0	0	−10236	0	−19654	113106	0	−4125
y	0	−650	−1952	0	0	0	0	0	0	0	−385937	0	0	729643	−1952
θ	0	1952	1305	0	0	0	0	0	0	19654	0	25157	−4125	−1952	102850

structure matrix non-singular. The only contribution to the structure matrix from this member is $\mathbf{Y}_{22(5)}$ in the last term, and the remarks concerning dependent coefficients no longer apply.

The numerical values of this matrix are given in Table 5.2. The digital computer has determined them from the first data sheet, using the properties of the beams to form the basic sub-matrices and the list of joints at member ends to sort them into their positions.

It follows from the way in which the conditions of equilibrium and compatibility have been introduced that:

if the stiffness matrix of the structure be partitioned into sub-matrices $\mathbf{Y}_{rs}$, equal in size with the member sub-matrices, then the four $\mathbf{Y}$ matrices for a member which has joint r at end 1 and joint s at end 2 are disposed as follows:

$\mathbf{Y}_{11}$ adds into position $\mathbf{Y}_{rr}$ of the structure matrix.

$\mathbf{Y}_{12}$ occupies position $\mathbf{Y}_{rs}$ of the structure matrix.

$\mathbf{Y}_{21}$ occupies position $\mathbf{Y}_{sr}$ of the structure matrix.

$\mathbf{Y}_{22}$ adds into position $\mathbf{Y}_{ss}$ of the structure matrix.

(ix) *The Effect of the Pinned Joint*

No equilibrium equation, or normal matrix row, is obtained for those directions which are constrained. In the example there are no rows or columns of the structure stiffness matrix corresponding to the fixed end of member 5. Similarly, only one equation for torque need have been introduced for joint 1, in place of the usual three, if the matrix had been set up by hand, and the resulting matrix would have been quite symmetric. However, for ease of programming joint 1 was treated at first like a normal joint and a subsequent correction made. The first two rows were replaced by zero coefficients, and a convenient arbitrary number then re-inserted on the leading diagonal (512, in fact, which as a power of two was easily generated). Provided that the load in the constrained direction is said to be zero, which is not restrictive since any non-zero load would be absorbed by the constraint, the first two equations implied by the matrix now simply state the restraint conditions. The remaining non-zero terms in the first two *columns*, while useless, are harmless.

(x) *Solution of the Equations*

The inverse of the stiffness matrix was found, and is given in Table 5.3. It may be called the flexibility matrix of the structure. Its terms are " influence coefficients ". When it is multiplied by any one of the load vectors, there results the corresponding vector of displacements.

TABLE 5.3.　INVERSE MATRIX × 10^{10}

Row 1	Row 2	Row 3	Row 10	Row 11	Row 12
19531248 +	00000002 −	03081305 +	18463427 −	00036291 −	00204819 +
00000037 −	19531213 +	03368584 −	13168040 +	00021711 +	03179630 −
00000000 +	00000000 +	00873690 +	01168181 −	00006339 +	00114867 +
00000000 +	00000000 +	00560827 −	00927796 +	00005231 +	00097019 −
00000000 −	00000000 −	00001645 −	00006432 +	00000011 +	00001553 −
00000000 +	00000000 +	00071134 +	00977201 −	00006003 +	00116764 +
00000000 −	00000000 −	01076289 −	03687374 +	00029772 −	00516959 −
00000000 −	00000000 −	00003853 −	00023302 +	00000060 +	00007394 −
00000000 +	00000000 +	00027605 −	00133830 −	00008238 +	00015536 −
00000000 −	00000000 −	01168181 −	03708884 +	00029676 −	00524706 −
00000000 +	00000000 +	00006339 +	00029676 −	00054999 +	00008216 +
00000000 +	00000000 +	00114867 +	00524706 −	00008216 +	00242639 +
00000000 −	00000000 −	00554529 −	01010991 +	00005546 −	00086188 −
00000000 +	00000000 +	00005028 +	00019653 −	00029117 +	00004746 +
00000000 +	00000000 +	00155137 +	00503255 −	00003764 +	00033149 +

Row 4	Row 5	Row 6	Row 13	Row 14	Row 15
17272420 +	00007591 +	01904658 +	16387097 +	00023189 −	03402196 −
02789284 +	19526257 +	03224467 −	02930572 +	00015231 +	01869094 +
00560827 −	00001645 −	00471134 +	00554529 −	00005028 +	00155137 +
00426257 +	00001362 +	00400694 +	00423264 +	00004163 −	00121483 −
00001362 +	00009538 +	00001575 +	00001431 −	00000007 +	00000913 −
00400694 +	00001575 −	00488786 +	00402604 −	00004812 −	00123594 +
00935033 +	00006455 +	00986830 +	01016615 +	00019722 +	00500450 −
00003160 +	00009532 +	00003578 −	00003404 +	00000024 +	00002552 −
00025949 +	00001420 −	00037466 −	00008278 +	00004339 +	00031239 +
00927796 +	00006432 +	00977201 −	01010992 +	00019653 +	00503255 −
00005231 −	00000011 +	00006003 +	00005548 −	00029117 +	00003764 +
00097019 −	00001553 −	00116765 +	00086188 −	00004746 +	00033149 +
00423264 +	00001431 +	00402603 −	00518022 +	00004374 −	00136163 −
00004163 −	00000007 +	00004812 +	00004374 −	00029127 +	00002790 +
00121483 −	00000913 −	00123594 +	00136163 −	00002790 +	00175207 +

Row 7	Row 8	Row 9
18627470 −	00029627 +	01063746 −
13214366 +	19515458 +	02907483 −
01176289 −	00003853 −	00027605 −
00935032 +	00003160 +	00025949 +
00006455 +	00009532 +	00001420 −
00986829 −	00003578 −	00037466 −
03748439 +	00023371 +	00143361 −
00023371 +	00053084 +	00007982 −
00143361 −	00007982 −	00270208 +
03687374 +	00023302 +	00133830 −
00029772 −	00000060 −	00008238 +
00516960 −	00007394 −	00015536 +
01016615 +	00003404 +	00008278 +
00019722 −	00000024 +	00004339 +
00500450 −	00002552 −	00031239 +

For few loading cases, or for a large structure, it would be more economical to solve the stiffness equations without forming the inverse matrix.

For the case in Fig. 5.3, the displacements are given (in inches and radians in Table 5.4.

TABLE 5.4. DISPLACEMENTS

$1x$	0
$1y$	0
1θ	-0.0032
$2x$	0.2597
$2y$	0.0018
2θ	-0.0027
$3x$	1.0324
$3y$	0.0065
3θ	-0.0004
$4x$	1.0385
$4y$	-0.0083
4θ	-0.0015
$5x$	0.2831
$5y$	-0.0055
5θ	-0.0014

The main deflexions are shown in Fig. 5.5.

(xi) *Member Forces*

The computer programme continues to find the magnitudes of the forces acting on the members. The forces on the left of member 3, for example, are given by a previous equation as

$$\mathbf{Y}_{11(3)} \mathbf{D}^3 + \mathbf{Y}_{12(3)} \mathbf{D}^4$$

The forces at the opposite end could be found from the similar equation including $\mathbf{Y}_{21}$ and $\mathbf{Y}_{22}$, but by the equilibrium of the member it is sufficient to compute the forces at one end of the member, and the couple only at both ends. Loads for all members are given in Fig. 5.9, the units being tons and tons-100 in. From these results the bending-moment diagram of Fig. 5.4 was produced.

E. A. RICHARDS

LOAD	MEMBER	FORCES	DP
+000003	+000000	+000000	+000003
X_1	Y_1	M_1	M_2
−029531	−018878	+000000	+024808
−007242	−010831	+001923	+025887
−007242	−010831	−025887	−039099
−020758	+010831	+040610	+039099
+001531	+018878	+012449	−019062
−022299	−008047	−026731	−021548

FIG. 5.9.   Specimen output forces.

5.9. APPLICATION TO STRUCTURAL DESIGN

It seems an attractive proposition to modify the section constants of the framework in the light of the results, and proceed in steps towards an optimum design with no intervention by a human operator. Unfortunately no suitable criterion as to the alterations required has been found, which is simple to include in a programme. At present it seems far more satisfactory to employ an engineer to make design alterations, using the computer merely to analyse the effects of these alterations.

5.10. SOME OTHER PROGRAMMES

The approach discussed above has been extended by Livesley to include the effects of instability and plasticity by a series of solutions converging to the true solution.

The general linear displacement method in three dimensions and two-dimensional simplifications have been outlined by Kron. The framework programme is one of the two special cases; the other is grids loaded perpendicular to their plane.

The matrix force method favoured by Argyris has also been programmed. This method is particularly advantageous for large regular structures of fairly low redundancy.

Plastic methods lead more directly to automatic design tools than either elastic approach and provide an example of a scheme to determine a structure of minimum weight.

5.11. FUTURE POSSIBILITIES

While it is still a *tour de force* to analyse a large irregular space structure, this will be reduced to a routine, and more attention given to the detailed distribution of stresses within members.

It will ultimately be possible to produce programmes which, given the general type of structure and the specification it must meet, will produce an economic design in full detail, including parts-lists and fabricating instructions.

Kron envisages even more complex structures being assembled, using in the analysis the recorded properties of sub-assemblies.

Even with existing designs of computers much more can be done to make this ambitious programming feasible. A measure of standardization is being sought on methods of constructing a fast programme by the computer itself, using as input only an algebraic statement of the problem, and there is much work being done on refined numerical methods of solving various kinds of equation.

Finally, improvements in computing equipment can be expected—the history of modern computers spans only fifteen years. Greater size and reliability will be demanded, and increased speed. The fastest circuits so far proposed use super-conducting elements immersed in liquid helium, whereby elementary operations are performed in a few millimicroseconds rather than microseconds. The limiting factor to increased speed will soon be the finite speed of light, which only travels about $1/100$ in. in $1 \mu\mu$ sec., and the computing elements must be of comparable magnitude.

REFERENCES

Displacement Methods

R. K. LIVESLEY, Application of an electronic digital computer to some problems of structural analysis. *Structural Engineer* January (1956).

G. KRON, Diakoptics the piecewise solution of large scale systems, chapter VIII. *Elec. J.* p. 399 (1958).

J. A. L. MATHESON, *Hyperstatic Structures*. Butterworth (1959). Covers both displacement and force methods and contains a chapter by Livesley on machine application.

Force Methods

MORICE, *Linear Structural Analysis*. Thames & Hudson (1959).

J. H. ARGYRIS, Energy theorems and structural analysis. *Aircraft Engng*. October (1954) to May (1955).

J. H. ARGYRIS and S. KELSEY, *Matrix Force Method and Some New Applications*. Ministry of Supply A.R.C. Rand M3034.

Plastic Methods

J. F. BAKER *et al.*, The steel skeleton, vol. 2, *Plastic Behaviour and Design*. Cambridge University Press (1954–56).

J. HEYMAN, On the absolute minimum weight design of framed structures. *Quart. J. Appl. Math.* **12**, 314–24 (1959).

General

Conference on Electronic Computation, Kansas City, November 20–21, 1958. Structural Division A.S.C.E. (1959).

Matrix Manipulation and Numerical Analysis

Those to whom this subject is unfamiliar are warned:

   (i) Any book devoted wholly to the subject will contain far more detail than is usually required by an engineer.

 (ii) A slight familiarity with determinants is more of a hindrance than a help. In particular, the method of solving equations by forming ratios of determinants is not to be regarded as having practical utility.

Modern Computing Methods. N.P.L. Notes on Applied Science No. 16. H.M.S.O. Contains an excellent bibliography.

The books by Matheson and Morice also contain adequate chapters on matrices.

Computers

F. L. ALT, *Electronic Digital Computers.* Academic Press (1958).

M. V. WILKES, *Automatic Digital Computers*, Methuen (1956); *The Computer Journal* (quarterly), British Computer Society.

CHAPTER 6

AN INTRODUCTION TO THE ELASTIC BEHAVIOUR OF SHELLS AND PLATES

A. H. CHILVER

INTRODUCTION

OF the many structural problems associated with nuclear reactors some of the most difficult, and most interesting, are concerned with the strength of thin metal shells and plates. In the gas-cooled graphite-moderated types of reactors, which are under construction at present in this country, thin steel shells are used to contain the gas coolant. The structural problems associated with these shells include those of supporting the shell and providing holes for the flow of the coolant gas; the problems of stresses in the shell due to discontinuities are perhaps the most difficult analytically. Shell problems range, however, from those of the large containment vessels to those of the fuel element tubes. Problems of flat plates are perhaps less important; they arise in certain grillages, designed to support the graphite core of the reactor.

The aim in this chapter is to review the fundamental behaviour of shells as elastic systems; for this reason the basic assumptions in engineering theories of the bending of shells are discussed at some length. Only a few practical problems are considered; fuller treatments of a wide range of practical problems are given in the books by Flügge,* and by Timoshenko and Woinowsky-Krieger.* In this chapter, the simple linear-elastic theory of thin shells is first reviewed; the forms this theory takes for spherical and circular cylindrical shells are then presented; flat plates are treated as an extreme case of shells. The chapter includes brief notes on the buckling of shells and plates.

The linear-elastic theory is presented largely in the form due to Novozhilov; his work is now available in English translation,* and reference should be made to his book for a fuller treatment of linear-elastic problems.

---

*See the short bibliography on p. 188.

PRINCIPAL NOTATION

x = Cartesian coordinates.
ξ = curvilinear coordinates.
f = function of a surface in space.
s = length along a curve.
θ, ϕ = angular coordinates.
u = displacement.
ψ = angle of rotation.
ε = linear strain.
β = bending strain, twisting strain.
σ = stress.
σ_{cr} = critical buckling stress.
N = force per unit length.
M = couple per unit length.
q = force per unit area.
E = Young's modulus.
v = Poisson's ratio.
B = bending stiffness, torsional stiffness.
R = radius of curvature.
k = curvature.
L, b, t = linear dimensions.
ρ = density.
g = acceleration.
w = weight per unit area.
μ = geometric constant.

6.1. LINEAR-ELASTIC THEORY OF THIN SHELLS

(i) *Geometrical Properties of a Surface in Space*

A thin shell is a continuous structural form in space with the property that one of its principal linear dimensions, namely its thickness, is small compared with its other principal linear dimensions—which may be its length, breadth, radius of curvature, and so on. A thin shell, in fact, is essentially a surface in space; the form of the surface defines the nature of the internal loading actions in the shell. It is not surprising, therefore, that in any general theory of shells we must make some use of the geometrical properties of a surface in space. For this purpose we consider any curved surface S in space, Fig. 6.1, and we shall refer the surface to the Cartesian co-ordinate system x_I, x_{II}, x_{III} which will be refered to briefly as the system $x_i (i = \text{I, II, III})$. Suppose P is a point on the surface having coordinates x_i.

The surface S may be defined by expressing the coordinates x_i in terms of *two* independent parameters, ξ_1, ξ_2; we may write

$$x_{\mathrm{I}} \equiv x_{\mathrm{I}}(\xi_1, \xi_2)$$

$$x_{\mathrm{II}} \equiv x_{\mathrm{II}}(\xi_1, \xi_2) \tag{6.1}$$

$$x_{\mathrm{III}} \equiv x_{\mathrm{III}}(\xi_1, \xi_2)$$

or, more briefly,

$$x_i \equiv x_i(\xi_1, \xi_2)$$

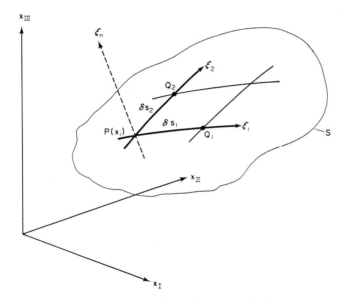

FIG. 6.1.   Coordinates of a point on a surface in space.

If the parameter ξ_2 is kept constant, then the parameter ξ_1 defines a line in the surface, which we shall call a ξ_1 co-ordinate line; in general this line is curved in space. Similarly, a curved line in space for which ξ_1 is constant defines a ξ_2 co-ordinate line. Positive directions along the co-ordinate lines correspond to ξ_1, ξ_2 increasing.

Now consider a point Q_1 near to the point P and lying on a ξ_1 co-ordinate line passing through P. The coordinates of P are x_i, while the coordinates of Q_1 are

$$x_i + \frac{\partial x_i}{\partial \xi_1} \delta \xi_1$$

if $\delta \xi_1$ is infinitesimally small. Then the infinitesimally small distance, δs_1, from P to Q_1 along the ξ_1 co-ordinate line is given by

$$\delta s_1^2 = \left[\left(\frac{\partial x_{\mathrm{I}}}{\partial \xi_1}\right)^2 + \left(\frac{\partial x_{\mathrm{II}}}{\partial \xi_1}\right)^2 + \left(\frac{\partial x_{\mathrm{III}}}{\partial \xi_1}\right)^2 \right] \delta \xi_1^2 = \sum_i \left(\frac{\partial x_i}{\partial \xi_1}\right)^2 \delta \xi_1^2$$

Suppose

$$1 = \sqrt{\left[\sum_i \left(\frac{\partial x_i}{\partial \xi_1}\right)^2\right]} \tag{6.2a}$$

Then if s_1 is taken positive in the direction of ξ_1 increasing, we have

$$\delta s_1 = f_1\,\delta\xi_1 \tag{6.3a}$$

In a similar way we take a neighbouring point Q_2 lying on the ξ_2 co-ordinate line through P; if

$$f_2 = \sqrt{\left[\sum_i \left(\frac{\partial x_i}{\partial \xi_2}\right)^2\right]} \tag{6.2b}$$

then

$$\delta s_2 = f_2\,\delta\xi_2 \tag{6.3b}$$

The direction cosines of the tangent to the ξ_1 co-ordinate line at P are

$$\left| \frac{\partial x_i}{\partial \xi_1}\frac{\delta\xi_1}{\delta s_1} \right._{\delta s_1 \to 0} = \frac{1}{f_1}\frac{\partial x_i}{\partial \xi_1}, \quad (i = \mathrm{I, II, III}) \tag{6.4a}$$

and, similarly, the direction cosines of the tangent to the ξ_2 co-ordinate line at P are

$$\frac{1}{f_2}\frac{\partial x_i}{\partial \xi_2}, \quad (i = \mathrm{I, II, III}) \tag{6.4b}$$

In general there is an unlimited choice of the parameters ξ_1, ξ_2 which define the surface in the x_i space. One suitable choice of parameters is that for which the co-ordinate lines ξ_1, ξ_2 coincide with the *axes of principal curvature* of the surface. Consider again the point P of the surface; suppose ξ_n is the normal to the surface at the point P, Fig. 6.2. If the ξ_1 co-ordinate line is a line of principal curvature, then the normal $(\xi_n)_1$ at a point Q_1 of the surface an infinitesimally small distance δs_1 along the ξ_1 line may be considered co-planar with the normal ξ_n at P. Similarly if ξ_2 is a line of principal curvature, the normal $(\xi_n)_2$ at the point Q_2 on the ξ_2 line may be considered co-planar with the normal ξ_n at P. If ξ_1, ξ_2 are both lines of principal curvature we have the further property that these lines intersect orthogonally. In general there is only one pair of lines of principal curvature at a point of a surface; for any other co-ordinate lines, normals at adjacent points along a co-ordinate line cannot be considered as co-planar.

If ξ_1, ξ_2 are lines of principal curvature, then for orthogonality the sum of the products of corresponding direction cosines of these lines is zero; that is, from equations (6.4),

$$\sum_i \frac{\partial x_i}{\partial \xi_1}\frac{\partial x_i}{\partial \xi_2} = 0$$

If l_{I}, l_{II}, l_{III}, are the direction cosines of the normal ξ_n, then

$$l_{\mathrm{I}}^2 + l_{\mathrm{II}}^2 + l_{\mathrm{III}}^2 = 1 \qquad (6.5a)$$

and, since ξ_n is orthogonal to ξ_1 and ξ_2,

$$\sum_i l_i \frac{\partial x_i}{\partial \xi_1} = 0, \quad \sum_i l_i \frac{\partial x_i}{\partial \xi_2} = 0, \quad (i = \mathrm{I}, \mathrm{II}, \mathrm{III}) \qquad (6.5b \text{ and } c)$$

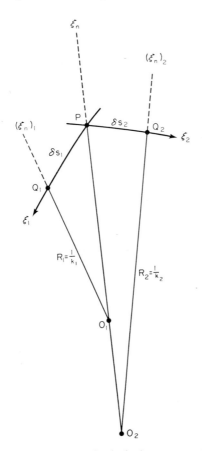

FIG. 6.2.   Co-ordinate lines of principal curvature of a surface.

The values of l_{I}, l_{II}, l_{III} are therefore determined, except possibly for sign, by the three equations (6.5). The positive direction along the normal ξ_n is that which forms a right-handed co-ordinate system with positive directions along ξ_1 and ξ_2, taken in the order ξ_1, ξ_2, ξ_n.

If the normal $(\xi_n)_1$ in Fig. 6.2 intersects the normal ξ_n at O_1, then the radius of curvature R_1 of the ξ_1-line in the plane of the normals is

$R_1 = O_1 Q_1 = O_1 P$; then R_1 is a *principal radius of curvature*; in a similar way the principal radius of curvature R_2 is defined in the plane of the normals ξ_n, $(\xi_n)_2$. The *principal curvatures*, k_1, k_2, are defined as

$$k_1 = \frac{1}{R_1}, \quad k_2 = \frac{1}{R_2} \tag{6.6}$$

For the lines of principal curvature, ξ_1, ξ_2, the functions f_1, f_2, defined by equations (6.2), and the curvatures k_1, k_2 are not entirely independent. They are related by the Codazzi–Gauss conditions

$$\frac{\partial}{\partial \xi_1}(k_2 f_2) - k_1 \frac{\partial f_2}{\partial \xi_1} = 0 \tag{6.7a}$$

$$\frac{\partial}{\partial \xi_2}(k_1 f_1) - k_2 \frac{\partial f_1}{\partial \xi_2} = 0 \tag{6.7b}$$

$$\frac{\partial}{\partial \xi_1}\left(\frac{1}{f_1}\frac{\partial f_2}{\partial \xi_1}\right) + \frac{\partial}{\partial \xi_2}\left(\frac{1}{f_2}\frac{\partial f_1}{\partial \xi_2}\right) + k_1 k_2 f_1 f_2 = 0 \tag{6.7c}$$

(ii) State of Strain of a Shell

If a shell were infinitesimally thin it could be defined completely by a surface in space; in fact the shell must have a finite thickness. We can, however, consider the surface which is formed by points at the mid-thickness of the shell. We shall show that the displacements of this *middle surface* define the strains throughout the wall thickness of the shell. We will use, therefore, the general geometrical properties of a surface to study deformations of the middle surface of a shell, and also to examine statical equilibrium of forces in the shell.

We take any point P, which we imagine to lie in the middle surface, S, of a shell; ξ_1, ξ_2 are co-ordinate lines of principal curvature of the middle surface at the point P, Fig. 6.3. We now consider the strains induced in the middle surface S when points of the surface suffer small displacements. Suppose the point P of the surface is displaced *small* amounts u_1, u_2 along tangents to the lines of principal curvature ξ_1, ξ_2, and a *small* amount u_n along the normal ξ_n. The resulting strains of the surface will be taken as infinitesimally small and linearly dependent on u_1, u_2, u_n. In evaluating the strains due to these displacements we may therefore superpose the strains caused separately by u_1, u_2, u_n.

In Fig. 6.4 points of the surface are displaced only by amounts u_1; the remaining displacements u_2, u_n are taken equal to zero. The displacements of points Q_1, Q_2 along the ξ_1 co-ordinate lines are

$$u_1 + \frac{\partial u_1}{\partial \xi_1}\delta\xi_1, \quad u_1 + \frac{\partial u_1}{\partial \xi_2}\delta\xi_2$$

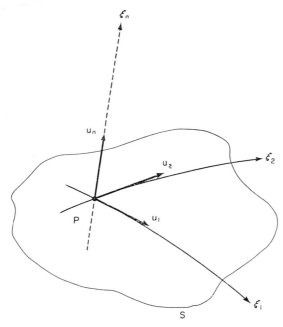

FIG. 6.3.   Displacements of a point of the middle surface of a shell.

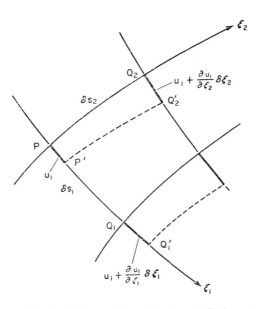

FIG. 6.4.   Strains of the middle surface due to displacement u_1.

respectively. The extension of PQ_1 due to u_1 is, to sufficient accuracy,

$$P'Q_1' - PQ_1 = \frac{\partial u_1}{\partial \xi_1} \delta \xi_1$$

The displacement of Q_2 along its ξ_1 co-ordinate line has a small effect on the length of PQ_2; the direction cosines at P of the tangent to the ξ_2 co-ordinate line are, from equations (6.4b),

$$\frac{1}{f_2} \frac{\partial x_i}{\partial \xi_2}, \quad (i = I, II, III)$$

and the direction cosines of the displacement $Q_2 Q_2'$ are, from equations (6.4a),

$$\frac{1}{f_1} \frac{\partial x_i}{\partial \xi_1} + \frac{\partial}{\partial \xi_2} \left(\frac{1}{f_1} \frac{\partial x_i}{\partial \xi_1} \right) \delta \xi_2, \quad (i = I, II, III)$$

The component of $Q_2 Q_2'$ along the tangent to the ξ_2 co-ordinate line at P is therefore

$$\left[u_1 + \frac{\partial u_1}{\partial \xi_2} \delta \xi_2 \right] \left[\sum_i \frac{1}{f_2} \frac{\partial x_i}{\partial \xi_2} \left\{ \frac{1}{f_1} \frac{\partial x_i}{\partial \xi_1} + \frac{\partial}{\partial \xi_2} \left(\frac{1}{f_1} \frac{\partial x_i}{\partial \xi_1} \right) \delta \xi_2 \right\} \right]$$

On making use of the orthogonality property of the ξ_1, ξ_2 co-ordinate lines, this component becomes

$$\left[u_1 + \frac{\partial u_1}{\partial \xi_2} \delta \xi_2 \right] \left[\sum_i \frac{1}{f_1 f_2} \left\{ \frac{\partial x_i}{\partial \xi_2} \frac{\partial^2 x_i}{\partial \xi_1 \partial \xi_2} \delta \xi_2 \right\} \right]$$

Now, from equation (6.2b) we have

$$\sum_i \frac{\partial x_i}{\partial \xi_2} \frac{\partial^2 x_i}{\partial \xi_1 \partial \xi_2} = f_2 \frac{\partial f_2}{\partial \xi_1}$$

Then the component of displacement becomes

$$\left[u_1 + \frac{\partial u_1}{\partial \xi_2} \delta \xi_2 \right] \left[\frac{1}{f_1} \frac{\partial f_2}{\partial \xi_1} \delta \xi_2 \right]$$

On ignoring small quantities of second order, this reduces to

$$\frac{u_1}{f_1} \frac{\partial f_2}{\partial \xi_1} \delta \xi_2$$

The extension of PQ_2 due to u_1 is therefore

$$P'Q_2' - PQ_2 = \frac{u_1}{f_1} \frac{\partial f_2}{\partial \xi_1} \delta \xi_2$$

The shearing strain in the middle surface due to u_1 arises from two causes: first, the increment of displacement

$$\frac{\partial u_1}{\partial \xi_2} \delta \xi_2$$

rotates the arc PQ_2 through a small angle, clockwise, of amount

$$\frac{\partial u_1}{\partial \xi_2} \frac{\partial \xi_2}{\partial s_2} = \frac{1}{f_2} \frac{\partial u_1}{\partial \xi_2}$$

to the position $P'Q_2'$; secondly, the component of displacement

$$u_1 + \frac{\partial u_1}{\partial \xi_1} \delta \xi_1$$

at Q_1 has a component

$$\left[u_1 + \frac{\partial u_1}{\partial \xi_1} \delta \xi_1 \right] \left[\sum_i \frac{1}{f_2} \frac{\partial x_i}{\partial \xi_2} \frac{\partial}{\partial \xi_1} \left(\frac{1}{f_1} \frac{\partial x_i}{\partial \xi_1} \right) \delta \xi_1 \right]$$

along the tangent to the ξ_2 co-ordinate line at P. On ignoring small quantities of second order, this component reduces to

$$- \frac{u_1}{f_2} \frac{\partial f_1}{\partial \xi_2} \delta \xi_1$$

so that the rotation of PQ_1 in being displaced to $P'Q_1'$ is a small angle, anti-clockwise, of amount

$$- \frac{u_1}{f_2} \frac{\partial f_1}{\partial \xi_2} \frac{\delta \xi_1}{\delta s_1} = - \frac{u_1}{f_1 f_2} \frac{\partial f_1}{\partial \xi_2}$$

The change of angle between PQ_1 and PQ_2 due to u_1 is therefore

$$\frac{1}{f_2} \frac{\partial u_1}{\partial \xi_2} - \frac{u_1}{f_1 f_2} \frac{\partial f_1}{\partial \xi_2}$$

The effect of u_2 on the strains of the middle surface can be dealt with similarly. The effect of the normal displacement u_n requires a separate treatment; we consider the surface subjected to displacements u_n, parallel to normals to the surface, and to no other displacements, Fig. 6.5. There is no change of angle between PQ_1 and PQ_2 during displacement, and there is therefore no shearing strain of the middle surface due to u_n. The extension of PQ_1 due to u_n is given with sufficient accuracy by

$$P'Q_1' - PQ = (R_1 + u_n) \frac{\delta s_1}{R_1} - \delta s_1 = k_1 u_n \delta s_1$$

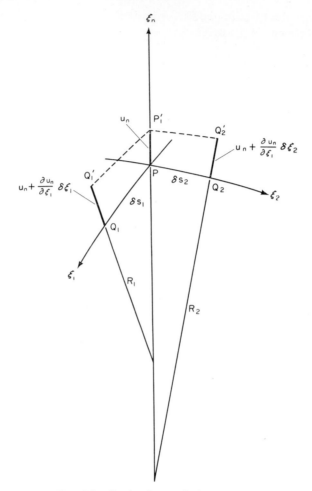

FIG. 6.5. Strains due to displacement u_n.

Similarly the extension of PQ_2 due to u_n is

$$k_2 u_n \, \delta s_2$$

We now add together the strain effects of u_1, u_2 and u_n. The total extension of PQ_1 is

$$\frac{\partial u_1}{\partial \xi_1} \delta \xi_1 + \frac{u_2}{f_2} \frac{\partial f_1}{\partial \xi_2} \delta \xi_1 + k_1 u_n \, \delta s_1$$

The total linear strain of PQ_1 is therefore

$$\varepsilon_1 = \frac{1}{f_1} \frac{\partial u_1}{\partial \xi_1} + \frac{1}{f_1 f_2} \frac{\partial f_1}{\partial \xi_2} u_2 + k_1 u_n \tag{6.8a}$$

Similarly the total linear strain of PQ_2 is

$$\varepsilon_2 = \frac{1}{f_2}\frac{\partial u_2}{\partial \xi_2} + \frac{1}{f_2 f_1}\frac{\partial f_2}{\partial \xi_1}u_1 + k_2 u_n \qquad (6.8b)$$

The shearing strain of the surface is

$$\varepsilon_{12} = \frac{1}{f_2}\frac{\partial u_1}{\partial \xi_2} - \frac{1}{f_1 f_2}\frac{\partial f_1}{\partial \xi_2}u_1 + \frac{1}{f_1}\frac{\partial u_2}{\partial \xi_1} - \frac{1}{f_2 f_1}\frac{\partial f_2}{\partial \xi_1}u_2 \qquad (6.8c)$$

The direct strains ε_1, ε_2 and the shearing strain ε_{12} define the state of strain in the surface.

We have considered the strains arising in a surface due to small displacements u_1, u_2, u_n of points of that surface. We have supposed this surface to correspond to the middle surface of a thin shell, that is, the surface which lies at the centre of the wall-thickness of the shell; the wall-thickness may vary continuously from one point of the middle surface to another.

We now make a simple assumption about any deformed condition of the shell; it will be assumed that points of the wall lying on a normal to the middle surface are displaced during deformation to points lying on a normal to the strained middle surface. The assumption that normals remain normals to the middle surface implies that there is no shearing strain through the wall-thickness of the shell; a shearing strain in the plane of the middle surface, or in planes parallel to it, is still possible. Such an assumption is justified if the shearing stresses across the wall-thickness, and acting parallel to the normal to the middle surface, are small compared with other stresses in the shell; this will be the case at points of a shell remote from supports or concentrated loads; moreover, shearing distortion effects will be localized around concentrated loads.

Consider a point P of the middle surface, where the thickness of the shell is t, Fig. 6.6; take another point P_n of the shell a distance s_n from P along the positive direction of the normal ξ_n at P. Then the extreme surfaces of the shell are defined by $s_n = \pm\frac{1}{2}t$. We now determine the displacements of the point P_n on the assumption that normals remain normal to the middle surface in the deformed state of the shell; this means that we can express the displacements of P_n in terms of s_n and the displacement functions u_1, u_2, u_n, if we assume that PP_n is unaltered in length. That PP_n is unaltered in length is a reasonable assumption since the stresses in the direction of the normal through the shell will be small compared with stresses acting parallel to the middle surface, for most practical problems. If the deformations are small then the displacements of P_n will be linearly dependent on u_1, u_2, u_n, and as before we can discuss the effects of u_1, u_2, u_n separately and superpose the results. In Fig. 6.6(a) the point P is given a displacement u_1 only, along the ξ_1 co-ordinate line; the middle surface then retains its curvature k_1 in the $\xi_1\xi_n$-plane, and the normal ξ_n is rotated clockwise through a small angle

$$\frac{u_1}{R_1} = k_1 u_1$$

in the $\xi_1\xi_n$-plane. A displacement u_2 of the middle surface along the ξ_2 co-ordinate line leads to no rotation of the normal ξ_n in the $\xi_1\xi_n$-plane.

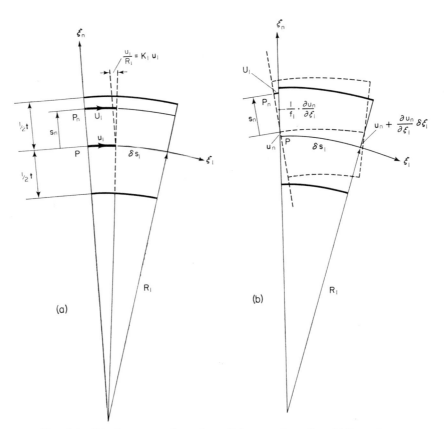

Fig. 6.6. Displacements of a point a distance s_n from the middle surface.

Again, in Fig. 6.6(b), the middle surface is given a displacement u_n only, along the normal ξ_n; the resulting rotation of the normal is a small angle

$$\frac{1}{f_1}\frac{\partial u_n}{\partial \xi_1}$$

anti-clockwise in the $\xi_1\xi_n$-plane. The total clockwise rotation ψ_1 of the normal ξ_n in the $\xi_1\xi_n$-plane is therefore

$$\psi_1 = k_1u_1 - \frac{1}{f_1}\frac{\partial u_n}{\partial \xi_1} \qquad (6.9a)$$

Similarly, the total rotation ψ_2 of the normal in the $\xi_2\xi_n$-plane is

$$\psi_2 = k_2u_2 - \frac{1}{f_2}\frac{\partial u_n}{\partial \xi_2} \qquad (6.9b)$$

Suppose the displacements of P_n parallel to ξ_1, ξ_2, ξ_n, respectively, are

$$U_1, U_2, U_n$$

Then to a sufficient degree of accuracy we have

$$U_1 = u_1 + s_n\psi_1$$
$$U_2 = u_2 + s_n\psi_2 \qquad (6.10)$$
$$U_n = u_n$$

The last relation implies that all points along a normal suffer the same normal displacement, u_n.

Since the displacements of the point P_n are now known in terms of u_1, u_2, u_n and s_n, we can easily find the strains parallel to the middle surface at P_n. We imagine a surface passing through P_n and parallel to the middle surface, Fig. 6.7; an element in the surface has sides of lengths

$$P_nQ_{1n} = (R_1 + s_n)\frac{\delta s_1}{R_1} = (1 + k_1s_n)f_1\,\delta\xi_1$$

$$P_nQ_{2n} = (R_2 + s_n)\frac{\delta s_2}{R_2} = (1 + k_2s_n)f_2\,\delta\xi_2$$

with radii of curvature

$$(R_1 + s_n), \quad (R_2 + s_n)$$

In equations (6.8), defining strains in the middle surface, we replace f_1, f_2 by

$$(1 + k_1s_n)f_1, \quad (1 + k_2s_n)f_2$$

respectively, and k_1, k_2 by

$$\frac{k_1}{1 + k_1s_n}, \quad \frac{k_2}{1 + k_2s_n}$$

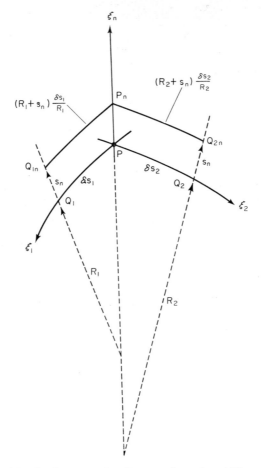

FIG. 6.7.   Strains at a point distant s_n from the middle surface.

respectively.   On making these replacements, equations (6.8) give for the
longitudinal strains $(\varepsilon_1)_n$, $(\varepsilon_2)_n$ and shearing strain $(\varepsilon_{12})_n$ at P_n the values

$$(\varepsilon_1)_n = \frac{1}{1+k_1 s_n}(\varepsilon_1 + \beta_1 s_n) \qquad (6.11a)$$

$$(\varepsilon_2)_n = \frac{1}{1+k_2 s_n}(\varepsilon_2 + \beta_2 s_n) \qquad (6.11b)$$

$$(\varepsilon_{12})_n = \frac{1}{(1+k_1 s_n)(1+k_2 s_n)}\left[\varepsilon_{12}(1-k_1 k_2 s_n^2) + 2\beta_{12}\{1+\tfrac{1}{2}(k_1+k_2)s_n\}s_n\right] \qquad (6.11c)$$

where
$$\beta_1 = \frac{1}{f_1}\frac{\partial \psi_1}{\partial \xi_1} + \frac{1}{f_1 f_2}\frac{\partial f_1}{\partial \xi_2}\psi_2 \tag{6.12a}$$

$$\beta_2 = \frac{1}{f_2}\frac{\partial \psi_2}{\partial \xi_2} + \frac{1}{f_2 f_1}\frac{\partial f_2}{\partial \xi_1}\psi_1 \tag{6.12b}$$

and
$$\beta_{12} = \frac{1}{f_1}\frac{\partial \psi_2}{\partial \xi_1} - \frac{1}{f_1 f_2}\frac{\partial f_1}{\partial \xi_2}\psi_1 + k_1\left(\frac{1}{f_2}\frac{\partial u_1}{\partial \xi_2} - \frac{1}{f_1 f_2}\frac{\partial f_2}{\partial \xi_1}u_2\right) \tag{6.12c}$$

The functions β_1, β_2 may be regarded as defining bending deformation of the middle surface, and the function β_{12} twisting of the middle surface. The state of strain of the shell is then completely defined by

$$\varepsilon_1, \varepsilon_2, \varepsilon_{12}, \beta_1, \beta_2, \beta_{12} \tag{6.13}$$

These six quantities are all functions of the three displacements u_1, u_2, u_n of the middle surface; the six quantities of strain are not therefore completely independent, and they are in fact related by three strain compatibility equations, which are found by eliminating u_1, u_2, u_n from the expressions for ε_1, ε_2, ε_{12}, β_1, β_2, β_{12}; in terms of u_1, u_2, u_n these strains are

$$\varepsilon_1 = \frac{1}{f_1}\frac{\partial u_1}{\partial \xi_1} + \frac{1}{f_1 f_2}\frac{\partial f_1}{\partial \xi_2}u_2 + k_1 u_n \tag{6.13a}$$

$$\varepsilon_2 = \frac{1}{f_2}\frac{\partial u_2}{\partial \xi_2} + \frac{1}{f_2 f_1}\frac{\partial f_2}{\partial \xi_1}u_1 + k_2 u_n \tag{6.13b}$$

$$\varepsilon_{12} = \frac{f_1}{f_2}\frac{\partial}{\partial \xi_2}\left(\frac{u_1}{f_1}\right) + \frac{f_2}{f_1}\frac{\partial}{\partial \xi_1}\left(\frac{u_2}{f_2}\right) \tag{6.13c}$$

$$\beta_1 = \frac{1}{f_1}\frac{\partial}{\partial \xi_1}(k_1 u_1) + \frac{1}{f_1 f_2}\frac{\partial f_1}{\partial \xi_2}(k_2 u_2) - \frac{1}{f_1}\frac{\partial}{\partial \xi_1}\left(\frac{1}{f_1}\frac{\partial u_n}{\partial \xi_1}\right) - \frac{1}{f_1 f_2}\frac{\partial f_1}{\partial \xi_2}\left(\frac{1}{f_2}\frac{\partial u_n}{\partial \xi_2}\right) \tag{6.13d}$$

$$\beta_2 = \frac{1}{f_2}\frac{\partial}{\partial \xi_2}(k_2 u_2) + \frac{1}{f_2 f_1}\frac{\partial f_2}{\partial \xi_1}(k_1 u_1) - \frac{1}{f_2}\frac{\partial}{\partial \xi_2}\left(\frac{1}{f_2}\frac{\partial u_n}{\partial \xi_2}\right) - \frac{1}{f_2 f_1}\frac{\partial f_2}{\partial \xi_1}\left(\frac{1}{f_1}\frac{\partial u_n}{\partial \xi_1}\right) \tag{6.13e}$$

$$\beta_{12} = k_1\frac{f_1}{f_2}\frac{\partial}{\partial \xi_2}\left(\frac{u_1}{f_1}\right) + k_2\frac{f_2}{f_1}\frac{\partial}{\partial \xi_1}\left(\frac{u_2}{f_2}\right) - \frac{1}{f_1 f_2}\left(\frac{\partial^2 u_n}{\partial \xi_1 \partial \xi_2} - \frac{1}{f_1}\frac{\partial f_1}{\partial \xi_2}\frac{\partial u_n}{\partial \xi_1} - \frac{1}{f_2}\frac{\partial f_2}{\partial \xi_1}\frac{\partial u_n}{\partial \xi_2}\right) \tag{6.13f}$$

(iii) *Internal Loading Actions*

We consider next the state of stress through the wall-thickness of the shell; we assume that the largest stresses are those acting parallel to the middle surface. Such stresses may arise either from stretching of the middle surface or bending of the shell. We take an elemental layer of the shell at a distance s_n from the middle surface and of thickness δs_n, Fig. 6.8. The only stresses causing appreciable strain of this layer are direct stresses σ_1, σ_2, parallel to ξ_1, ξ_2, respectively, and a shearing stress σ_{12}, again acting

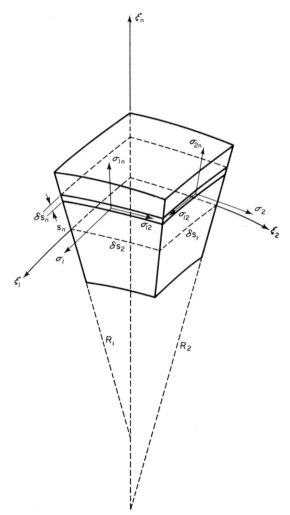

FIG. 6.8. Stresses on an element of the wall thickness.

parallel to the $\xi_1 \xi_2$-plane. Small shearing stresses σ_{1n}, σ_{2n} act on the layer parallel to ξ_n; there are assumed to be no direct stresses acting through the wall thickness in the ξ_n-direction.

We now integrate the effects of the stresses σ_1, σ_2, σ_{12}, σ_{1n}, σ_{2n}, and consider the resultant forces and couples as acting on the middle surface of the shell.   The integrated force actions on the middle surface are shown in Fig. 6.9;   they are expressed in terms of forces per unit length of the middle surface: N_1, N_2 are normal forces, N_{12}, N_{21} are shearing forces in the $\xi_1\xi_2$-plane, and N_{1n}, N_{2n} are lateral shearing forces, Fig. 6.9(a).   The in-

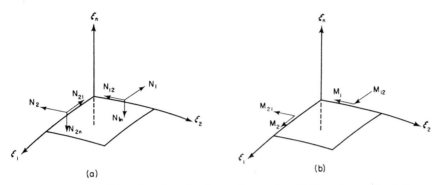

(a)   (b)

FIG. 6.9.   Intensities of resultant loading actions at the middle surface of the shell.

tegrated couples in the middle surface are shown in Fig. 6.9(b);   they are expressed in terms of couples per unit length of the middle surface: M_1, M_2 are bending couples, M_{12}, M_{21} are twisting couples.   Then we have

$$N_1 = \int_t \sigma_1(1+k_2 s_n)\, ds_n, \qquad N_2 = \int_t \sigma_2(1+k_1 s_n)\, ds_n$$

$$N_{12} = \int_t \sigma_{12}(1+k_2 s_n)\, ds_n, \qquad N_{21} = \int_t \sigma_{12}(1+k_1 s_n)\, ds_n$$

$$M_1 = \int_t \sigma_1(1+k_2 s_n)s_n\, ds_n, \qquad M_2 = \int_t \sigma_2(1+k_1 s_n)s_n\, ds_n$$

$$M_{12} = \int_t \sigma_{12}(1+k_2 s_n)s_n\, ds_n, \qquad M_{21} = \int_t \sigma_{12}(1+k_1 s_n)s_n\, ds_n$$

(6.14)

It is implicit in these relations that if k_1, k_2 are the undeformed curvatures of the shell, then the resultant loading actions are evaluated on the undeformed geometry of the shell.   This will be sufficiently accurate if the deformations are small.   The lateral shearing forces are given by

$$N_{1n} = \int_t \sigma_{1n}(1+k_2 s_n)\, ds_n, \qquad N_{2n} = \int_t \sigma_{2n}(1+k_1 s_n)\, ds_n \qquad (6.15)$$

In general, the internal loading actions will vary from one point of the middle surface to another.   The variations over elemental distances are shown in Fig. 6.10;   in considering the statical equilibrium of an element of the middle surface of the shell we must take account of external surface

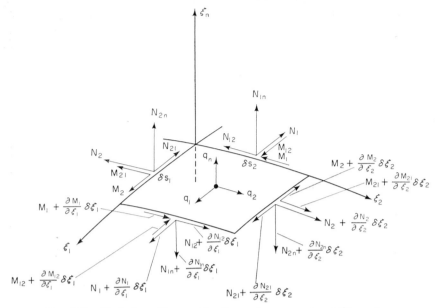

FIG. 6.10. Variation of internal loading actions over the middle surface.

loads, and we suppose these can be reduced to loads of intensities q_1, q_2, q_n, acting parallel to ξ_1, ξ_2, ξ_n, at the middle surface. For equilibrium of forces in the directions ξ_1, ξ_2, ξ_n, respectively, we then have

$$\frac{\partial}{\partial \xi_1}(f_2 N_1) + \frac{\partial}{\partial \xi_2}(f_1 N_{21}) + \frac{\partial f_1}{\partial \xi_2} N_{12} - \frac{\partial f_2}{\partial \xi_1} N_2 + k_1 f_1 f_2 N_{1n} + f_1 f_2 q_1 = 0 \tag{6.16a}$$

$$\frac{\partial}{\partial \xi_2}(f_1 N_2) + \frac{\partial}{\partial \xi_1}(f_2 N_{12}) + \frac{\partial f_2}{\partial \xi_1} N_{21} - \frac{\partial f_1}{\partial \xi_2} N_1 + k_1 f_2 f_1 N_{2n} + f_2 f_1 q_2 = 0 \tag{6.16b}$$

$$\frac{\partial}{\partial \xi_1}(f_2 N_{1n}) + \frac{\partial}{\partial \xi_2}(f_1 N_{2n}) - k_1 f_1 f_2 N_1 - k_2 f_2 f_1 N_2 + f_1 f_2 q_n = 0 \tag{6.16c}$$

For equilibrium of bending and twisting actions we have

$$\frac{\partial}{\partial \xi_1}(f_2 M_1) + \frac{\partial}{\partial \xi_2}(f_1 M_{21}) + \frac{\partial f_1}{\partial \xi_2} M_{12} - \frac{\partial f_2}{\partial \xi_1} M_2 - f_1 f_2 N_{1n} = 0 \tag{6.17a}$$

$$\frac{\partial}{\partial \xi_2}(f_1 M_2) + \frac{\partial}{\partial \xi_1}(f_2 M_{12}) + \frac{\partial f_2}{\partial \xi_1} M_{21} - \frac{\partial f_1}{\partial \xi_2} M_1 - f_2 f_1 N_{2n} = 0 \tag{6.17b}$$

$$N_{12} - N_{21} + k_1 M_{12} - k_2 M_{21} = 0 \tag{6.17c}$$

The last of the equations (6.17) is identically satisfied when N_{12}, N_{21}, M_{12}, M_{21} are expressed in terms of σ_{12} from equations (6.14).

(iv) *Elastic Strain Energy of the Shell*

We shall assume that the material of the shell remains elastic during deformation. If the strains are infinitesimally small, then Hooke's law can be applied, and at the point P_n of the shell in Figs. 6.6 and 6.7,

$$E(\varepsilon_1)_n = \sigma_1 - v\sigma_2 - v\sigma_n$$

$$E(\varepsilon_2)_n = \sigma_2 - v\sigma_n - v\sigma_1$$

$$E(\varepsilon_n)_n = \sigma_n - v\sigma_1 - v\sigma_2$$

$$E(\varepsilon_{12})_n = 2(1+v)\sigma_{12}$$

where E is Young's modulus, v is Poisson's ratio, and σ_n, ε_n are the stress and strain, respectively, in the ξ_n direction. We suppose $\sigma_n = 0$, and then

$$E(\varepsilon_1)_n = \sigma_1 - v\sigma_2$$

$$E(\varepsilon_2)_n = \sigma_2 - v\sigma_1$$

$$E(\varepsilon_n)_n = -v\sigma_1 - v\sigma_2$$

$$E(\varepsilon_{12})_n = 2(1+v)\sigma_{12}$$

On solving for the stresses, we have

$$\sigma_1 = \frac{E}{1-v^2}\left[(\varepsilon_1)_n + v(\varepsilon_2)_n\right]$$

$$\sigma_2 = \frac{E}{1-v^2}\left[(\varepsilon_2)_n + v(\varepsilon_1)_n\right]$$

$$\sigma_{12} = \frac{E}{2(1+v)}(\varepsilon_{12})_n$$

The strain energy per unit volume of the shell is

$$\tfrac{1}{2}\sigma_1(\varepsilon_1)_n + \tfrac{1}{2}\sigma_2(\varepsilon_2)_n + \tfrac{1}{2}\sigma_{12}(\varepsilon_{12})_n$$

so that the total strain energy, U, of the shell is

$$U = \int_V \left[\tfrac{1}{2}\sigma_1(\varepsilon_1)_n + \tfrac{1}{2}\sigma_2(\varepsilon_2)_n + \tfrac{1}{2}\sigma_{12}(\varepsilon_{12})_n\right] \mathrm{d} \tag{6.18}$$

where the integration is extended throughout the whole volume V of the shell. In the relation for U we substitute for σ_1, σ_2, σ_{12}, thus deriving an expression for U in terms of $(\varepsilon_1)_n$, $(\varepsilon_2)_n$, $(\varepsilon_{12})_n$; but these latter strains may themselves be expressed in terms of s_n, the distance of a point from the middle surface, and ε_1, ε_2, ε_{12}, β_1, β_2, β_{12}, the strain functions at the middle surface; on integrating the volume integral (6.18) over the wall-thickness t, and ignoring quantities of order (t/R_1), (t/R_2), compared with unity, we have, for a shell of uniform wall-thickness,

$$U = \frac{Et}{1-v^2} \int_S \frac{1}{2}[(\varepsilon_1+\varepsilon_2)^2 - 2(1-v)(\varepsilon_1\varepsilon_2 - \tfrac{1}{4}\varepsilon_{12}^2)]f_1 f_2 \, d\xi_1 \, d\xi_2 +$$

$$+ \frac{Et^3}{12(1-v^2)} \int_S \frac{1}{2}[(\beta_1+\beta_2)^2 - 2(1-v)(\beta_1\beta_2 - \tfrac{1}{4}\beta_{12}^2)]f_1 f_2 \, d\xi_1 \, d\xi_2 \quad (6.19)$$

where the integration is now extended over the whole of the middle surface S. The first of the integrals in equation (6.19) represents the strain energy of extension and shearing of the middle surface; the second term represents the strain energy of bending and twisting.

Now consider a small variation, δU, of the strain energy, resulting from small variations in ε_1, ε_2, ε_{12}, β_1, β_2, β_{12}. We have

$$\delta U = \frac{Et}{1-v^2} \int_S [(\varepsilon_1+v\varepsilon_2)\,\delta\varepsilon_1 + (\varepsilon_2+v\varepsilon_1)\delta\varepsilon_2 + \tfrac{1}{2}(1-v)\varepsilon_{12}\,\delta\varepsilon_{12}]f_1 f_2 \, d\xi_1 \, d\xi_2 +$$

$$+ \frac{Et^3}{12(1-v^2)} \int_S [(\beta_1+v\beta_2)\,\delta\beta_1 + (\beta_2+v\beta_1)\,\delta\beta_2 +$$

$$+ \tfrac{1}{2}(1-v)\beta_{12}\,\delta\beta_{12}]f_1 f_2 \, d\xi_1 \, d\xi_2 \quad (6.20)$$

A small variation of strain energy could also be evaluated by considering the work done by the internal loading actions N_1, N_2, N_{12}, N_{21}, M_1, M_2, M_{12}, M_{21} at the middle surface during small strain variations $\delta\varepsilon_1$, $\delta\varepsilon_2$, $\delta\varepsilon_{12}$, $\delta\beta_1$, $\delta\beta_2$, $\delta\beta_{12}$. We find that

$$\delta U = \int_S (N_1 \,\delta\varepsilon_1 + N_2 \,\delta\varepsilon_2 + \bar{N}_{12} \,\delta\varepsilon_{12} +$$

$$+ M_1 \,\delta\beta_1 + M_2 \,\delta\beta_2 + \bar{M}_{12}\delta\beta_{12})f_1 f_2 \, d\xi_1 \, d\xi_2 \quad (6.21)$$

where $\bar{N}_{12}$ and $\bar{M}_{12}$ are two *effective* internal loading actions, defined by

$$\bar{N}_{12} = N_{12} - k_2 M_{21} = N_{21} - k_1 M_{12} \quad (6.22a)$$

$$\bar{M}_{12} = \tfrac{1}{2}(M_{12} + M_{21}) \quad (6.22b)$$

If equations (6.20) and (6.21) are valid for all possible small variations $\delta\varepsilon_1$, $\delta\varepsilon_2$, $\delta\varepsilon_{12}$, $\delta\beta_1$, $\delta\beta_2$, $\delta\beta_{12}$, we have, by comparing terms within the two integrals,

$$N_1 = \frac{Et}{1-v^2}(\varepsilon_1 + v\varepsilon_2), \qquad N_2 = \frac{Et}{1-v^2}(\varepsilon_2 + v\varepsilon_1), \qquad \overline{N}_{12} = \frac{Et}{2(1+v)}\varepsilon_{12}$$

$$(6.23a)$$

$$M_1 = \frac{Et^3}{12(1-v^2)}(\beta_1 + v\beta_2), \quad M_2 = \frac{Et^3}{12(1-v^2)}(\beta_2 + v\beta_1), \quad \overline{M}_{12} = \frac{Et^3}{12(1+v)}\beta_{12}$$

$$(6.23b)$$

If $\overline{N}_{12}$ and $\overline{M}_{12}$ are determined by the state of strain, then we notice from the three equations (6.22) that there is an element of arbitrariness in the values of $N_{12}, N_{21}, M_{12}, M_{21}$. Anomalies of this type will not arise if the internal loading actions $\overline{N}_{12}, \overline{M}_{12}$ are considered. Since the strains may be written in terms of the displacements u_1, u_2, u_n, the internal loading actions may also be written in terms of displacements.

The equilibrium equations (6.16) and (6.17) may now be written in terms of

$$N_1, N_2, \overline{N}_{12}, M_1, M_2, \overline{M}_{12}$$

the shearing forces N_{1n}, N_{2n} being eliminated. The last of equations (6.17) is satisfied identically, and on eliminating N_{1n}, N_{2n} from the remaining five equations (6.16) and (6.17) we have the three equations

$$\frac{\partial}{\partial \xi_1}(f_2 N_1) - \frac{\partial f_2}{\partial \xi_1}N_2 + \frac{\partial}{\partial \xi_2}(f_1 \overline{N}_{12}) + \frac{\partial f_1}{\partial \xi_2}\overline{N}_{12} +$$

$$+ k_1 \left[\frac{\partial}{\partial \xi_1}(f_2 M_1) - \frac{\partial f_2}{\partial \xi_1}M_2 + 2\frac{\partial}{\partial \xi_2}(f_1 \overline{M}_{12}) + \right.$$

$$\left. + 2\frac{k_2}{k_1}\frac{\partial f_1}{\partial \xi_2}\overline{M}_{12} \right] + f_1 f_2 q_1 = 0 \qquad (6.24a)$$

$$\frac{\partial}{\partial \xi_2}(f_1 N_2) - \frac{\partial f_1}{\partial \xi_2}N_1 + \frac{\partial}{\partial \xi_1}(f_2 \overline{N}_{12}) + \frac{\partial f_2}{\partial \xi_1}\overline{N}_{12} +$$

$$+ k_2 \left[\frac{\partial}{\partial \xi_2}(f_1 M_2) - \frac{\partial f_1}{\partial \xi_2}M_1 + 2\frac{\partial}{\partial \xi_1}(f_2 \overline{M}_{12}) + \right.$$

$$\left. + 2\frac{k_1}{k_2}\frac{\partial f_2}{\partial \xi_1}\overline{M}_{12} \right] + f_2 f_1 q_2 = 0 \qquad (6.24b)$$

$$k_1 N_1 + k_2 N_2 - \frac{1}{f_1 f_2}\left\{ \frac{\partial}{\partial \xi_1}\left[\frac{1}{f_1}\left\{ \frac{\partial}{\partial \xi_1}(f_2 M_1) - \frac{\partial f_2}{\partial \xi_1}M_2 + \right. \right.\right.$$

$$+ \frac{\partial}{\partial \xi_2}(f_1 \overline{M}_{12}) + \frac{\partial f_1}{\partial \xi_2}\overline{M}_{12} \bigg\} \bigg] +$$

$$+ \frac{\partial}{\partial \xi_2}\left[\frac{1}{f_2}\left\{ \frac{\partial}{\partial \xi_2}(f_1 M_2) - \frac{\partial f_1}{\partial \xi_2}M_1 + \right. \right.$$

$$\left. + \frac{\partial}{\partial \xi_1}(f_2 \overline{M}_{12}) + \frac{\partial f_2}{\partial \xi_1}\overline{M}_{12} \bigg\} \bigg] \right\} - q_n = 0 \qquad (6.24c)$$

If the six internal loading actions N_1, N_2, $\overline{N}_{12}$, M_1, M_2, $\overline{M}_{12}$ were now written in terms of the displacements u_1, u_2, u_n of the middle surface, there would result three simultaneous partial differential equations in u_1, u_2, u_n. The general solution of the shell problem reduces therefore to these three equations, subject to the boundary conditions of the shell.

(v) *Loading Actions at a Boundary*

In our analysis so far it has been convenient to introduce five loading actions on any section of the shell at any point of the middle surface; these consist of three forces and two couples. Along a ξ_1 co-ordinate line, for example, a length PQ of the middle surface is subjected to forces N_2, N_{21}, N_{2n}, and couples M_2, M_{21}, Fig. 6.11. Suppose the line PQ is a boundary

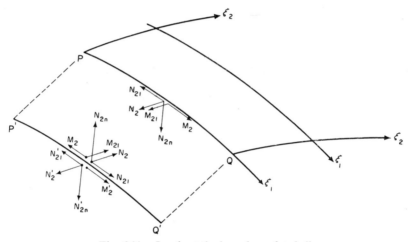

Fig. 6.11. Loads at the boundary of a shell.

of the middle surface: suppose $P'Q'$, which is identical with PQ, is an imaginary boundary, detached from the shell itself; then $P'Q'$ is acted on by the reversed loading actions on PQ. We suppose that $P'Q'$ is now supported by only four types of external loading actions—forces N_2', N_{21}', N_{2n}', and a couple M_2'; we consider the possibility that no twisting couple is required to support the boundary; we now find the relationship of the external loading actions N_2', N_{21}', N_{2n}', M_2' to the internal loading actions N_2, N_{21}, N_{2n}, M_2, M_{21}. We can consider these two loading systems as forming a self-equilibrating system, with perhaps external concentrated loading actions at certain points along the boundary. The work done in any virtual displacement of the imaginary boundary $P'Q'$ is zero, therefore; suppose $P'Q'$ is given any set of continuous displacements u_1, u_2, u_n, these being zero at any points of the boundary carrying concentrated external loading actions and zero at P and Q. The principle of virtual work, applied to the loading actions along $P'Q'$, then gives

$$\int_{P'}^{Q'} (N_{21} - N'_{21}) u_1 f_1 \, d\xi_1 + \int_{P'}^{Q'} (N_2 - N'_2) u_2 f_1 \, d\xi_1 + \int_{P'}^{Q'} (N_{2n} - N'_{2n}) u_n f_1 \, d\xi_1 +$$

$$+ \int_{P'}^{Q'} (M_2 - M'_2) \left(k_2 u_2 - \frac{1}{f_2} \frac{\partial u_n}{\partial \xi_2} \right) f_1 \, d\xi_1 +$$

$$+ \int_{P'}^{Q'} M_{21} \left(k_1 u_1 - \frac{1}{f_1} \frac{\partial u_n}{\partial \xi_1} \right) f_1 \, d\xi_1 = 0$$

On rearranging, this may be written

$$\int_{P'}^{Q'} (N_{21} - N'_{21} + k_1 M_{21}) u_1 f_1 \, d\xi_1 + \int_{P'}^{Q'} [N_2 - N'_2 + k_2 (M_2 - M'_2)] u_2 f_1 \, d\xi_1 +$$

$$+ \int_{P'}^{Q'} (N_{2n} - N'_{2n}) u_n f_1 \, d\xi_1 - \int_{P'}^{Q'} \frac{1}{f_2} (M_2 - M'_2) \frac{\partial u_n}{\partial \xi_2} f_1 \, d\xi_1 -$$

$$- \int_{P'}^{Q'} M_{21} \frac{\partial u_n}{\partial \xi_1} \, d\xi_1 = 0 \tag{6.25}$$

The last integral may be written in the form

$$\int_{P'}^{Q'} M_{21} \frac{\partial u_n}{\partial \xi_1} \, d\xi_1 = \left[M_{21} u_n - \int u_n \frac{\partial M_{21}}{\partial \xi_1} \, d\xi_1 \right]_{P'}^{Q'}$$

on integrating by parts; since $u_n = 0$ at P', Q', we have

$$\int_{P'}^{Q'} M_{21} \frac{\partial u_n}{\partial \xi_1} \, d\xi_1 = - \int_{P'}^{Q'} \frac{\partial M_{21}}{\partial \xi_1} u_n \, d\xi_1$$

Then equation (6.25) becomes

$$\int_{P'}^{Q'} (N_{21} - N'_{21} + k_1 M_{21}) u_1 f_1 \, d\xi_1 + \int_{P'}^{Q'} [N_2 - N'_2 + k_2 (M_2 - M'_2)] u_2 f_1 \, d\xi_1 +$$

$$+ \int_{P'}^{Q'} \left(N_{2n} - N'_{2n} + \frac{1}{f_1} \frac{\partial M_{21}}{\partial \xi_1} \right) u_n \, d\xi_1 - \int_{P'}^{Q'} \frac{1}{f_2} (M_2 - M'_2) \frac{\partial u_n}{\partial \xi_2} f_1 \, d\xi_1 = 0 \tag{6.26}$$

11

N.R.E.

If u_1, u_2 are to have *any* continuous values, then we must have

$$N_{21} - N'_{21} + k_1 M_{21} = 0 \tag{6.27}$$

$$N_2 - N'_2 + k_2(M_2 - M'_2) = 0 \tag{6.28}$$

at all points along $P'Q'$. Now if u_n is specified along $P'Q'$, then $(\partial u_n / \partial \xi_2)$ can be chosen completely independently; then we have, also,

$$N_{2n} - N'_{2n} + \frac{1}{f_1} \frac{\partial M_{21}}{\partial \xi_1} = 0 \tag{6.29}$$

$$M_2 - M'_2 = 0 \tag{6.30}$$

Equations (6.27), (6.28), (6.29) and (6.30) give

$$N'_2 = N_2, \; N'_{21} = N_{21} + k_1 M_{21}, \; N'_{2n} = N_{2n} + \frac{1}{f_1} \frac{\partial M_{21}}{\partial \xi_1}, \; M'_2 = M_2 \tag{6.31a}$$

The relevant loading actions along a boundary are therefore N_2, N'_{21}, N'_{2n}, M_2; the shearing forces N'_{21}, N'_{2n} may be regarded as *effective* shearing forces at the boundary. The relevant loading actions along a boundary which lies on a ξ_1 co-ordinate line are

$$N'_1 = N_1, \; N'_{12} = N_{12} + k_2 M_{12}, \; N'_{1n} = N_{1n} + \frac{1}{f_2} \frac{\partial M_{12}}{\partial \xi_2}, \; M'_1 = M_1 \tag{6.31b}$$

The effective shearing forces at the boundary may be expressed in terms of $\bar{N}_{12}$ and $\bar{M}_{12}$ in the forms

$$N'_{21} = N_{21} + k_1 M_{21} = \bar{N}_{12} + 2k_1 \bar{M}_{12} \tag{6.32a}$$

$$N'_{12} = N_{12} + k_2 M_{12} = \bar{N}_{12} + 2k_2 \bar{M}_{12} \tag{6.32b}$$

$$N'_{2n} = N_{2n} + \frac{1}{f_1} \frac{\partial M_{21}}{\partial \xi_1} = \frac{1}{f_1 f_2} \left[\frac{\partial}{\partial \xi_2}(f_1 M_2) - \frac{\partial f_1}{\partial \xi_2} M_1 + 2 \frac{\partial}{\partial \xi_1}(f_2 \bar{M}_{12}) \right] \tag{6.33a}$$

$$N'_{1n} = N_{1n} + \frac{1}{f_2} \frac{\partial M_{12}}{\partial \xi_2} = \frac{1}{f_2 f_1} \left[\frac{\partial}{\partial \xi_1}(f_2 M_1) - \frac{\partial f_2}{\partial \xi_1} M_2 + 2 \frac{\partial}{\partial \xi_2}(f_1 \bar{M}_{12}) \right] \tag{6.33b}$$

Boundary conditions are formulated in terms of the displacements

$$u_1, u_2, u_n$$

at the boundaries, in terms of the rotations

$$\psi_1, \psi_2$$

of the normals to the middle surface at the boundaries, and in terms of the loading actions

$$N_1, N'_{12}, N'_{1n}, M_1; \; N_2, N'_{21}, N'_{2n}, M_2$$

at the boundaries. Not all these quantities can be specified independently; for example, if u_1, u_n are specified along a boundary ξ_1, then

$$\psi_1 = k_1 u_1 - \frac{1}{f_1}\frac{\partial u_n}{\partial \xi_1}$$

cannot be specified independently.

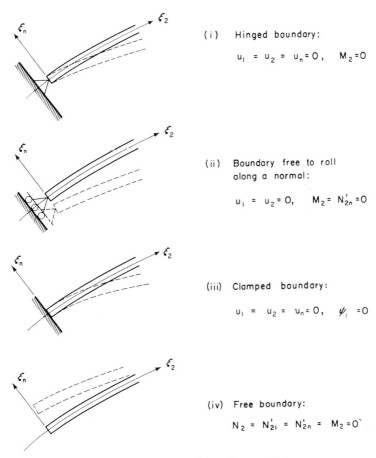

(i) Hinged boundary:

$$u_1 = u_2 = u_n = 0, \quad M_2 = 0$$

(ii) Boundary free to roll along a normal:

$$u_1 = u_2 = 0, \quad M_2 = N'_{2n} = 0$$

(iii) Clamped boundary:

$$u_1 = u_2 = u_n = 0, \quad \psi_1 = 0$$

(iv) Free boundary:

$$N_2 = N'_{21} = N'_{2n} = M_2 = 0$$

FIG. 6.12. Simple types of boundary conditions.

Four simple types of boundary conditions are shown in Fig. 6.12; the boundary lies on a ξ_1 co-ordinate line. On each of the boundaries shown in Fig. 6.12, four zero boundary conditions apply; in (ii) the rollers offer no restraint to movement of the boundary in the ξ_n-direction.

6.2. SHELLS OF REVOLUTION

(i) *General*

Many of the shells used in nuclear reactor structures are shells of revolution; the middle surface of such a shell is formed by rotating a curved line such as *AB*, Fig. 6.13, in space about the axis of symmetry *AA*. A plane through the axis of symmetry *AA* cuts the middle surface in *meridian lines*;

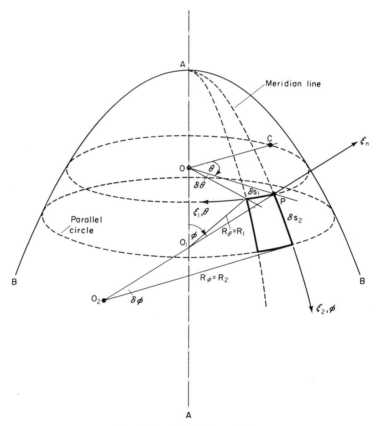

Fig. 6.13.   Shell of revolution.

a plane perpendicular to *AA* cuts the middle surface in a *parallel circle*. We take the ξ_1 co-ordinate line along a parallel circle, and the ξ_2 line along a meridian. For all points on the same parallel circle as *P* in Fig. 6.13, normals intersect *AA* at the same point O_1, which defines the centre of curvature of the ξ_1 co-ordinate lines; the centre of curvature of the ξ_2 co-ordinate line at *P* lies at O_2, which is in the meridional plane through *P*. We can associate the co-ordinate ξ_1 with the angle θ at the centre *O* of the parallel circle through *P*, and the co-ordinate ξ_2 with the angle ϕ which the normal at *P* makes with AA. Suppose

$$\xi_1 = \theta, \quad \xi_2 = \phi \tag{6.34}$$

Then we replace subscripts 1 by θ, and subscripts 2 by ϕ; we write then

$$R_1 = R_\theta, \quad R_2 = R_\phi, \quad k_1 = k_\theta, \quad k_2 = k_\phi, \quad \text{etc.}$$

The functions f_1, f_2, which are geometric properties of the middle surface, become

$$f_1 = R_\theta \sin \phi = \frac{\sin \phi}{k_\theta}, \quad f_2 = R_\phi = \frac{1}{k_\phi} \tag{6.35}$$

The conditions of Codazzi and Gauss reduce to the single equation

$$\frac{\partial f_1}{\partial \xi_2} = \frac{\cos \phi}{k_2}, \quad \text{or} \quad \frac{\partial}{\partial \phi}\left(\frac{\sin \phi}{k_\theta}\right) = \frac{\cos \phi}{k_\phi} \tag{6.36}$$

The strains given by equations (6.13) become

$$\varepsilon_1 = \varepsilon_\theta = \frac{k_\theta}{\sin \phi} u_\theta^\theta + k_\theta \cot \phi \, u_\phi + k_\theta u_n$$

$$\varepsilon_2 = \varepsilon_\phi = k_\phi u_\phi^\phi + k_\phi u_n$$

$$\varepsilon_{12} = \varepsilon_{\theta\phi} = \frac{k_\phi}{k_\theta} \sin \phi \left(\frac{k_\theta u_\theta}{\sin \phi}\right)^\phi + \frac{k_\theta}{\sin \phi} u_\phi^\theta$$

$$\beta_1 = \beta_\theta = \frac{k_\theta^2}{\sin \phi} u_\theta^\theta + k_\theta k_\phi \cot \phi \, u_\phi - \frac{k_\theta^2}{\sin^2 \phi} u_n^{\theta\theta} - k_\theta k_\phi \cot \phi \, u_n^\phi \tag{6.37}$$

$$\beta_2 = \beta_\phi = k_\phi (k_\phi u_\phi)^\phi - k_\phi (k_\phi u_n^\phi)^\phi$$

$$\beta_{12} = \beta_{\theta\phi} = k_\phi \sin \phi \left(\frac{k_\theta u_\theta}{\sin \phi}\right)^\phi + \frac{k_\theta k_\phi}{\sin \phi} u_\phi^\theta - \frac{k_\theta k_\phi}{\sin \phi}\left(u_n^{\theta\phi} - \frac{k_\theta}{k_\phi} \cot \phi \, u_n^\theta\right)$$

where superscripts denote differentiation with respect to θ or ϕ; thus

$$\frac{\partial u}{\partial \theta} = u^\theta, \quad \frac{\partial u}{\partial \phi} = u^\phi, \quad \frac{\partial^2 u}{\partial \theta^2} = u^{\theta\theta}, \quad \frac{\partial^2 u}{\partial \theta \, \partial \phi} = u^{\theta\phi}, \quad \text{etc.}$$

The internal loads given by equations (6.23) become

$$N_1 = N_\theta = \frac{Et}{1-v^2}\left[\frac{k_\theta}{\sin \phi} u_\theta^\theta + vk_\phi u_\phi^\phi + k_\theta \cot \phi \, u_\phi + (k_\theta + vk_\phi)u_n\right]$$

$$N_2 = N_\phi = \frac{Et}{1-v^2}\left[\frac{vk_\theta}{\sin \phi} u_\theta^\theta + k_\phi u_\phi^\phi + vk_\theta \cot \phi \, u_\phi + (k_\phi + vk_\theta)u_n\right]$$

$$\bar{N}_{12} = \bar{N}_{\theta\phi} = \frac{Et}{2(1+v)}\left[\frac{k_\phi}{k_\theta} \sin \phi \left(\frac{k_\theta u_\theta}{\sin \phi}\right)^\phi + \frac{k_\theta}{\sin \phi} u_\phi^\theta\right]$$

$$M_1 = M_\theta = \frac{Et^3}{12(1-v^2)}\left[\frac{k_\theta^2}{\sin\phi}u_\theta^\theta + vk_\phi(k_\phi u_\phi)^\phi + k_\theta k_\phi \cot\phi\, u_\phi -\right.$$

$$\left. -\left\{\frac{k_\theta^2}{\sin^2\phi}u_n^{\theta\theta} + vk_\phi(k_\phi u_n^\phi)^\phi + k_\theta k_\phi \cot\phi\, u_n^\phi\right\}\right]$$

$$M_2 = M_\phi = \frac{Et^3}{12(1-v)^2}\left[\frac{vk_\theta^2}{\sin\phi}u_\theta^\theta + k_\phi(k_\phi u_\phi)^\phi + vk_\theta k_\phi \cot\phi\, u_\phi -\right.$$

$$\left. -\left\{\frac{vk_\theta^2}{\sin^2\phi}u_n^{\theta\theta} + k_\phi(k_\phi u_n^\phi)^\phi + vk_\theta k_\phi \cot\phi\, u_n^\phi\right\}\right]$$

$$\overline{M}_{12} = \overline{M}_{\theta\phi} = \frac{Et^3}{12(1+v)}\left[k_\phi \sin\phi\left(\frac{k_\theta u_\theta}{\sin\phi}\right)^\phi + \frac{k_\theta k_\phi}{\sin\phi}u_\phi^\theta -\right.$$

$$\left. -\frac{k_\theta k_\phi}{\sin\phi}\left\{u_n^{\theta\phi} - \frac{k_\theta}{k_\phi}\cot\phi\, u_n^\theta\right\}\right] \qquad (6.38)$$

The three equilibrium equations (6.24) take the forms

$$\frac{1}{k_\phi}N_\theta^\theta + \left(\frac{\sin\phi}{k_\theta}\overline{N}_{\theta\phi}\right)^\phi + \frac{\cos\phi}{k_\phi}\overline{N}_{\theta\phi} +$$

$$+ k_\theta\left[\frac{1}{k_\phi}M_\theta^\theta + 2\left(\frac{\sin\phi}{k_\theta}\overline{M}_{\theta\phi}\right)^\phi + \frac{2}{k_\theta}\cos\phi\,\overline{M}_{\theta\phi}\right] = -q_\theta\frac{\sin\phi}{k_\theta k_\phi}$$

$$\frac{1}{k_\phi}\overline{N}_{\theta\phi}^\theta + \left(\frac{\sin\phi}{k_\theta}N_\phi\right)^\phi - \frac{\cos\phi}{k_\phi}N_\theta +$$

$$\qquad\qquad (6.39)$$

$$+ k_\phi\left[\left(\frac{\sin\phi}{k_\theta}M_\phi\right)^\phi - \frac{\cos\phi}{k_\phi}M_\theta + \frac{2}{k_\phi}\overline{M}_{\theta\phi}^\theta\right] = -q_\phi\frac{\sin\phi}{k_\theta k_\phi}$$

$$k_\theta N_\theta + k_\phi N_\phi - \frac{k_\theta k_\phi}{\sin\phi}\left\{\frac{k_\theta}{k_\phi\sin\phi}M_\theta^{\theta\theta} + \frac{k_\theta}{\sin\phi}\left(\frac{\sin\phi}{k_\theta}\overline{M}_{\theta\phi}\right)^\phi +\right.$$

$$\left. +\frac{k_\theta}{k_\phi}\cot\phi\,\overline{M}_{\theta\phi}^\theta + \left[\overline{M}_{\theta\phi}^\theta + k_\phi\left(\frac{\sin\phi}{k_\theta}M_\phi\right)^\phi - \cos\phi\, M_\theta\right]^\phi\right\} = q_n$$

(ii) Spherical Shells

In the special case of a spherical shell the principal radii of curvature are each equal to the radius R of the middle surface, Fig. 6.14. The strains given by equations (6.37) become

$$\varepsilon_\theta = \frac{1}{R}\left(\frac{1}{\sin\phi}u_\theta^\theta + \cot\phi\, u_\phi + u_n\right)$$

$$\varepsilon_\phi = \frac{1}{R}(u_\phi^\phi + u_n)$$

$$\varepsilon_{\theta\phi} = \frac{1}{R}\left[\sin\phi\left(\frac{u_\theta}{\sin\phi}\right)^\phi + \frac{1}{\sin\phi}u_\phi^\theta\right]$$

$$\beta_\theta = \frac{1}{R^2}\left[\frac{1}{\sin\phi}u_\theta^\theta + \cot\phi\, u_\phi - \left\{\frac{1}{\sin^2\phi}u_n^{\theta\theta} + \cot\phi\, u_n^\phi\right\}\right]$$

$$\beta_\phi = \frac{1}{R^2}[u_\phi^\phi - u_n^{\phi\phi}]$$

$$\beta_{\theta\phi} = \frac{1}{R^2}\left[\sin\phi\left(\frac{u_\theta}{\sin\phi}\right)^\phi + \frac{1}{\sin\phi}u_\phi^\theta - \frac{1}{\sin\phi}\{u_n^{\theta\phi} - \cot\phi\, u_n^\theta\}\right]$$

$$(6.40)$$

The internal loading actions become

$$N_\theta = \frac{Et}{(1-v^2)R}\left[\frac{1}{\sin\phi}u_\theta^\theta + vu_\phi^\phi + \cot\phi\, u_\phi + (1+v)u_n\right]$$

$$N_\phi = \frac{Et}{(1-v^2)R}\left[\frac{v}{\sin\phi}u_\theta^\theta + u_\phi^\phi + v\cot\phi\, u_\phi + (1+v)u_n\right]$$

$$\overline{N}_{\theta\phi} = \frac{Et}{2(1+v)R}\left[\sin\phi\left(\frac{u_\theta}{\sin\phi}\right)^\phi + \frac{1}{\sin\phi}u_\phi^\theta\right]$$

$$M_\theta = \frac{Et^3}{12(1-v^2)R^2}\left[\frac{1}{\sin\phi}u_\theta^\theta + vu_\phi^\phi + \cot\phi\, u_\phi - \right.$$
$$\left. - \left\{\frac{1}{\sin^2\phi}u_n^{\theta\theta} + vu_n^{\phi\phi} + \cot\phi\, u_n^\phi\right\}\right]$$

$$(6.41)$$

$$M_\phi = \frac{Et^3}{12(1-v^2)R^2}\left[\frac{v}{\sin\phi}u_\theta^\theta + u_\phi^\phi + v\cot\phi\, u_\phi - \right.$$
$$\left. - \left\{\frac{v}{\sin^2\phi}u_n^{\theta\theta} + u_n^{\phi\phi} + v\cot\phi\, u_n^\phi\right\}\right]$$

$$\overline{M}_{\theta\phi} = \frac{Et^3}{12(1+v)R^2}\left[\sin\phi\left(\frac{u_\theta}{\sin\phi}\right)^\phi + \frac{1}{\sin\phi}u_\phi^\theta - \right.$$
$$\left. - \frac{1}{\sin\phi}\{u_n^{\theta\phi} - \cot\phi\, u_n^\theta\}\right]$$

The equilibrium equations (6.39) take the forms

$$N_\theta^\theta + (\sin\phi\,\bar{N}_{\theta\phi})^\phi + \cos\phi\,\bar{N}_{\theta\phi} +$$

$$+ \frac{1}{R}[M_\theta^\theta + 2(\sin\phi\,\bar{M}_{\theta\phi})^\phi + 2\cos\phi\,\bar{M}_{\theta\phi}] = -q_\theta R\sin\phi$$

$$\bar{N}_{\theta\phi}^\theta + (\sin\phi\,N_\phi)^\phi - \cos\phi\,N_\theta +$$

$$+ \frac{1}{R}[2\bar{M}_{\theta\phi}^\theta + (\sin\phi\,M_\phi)^\phi - \cos\phi\,M_\theta] = -q_\phi R\sin\phi \qquad (6.42)$$

$$N_\theta + N_\phi - \frac{1}{R\sin\phi}\left[\frac{1}{\sin\phi}M_\theta^{\theta\theta} + \frac{1}{\sin\phi}(\sin\phi\,\bar{M}_{\theta\phi})^\phi + \cot\phi\,\bar{M}_{\theta\phi} + \right.$$

$$\left. + \bar{M}_{\theta\phi}^\theta + (\sin\phi\,M_\phi)^{\phi\phi} - \cos\phi\,M_\theta^\phi + \sin\phi\,M_\theta\right] = q_n R$$

In terms of displacements the equilibrium equations become

$$\frac{1}{\sin\phi}u_\theta^{\theta\theta} + \tfrac{1}{2}(1-v)\sin\phi\,u_\theta^{\phi\phi} + \tfrac{1}{2}(1-v)\cos\phi\,u_\theta^\phi +$$

$$+ \tfrac{1}{2}(1-v)\sin\phi\,(1-\cot^2\phi)u_\theta + \tfrac{1}{2}(1+v)u_\phi^{\theta\phi} + \tfrac{1}{2}(3-v)\cot\phi\,u_\phi^\theta +$$

$$+ (1+v)u_n^\theta + \mu\left[\frac{1}{\sin\phi}u_\theta^{\theta\theta} + 2(1-v)\sin\phi\,u_\theta^{\phi\phi} + 2(1-v)\cos\phi\,u_\theta^\phi + \right.$$

$$+ 2(1-v)\sin\phi\,(1-\cot^2\phi)u_\theta + (2-v)u_\phi^{\theta\phi} + (3-2v)\cot\phi\,u_\phi^\theta -$$

$$\left. - \frac{1}{\sin^2\phi}u_n^{\theta\theta\theta} - (2-v)u_n^{\theta\phi\phi} - \cot\phi\,u_n^{\theta\phi} - 2(1-v)u_n^\theta\right]$$

$$= -\frac{(1-v^2)}{Et}q_\theta R^2\sin\phi \quad (6.43a)$$

$$\tfrac{1}{2}(1+v)u_\theta^{\theta\phi} - \tfrac{1}{2}(3-v)\cot\phi\,u_\theta^\theta + \frac{1-v}{2\sin\phi}u_\phi^{\theta\theta} + \sin\phi\,u_\phi^{\phi\phi} +$$

$$+ \cos\phi\,u_\phi^\theta + \cos\phi\,u_\phi^\phi - \sin\phi\,(v+\cot^2\phi)u_\phi + (1+v)\sin\phi\,u_n^\phi +$$

$$+ \mu\left[(2-v)u_\theta^{\theta\phi} - (3-2v)\cot\phi\,u_\theta^\theta + \frac{2(1-v)}{\sin\phi}u_\phi^{\theta\theta} + \sin\phi\,u_\phi^{\phi\phi} + \right.$$

$$+ \cos\phi\,u_\phi^\phi - \sin\phi\,(v+\cot^2\phi)u_\phi -$$

$$- \frac{(2-v)}{\sin\phi}u_n^{\theta\theta\phi} - \sin\phi\,u_n^{\phi\phi\phi} + (3-v)\frac{\cot\phi}{\sin\phi}u_n^{\theta\theta} - \cos\phi\,u_n^{\phi\phi} +$$

$$\left. + \sin\phi\,(v+\cot^2\phi)u_n^\phi\right] = -\frac{(1-v^2)}{Et}q_\phi R^2\sin\phi \quad (6.43b)$$

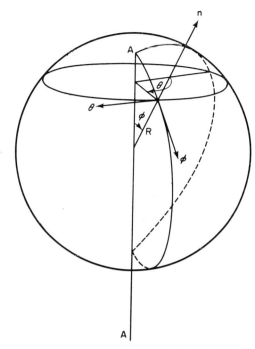

FIG. 6.14.   Spherical shell of radius R.

$$(1+v)u_\theta^\theta + (1+v)\sin\phi\, u_\phi^\phi + (1+v)\cos\phi\, u_\phi + 2(1+v)\sin\phi\, u_n -$$

$$-\frac{\mu}{\sin\phi}\left[\frac{1}{\sin\phi}u_\theta^{\theta\theta\theta} + (2-v)\sin\phi\, u_\theta^{\theta\phi\phi} - \cos\phi\, u_\theta^{\theta\phi} +\right.$$

$$+\frac{1}{\sin\phi}\{1+2(1-v)\sin^2\phi\}u_\theta^\theta + (2-v)u_\phi^{\theta\theta} + \sin^2\phi\, u_\phi^{\phi\phi\phi} +$$

$$+ 2\cos\phi\sin\phi\, u_\phi^{\phi\phi} + \cot\phi\, u_\phi^{\theta\theta} - (1+v\sin^2\phi)u_\phi^\phi +$$

$$+ \cot\phi\{1+(1-v)\sin^2\phi\}u_\phi - \frac{1}{\sin^2\phi}u_n^{\theta\theta\theta\theta} - 2u_n^{\theta\theta\phi\phi} -$$

$$- \sin^2\phi\, u_n^{\phi\phi\phi\phi} + 2\cot\phi\, u_n^{\theta\theta\phi} - 2\sin\phi\cos\phi\, u_n^{\phi\phi\phi} -$$

$$-\frac{1}{\sin^2\phi}\{(3-v)+(1+v)\cos^2\phi\}u_n^{\theta\theta} + (1+v\sin^2\phi)u_n^{\phi\phi} -$$

$$\left. - \cot\phi\{1+(1-v)\sin^2\phi\}u_n^\phi\right] = \frac{1-v^2}{Et}q_n R^2 \sin\phi \quad (6.43c)$$

in which $\qquad\qquad\qquad\qquad \mu = \dfrac{t^2}{12R^2} \qquad\qquad\qquad\qquad (6.44)$

If the external loading on the sphere is also symmetric about the axis AA, Fig. 6.14, then there is complete axial symmetry of the problem. We put

$$q_\theta = 0, \quad u_\theta = 0, \quad \frac{\partial}{\partial \theta} = 0$$

The first of equations (6.43) vanishes, while the second and third give

$$\sin \phi \, u_\phi^{\phi\phi} + \cos \phi \, u_\phi^\phi - \sin \phi (v + \cot^2 \phi) u_\phi + (1+v) \sin \phi \, u_n^\phi +$$
$$+ \mu [\sin \phi \, u_\phi^{\phi\phi} + \cos \phi \, u_\phi^\phi - \sin \phi (v + \cot^2 \phi) u_\phi -$$
$$- \sin \phi \, u_n^{\phi\phi\phi} - \cos \phi \, u_n^{\phi\phi} + \sin \phi (v + \cot^2 \phi) u_n^\phi]$$
$$= -\frac{(1-v^2)}{Et} q_\phi R^2 \sin \phi \quad (6.45\text{a})$$

$$(1+v) u_\phi^\phi + (1+v) \cos \phi \, u_\phi + 2(1+v) \sin \phi \, u_n - \frac{\mu}{\sin \phi} [\sin^2 \phi \, u_\phi^{\phi\phi\phi} +$$
$$+ 2 \cos \phi \sin \phi \, u_\phi^{\phi\phi} - (1 + v \sin^2 \phi) u_\phi^\phi + \cot \phi \{1 + (1-v) \sin^2 \phi\} u_\phi -$$
$$- \sin^2 \phi \, u_n^{\phi\phi\phi\phi} - 2 \sin \phi \cos \phi \, u_n^{\phi\phi\phi} + (1 + v \sin^2 \phi) u_n^{\phi\phi} -$$
$$- \cot \phi \{1 + (1-v) \sin^2 \phi\} u_n^\phi] = \frac{1-v^2}{Et} q_n R^2 \sin \phi \quad (6.45\text{b})$$

The solution of equations of this type has been discussed by Flügge (see Bibliography, p. 188).

(iii) Circular Cylindrical Shells

In the case of a circular cylindrical shell, we take the co-ordinate axes ξ_1, ξ_2 around the circumference and along a generator, respectively, Fig. 6.15. If R is the radius of the middle surface, then

$$R_1 = R, \quad R_2 = \infty$$

We introduce coordinates θ, ζ, such that

$$\xi_1 = \theta, \quad \xi_2 = \frac{z}{R} = \zeta \quad (6.46)$$

where z is measured along the length of the cylinder; the subscript 1 is replaced by θ, and subscript 2 by ζ. Then

$$\delta s_1 = f_1 \delta \xi_1 = R \, \delta\theta, \quad \delta s_2 = f_2 \delta \xi_2 = \delta z = R \, \delta \zeta$$

so that

$$_1 = R, \quad f_2 = R \quad (6.47)$$

The conditions of Codazzi and Gauss are satisfied identically; the strains reduce to

$$\varepsilon_\theta = \frac{1}{R}(u_\theta^\theta + u_n), \qquad \varepsilon_\zeta = \frac{1}{R}u_\zeta^\zeta, \qquad \varepsilon_{\theta\zeta} = \frac{1}{R}(u_\theta^\zeta + u_\zeta^\theta) \tag{6.48}$$

$$\beta_\theta = \frac{1}{R^2}(u_\theta^\theta - u_n^{\theta\theta}), \quad \beta_\zeta = -\frac{1}{R^2}u_n^{\zeta\zeta}, \quad \beta_{\theta\zeta} = \frac{1}{R^2}(u_\theta^\zeta - u_n^{\theta\zeta})$$

The internal loading actions become

$$N_\theta = \frac{Et}{(1-v^2)R}[u_\theta^\theta + v u_\zeta^\zeta + u_n]$$

$$N_\zeta = \frac{Et}{(1-v^2)R}[v u_\theta^\theta + u_\zeta^\zeta + v u_n]$$

$$\overline{N}_{\theta\zeta} = \frac{Et}{2(1+v)R}[u_\theta^\zeta + u_\zeta^\theta]$$

$$M_\theta = \frac{Et^3}{12(1-v^2)R^2}[u_\theta^\theta - u_n^{\theta\theta} - v u_n^{\zeta\zeta}] \tag{6.49}$$

$$M_\zeta = \frac{Et^3}{12(1-v^2)R^2}[v u_\theta^\theta - v u_n^{\theta\theta} - u_n^{\zeta\zeta}]$$

$$\overline{M}_{\theta\zeta} = \frac{Et^3}{12(1+v)R^2}[u_\theta^\zeta - u_n^{\theta\zeta}]$$

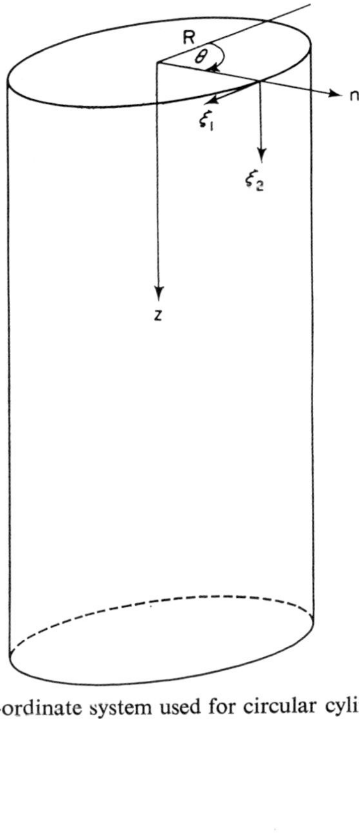

FIG. 6.15. Co-ordinate system used for circular cylindrical shells.

The equilibrium equations in terms of displacements become

$$
\begin{bmatrix}
\left\{\begin{aligned}(1+\mu)\dfrac{\partial^2}{\partial\theta^2}+\\+(1-v)(\tfrac{1}{2}+2\mu)\dfrac{\partial^2}{\partial\zeta^2}\end{aligned}\right\} & \tfrac{1}{2}(1+v)\dfrac{\partial^2}{\partial\theta\,\partial\zeta} & \left\{\begin{aligned}\dfrac{\partial}{\partial\theta}-\mu\dfrac{\partial^3}{\partial\theta^3}-\\-\mu(2-v)\dfrac{\partial^3}{\partial\theta\,\partial\zeta^2}\end{aligned}\right\} \\[3ex]
\tfrac{1}{2}(1+v)\dfrac{\partial^2}{\partial\theta\,\partial\zeta} & \left\{\dfrac{\partial^2}{\partial\zeta^2}+\tfrac{1}{2}(1-v)\dfrac{\partial^2}{\partial\theta^2}\right\} & \mu\dfrac{\partial}{\partial\zeta} \\[3ex]
\left\{\begin{aligned}\dfrac{\partial}{\partial\theta}-\mu\dfrac{\partial^3}{\partial\theta^3}-\\-\mu(2-v)\dfrac{\partial^3}{\partial\theta\,\partial\zeta^2}\end{aligned}\right\} & \mu\dfrac{\partial}{\partial\zeta} & 1+\mu\nabla^4
\end{bmatrix}
\begin{bmatrix} u_\theta \\[2ex] u_\zeta \\[2ex] u_n \end{bmatrix}
$$

$$
=\frac{R^2(1-v^2)}{Et}\begin{bmatrix}-q_\theta \\[2ex] -q_\zeta \\[2ex] q_n\end{bmatrix}
\tag{6.50}
$$

in which

$$
\nabla^4 = \frac{\partial^4}{\partial\theta^4}+2\frac{\partial^4}{\partial\theta^2\,\partial\zeta^2}+\frac{\partial^4}{\partial\zeta^4}
$$

In some problems the shell is subjected to loads at the ends and in a plane normal to the longitudinal axis of the cylinder, as for example the diametrally opposed loads W_1, W_2, W_3 shown in Fig. 6.16. In such cases there is no surface loading on the shell, and in equations (6.50) we may write $q_\theta = q_\zeta = q_n = 0$. Any distorted form of the shell may then be taken in the form of a Fourier series in the circumferential direction, i.e. in θ; we take the values of u_θ, u_ζ, u_n in the forms

$$
u_\theta = \sum_{p=0}^{\infty} U_\theta^p \cos p\theta, \quad u_\zeta = \sum_{p=1}^{\infty} U_\zeta^p \sin p\theta, \quad u_n = \sum_{p=1}^{\infty} U_n^p \sin p\theta \tag{6.51}
$$

Equations (6.50), with $q_\theta = q_\zeta = q_n = 0$, then become total differential equations, and we may take the values of U_θ^p, U_ζ^p, U_n^p in the forms

$$
U_\theta^p = C_\theta^p e^{\lambda\zeta}, \quad U_\zeta^p = C_\zeta^p e^{\lambda\zeta}, \quad U_n^p = C_n^p e^{\lambda\zeta} \tag{6.52}
$$

where C_θ^p, C_ζ^p, C_n^p are constants. Equations (6.49) then reduce to

$$
\begin{bmatrix}
\{(1+\mu)p^2-(1-v)(\tfrac{1}{2}+2\mu)\lambda^2\} & \tfrac{1}{2}(1+v)p\lambda & \{p+\mu p^3-\mu(2-v)p\lambda^2\} \\[2ex]
\tfrac{1}{2}(1+v)p\lambda & \lambda^2-\tfrac{1}{2}(1-v)p^2 & v\lambda \\[2ex]
p+\mu p^3-\mu(2-v)p\lambda^2 & v\lambda & 1+\mu(p^2-\lambda^2)^2
\end{bmatrix}
\begin{bmatrix} C_\theta^p \\[2ex] C_\zeta^p \\[2ex] C_n^p \end{bmatrix} = 0
\tag{6.53}
$$

The condition for non-zero values of C_θ^p, C_ζ^p, C_n^p is that the determinant of the coefficients of C_θ^p, C_ζ^p, C_n^p in equations (6.53) should vanish. This zero determinant is the *characteristic equation*, and the values of λ which are defined by this equation correspond to different forms of the displacements given by equations (6.52). The zero determinant reduces to

$$(1+4\mu)\lambda^8 - 4(1+\mu)p^2\lambda^6 +$$

$$+ \left[\{6+\mu(1-v^2)\}p^4 - 2(4-v^2)p^2 + (1-v^2)\left(\frac{1}{\mu}+4\right) \right]\lambda^4 -$$

$$- 4p^2(p^2-1)^2\lambda^2 + p^4(p^2-1)^2 = 0 \qquad (6.54)$$

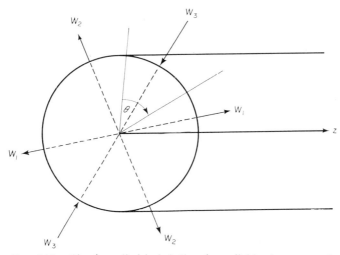

Fig. 6.16.   Circular cylindrical shell under radial loads at one end.

For given values of μ, which is a geometrical parameter, and p, which defines the harmonic component under discussion, the roots of this equation determine the displaced forms due to edge loading of the shell.

For the case of a circular cylindrical shell with axially symmetric loading we put

$$q_\theta = 0, \quad u_\theta = 0, \quad \frac{\partial}{\partial\theta} = 0$$

The strains reduce to

$$\varepsilon_\theta = u_n/R, \quad \varepsilon_\zeta = u_\zeta^\zeta/R, \quad \varepsilon_{\theta\zeta} = 0$$

$$\beta_\theta = 0, \quad \beta_\zeta = -u_n^{\zeta\zeta}/R^2, \quad \beta_{\theta\zeta} = 0 \qquad (6.55)$$

Equations (6.50) reduce to

$$u_\zeta^{\zeta\zeta} + vu_n^\zeta = -q_\zeta R^2(1-v^2)/Et$$

$$vu_\zeta^\zeta + u_n + \mu u_n^{\zeta\zeta\zeta\zeta} = q_n R^2(1-v^2)/Et \qquad (6.56)$$

If, in addition, $q_\zeta = 0$ and $N_\zeta = 0$ at all points (i.e. there is no longitudinal thrust on the cylinder) then

$$u_n^{\zeta\zeta\zeta\zeta} + \frac{1-v^2}{\mu} u_n = \frac{R^2(1-v^2)}{\mu E t} q_n \qquad (6.57)$$

which is of the form of the equation for a beam on an elastic foundation; solutions of this equation have been discussed by Timoshenko (see Bibliography, p. 188).

6.3. MEMBRANE SHELLS

(i) *General*

If we imagine a shell with a free edge, we can, by loading the shell near the free edge, induce large bending distortions around that edge. Cases of this type are an open-ended cylindrical shell carrying radial loads at the open ends, and an open hemispherical shell carrying radial loads in the open diametral plane. Shells of this type clearly offer little resistance to bending actions.

If, on the other hand, we consider a completely closed shell, or a shell supported along its edges, the primary resistance of the shell to loading actions may be derived from stresses in the middle surface of the shell. The simplest practical case of this type is a thin spherical shell under internal pressure; the internal pressure is resisted by stresses in the middle surface of the shell only, except possibly at connections where there may be bending actions.

Shells in which stresses in the middle surface are of primary importance are called *membrane shells*, since we can treat the shell as a membrane concentrated at the middle surface. Again, if we choose to ignore the bending stiffness of the wall of the shell, then the shell becomes one of the membrane type.

In the linear theory of the elastic bending of thin shells we have considered bending stresses through the wall thickness. In the case of a very thin shell the bending and twisting actions

$$M_1, \quad M_2, \quad M_{12}, \quad M_{21}$$

which are proportional to the cube of the wall thickness, may be neglected. On putting

$$M_1 = M_2 = M_{12} = M_{21} = 0$$

in equations (6.17), we have

$$N_{1n} = N_{2n} = 0, \quad N_{21} = N_{21} \qquad (6.58)$$

so that there are no normal shearing forces N_{1n}, N_{2n}, and the shearing forces

N_{12}, N_{21} are *complementary*. Lateral forces on the shell are resisted entirely by internal loading actions in the plane $\xi_1 \xi_2$ of the middle surface; the shell has become then a membrane shell. If we put

$$N_{12} = N_{21} = \bar{N}_{12} \tag{6.59}$$

then equations (6.16) become

$$\frac{\partial}{\partial \xi_1}(f_2 N_1) + \frac{\partial}{\partial \xi_2}(f_1 \bar{N}_{12}) + \frac{\partial f_1}{\partial \xi_2}\bar{N}_{12} - \frac{\partial f_2}{\partial \xi_1}N_2 + f_1 f_2 q_1 = 0$$

$$\frac{\partial}{\partial \xi_2}(f_1 N_2) + \frac{\partial}{\partial \xi_1}(f_2 \bar{N}_{12}) + \frac{\partial f_2}{\partial \xi_1}\bar{N}_{12} - \frac{\partial f_1}{\partial \xi_2}N_1 + f_2 f_1 q_2 = 0 \tag{6.60}$$

$$k_1 N_1 + k_2 N_2 - q_n = 0$$

The strains in the middle surface of the shell are given by equations (6.13), and these become

$$\varepsilon_1 = \frac{1}{f_1}\frac{\partial u_1}{\partial \xi_1} + \frac{1}{f_1 f_2}\frac{\partial f_1}{\partial \xi_2}u_2 + k_1 u_n$$

$$\varepsilon_2 = \frac{1}{f_2}\frac{\partial u_2}{\partial \xi_2} + \frac{1}{f_2 f_1}\frac{\partial f_2}{\partial \xi_1}u_1 + k_2 u_n \tag{6.61}$$

$$\varepsilon_{12} = \frac{1}{f_2}\frac{\partial u_1}{\partial \xi_2} - \frac{1}{f_1 f_2}\frac{\partial f_1}{\partial \xi_2}u_1 + \frac{1}{f_1}\frac{\partial u_2}{\partial \xi_1} - \frac{1}{f_2 f_1}\frac{\partial f_2}{\partial \xi_1}u_2$$

Consider the possibility that throughout the middle surface we have

$$\varepsilon_1 = \varepsilon_2 = \varepsilon_{12} = 0$$

Then any set of displacement functions satisfying the equations

$$\frac{1}{f_1}\frac{\partial u_1}{\partial \xi_1} + \frac{1}{f_1 f_2}\frac{\partial f_1}{\partial \xi_2}u_2 + k_1 u_n = 0$$

$$\frac{1}{f_2}\frac{\partial u_2}{\partial \xi_2} + \frac{1}{f_2 f_1}\frac{\partial f_2}{\partial \xi_1}u_1 + k_2 u_n = 0 \tag{6.62}$$

$$\frac{1}{f_2}\frac{\partial u_1}{\partial \xi_2} - \frac{1}{f_1 f_2}\frac{\partial f_1}{\partial \xi_2}u_1 + \frac{1}{f_1}\frac{\partial u_2}{\partial \xi_1} - \frac{1}{f_2 f_1}\frac{\partial f_2}{\partial \xi_1}u_2 = 0$$

gives rise to no strains; such displacements are *inextensional*. They correspond to bending of the shell or to rigid-body movements; unless a membrane shell is given adequate boundary supports it may become a mechanism by developing local bending displacements. A complete spherical shell cannot suffer inextensional deformation; on the other hand, a spherical cap can undergo inextensional deformations unless a stiffening ring is provided along the edge of the shell. On the boundaries of a membrane shell the conditions will be expressed in terms of the membrane forces N_1, N_2, $\bar{N}_{12}$ and the displacements u_1, u_2; in general the boundary conditions for membrane shells cannot be given solely in terms of forces; however, in cases where the boundary conditions are given completely in terms of forces, the problems become statically determinate.

(ii) *Membrane Shells of Revolution*

It has already been pointed out that many of the thin shells used in nuclear reactor structures have one axis of symmetry for the geometrical form of the shell. We make use again of Fig. 6.13, in which AA is the axis of symmetry; we put

$$\xi_1 = 0, \quad \xi_2 = \phi; \quad f_1 = \frac{\sin \phi}{k_\theta}, \quad f_2 = \frac{1}{k_\phi} \tag{6.63}$$

The equilibrium equations (6.60) become

$$\frac{1}{k_\phi} \frac{\partial N_\theta}{\partial \theta} + \frac{\partial}{\partial \phi} \left(\frac{\sin \phi}{k_\theta} \bar{N}_{\theta\phi} \right) + \frac{\cos \phi}{k_\phi} \bar{N}_{\theta\phi} + \frac{\sin \phi}{k_\theta k_\phi} q_\theta = 0$$

$$\frac{\partial}{\partial \phi} \left(\frac{\sin \phi}{k_\theta} N_\phi \right) + \frac{1}{k_\phi} \frac{\partial \bar{N}_{\theta\phi}}{\partial \theta} - \frac{\cos \phi}{k_\phi} N_\theta + \frac{\sin \phi}{k_\theta k_\phi} q_\phi = 0 \tag{6.64}$$

$$k_\theta N_\theta + k_\phi N_\phi - q_n = 0$$

In general the external loading intensities q_θ, q_ϕ, q_n may be represented by Fourier series in θ, in the forms

$$q_\theta = \sum_{p=1}^{\infty} q_\theta^p \sin p\theta + \sum_{m=0}^{\infty} q_\theta'^p \cos p\theta$$

$$q_\phi = \sum_{p=0}^{\infty} q_\phi^p \cos p\theta + \sum_{p=1}^{\infty} q_\phi'^p \sin p\theta \tag{6.65}$$

$$q_n = \sum_{p=0}^{\infty} q_n^p \cos p\theta + \sum_{p=1}^{\infty} q_n'^p \sin p\theta$$

where q_θ^p, $q_\theta'^p$, q_ϕ^p, $q_\phi'^p$, q_n^p, $q_n'^p$ are functions of ϕ only. The values of the internal loads may then be written in the forms

$$N_\theta = \sum_{p=0}^{\infty} N_\theta^p \cos p\theta + \sum_{p=1}^{\infty} N_\theta'^p \sin p\theta$$

$$N_\phi = \sum_{p=0}^{\infty} N_\phi^p \cos p\theta + \sum_{p=1}^{\infty} N_\phi'^p \sin p\theta \tag{6.66}$$

$$\bar{N}_{\theta\phi} = \sum_{p=1}^{\infty} \bar{N}_{\theta\phi}^p \sin p\theta + \sum_{p=0}^{\infty} \bar{N}_{\theta\phi}'^p \cos p\theta$$

where N_θ^p, $N_\theta'^p$, N_ϕ^p, $N_\phi'^p$, $\overline{N}_{\theta\phi}^p$, $\overline{N}_{\theta\phi}'^p$ are functions of ϕ only. The equilibrium equations then take the forms

$$\frac{1}{k_\phi}pN_\theta^p - \frac{\cos\phi}{k_\phi}\overline{N}_{\theta\phi}^p - \frac{d}{d\phi}\left(\frac{\sin\phi}{k_\theta}\overline{N}_{\theta\phi}^p\right) = \frac{\sin\phi}{k_\theta k_\phi}q_\theta^p$$

$$\frac{\cos\phi}{k_\phi}N_\theta^p - \frac{d}{d\phi}\left(\frac{\sin\phi}{k_\theta}N_\phi^p\right) - \frac{p}{k_\phi}\overline{N}_{\theta\phi}^p = \frac{\sin\phi}{k_\theta k_\phi}q_\phi^p \qquad (6.67)$$

$$k_\theta N_\theta^p + k_\phi N_\phi^p = q_n^p$$

together with similar equations in $N_\phi'^p$, $N_\phi'^p$, $\overline{N}_{\theta\phi}'^p$, $q_\theta'^p$, $q_\phi'^p$, $q_n'^p$.

The equations (6.64) are the equilibrium equations for the membrane shell of revolution; the equations define the values of the internal loads N_θ, N_ϕ, $\overline{N}_{\theta\phi}$. If two of the loads, N_θ, $\overline{N}_{\theta\phi}$, say, are eliminated from the equations then the resulting differential equation is of the form

$$\frac{k_\theta}{k_\phi}\sin^2\phi\,\frac{\partial^2 N_\phi}{\partial\phi^2} + \frac{\partial^2 N_\phi}{\partial\theta^2} + h(\phi)\frac{\partial N_\phi}{\partial\phi} + i(\phi)N_\phi + j(q_\theta, q_\phi, q_n) = 0 \qquad (6.68)$$

where $h(\phi)$, $i(\phi)$ are functions of ϕ only, depending on the geometry of the shell, and j is a function depending on the external loads on the shell. The *form* of the solution of equation (6.68) is governed largely by the signs of the coefficients of the terms

$$\frac{\partial^2 N_\phi}{\partial\phi^2}, \quad \frac{\partial^2 N_\phi}{\partial\theta^2}$$

Now, the value of $\sin^2\phi$ is always positive, so that $\partial^2 N_\phi/\partial\phi^2$, $\partial^2 N_\phi/\partial\theta^2$ will have coefficients of the same sign if k_θ and k_ϕ are of the same sign, and coefficients of opposite sign if k_θ and k_ϕ are of opposite sign. When $(k_\theta/k_\phi)\sin^2\phi$ is positive, equation (6.68) is *elliptic* in form; a load applied to the boundary of a shell of this type is diffused rapidly into the shell; this property is true of spherical shells, for example. In cases where $(k_\theta/k_\phi)\sin^2\phi$ is negative, equation (6.68) is *hyperbolic* in form; in shells of this type an isolated load applied to the boundary is not diffused by membrane action alone. If the wall of a shell has appreciable bending stiffness, the problem may become elliptic.

(iii) *Spherical Membrane Shells*

A simple example of membrane stresses in a spherical shell is that of a complete sphere supported on a horizontal ring. In some nuclear reactors the shell may not be supported continuously on a ring, but may rest on isolated supports. Gas circulating within the shell gives rise to uniform membrane stress throughout the shell, and we shall not be concerned with

12

this uniform state of stress; the shell is assumed to be of uniform thickness. Membrane stresses are also set up by the self-weight of the shell, and these stresses will not be uniform throughout. Suppose ρ is the density of the material of the shell, and t its uniform thickness; then the weight per unit area of the middle surface is

$$w = \rho g t \tag{6.69}$$

where g is the acceleration due to gravity. Suppose R is the radius of the middle surface of the shell, and that the supporting ring is defined by the angle $\phi = \phi_0$. Since there is axial symmetry, we have $\bar{N}_{\theta\phi} = 0$, at all points of the shell. For the shell considered as a membrane it is easily shown that for the upper spherical shell ($\phi < \phi_0$),

$$N_\theta = wR\left[\frac{\sin^2\phi - \cos\phi}{1 + \cos\phi}\right], \quad N_\phi = -wR\left[\frac{1}{1 + \cos\phi}\right] \tag{6.70}$$

and for the lower shell ($\phi > \phi_0$),

$$N_\theta = -wR\left[\frac{\sin^2\phi + \cos\phi}{1 - \cos\phi}\right], \quad N_\phi = wR\left[\frac{1}{1 - \cos\phi}\right] \tag{6.71}$$

At the junction of the upper and lower sections, for the upper shell

$$N_\phi = N_{\phi_0}(\text{say}) = -wR/(1 + \cos\phi_0) \tag{6.72}$$

and for the lower shell

$$N_\phi = N'_{\phi_0}(\text{say}) = wR/(1 - \cos\phi_0) \tag{6.73}$$

N_{ϕ_0} is a compressive load, and N'_{ϕ_0} a tensile load. The strain along a parallel circle in the upper shell at the junction is

$$\varepsilon_{\theta_0}(\text{say}) = \frac{1}{Et}[N_\theta - vN_\phi]_{\phi=\phi_0} = \frac{wR}{Et}\left[\frac{\sin^2\phi_0 - \cos\phi_0 + v}{1 + \cos\phi_0}\right] \tag{6.74}$$

and in the lower shell at the junction is

$$\varepsilon'_{\theta_0}(\text{say}) = \frac{1}{Et}[N'_\theta - vN'_\phi]_{\phi=\phi_0} = -\frac{wR}{Et}\left[\frac{\sin^2\phi_0 + \cos\phi_0 + v}{1 - \cos\phi_0}\right] \tag{6.75}$$

It is impossible to choose ϕ_0 in the range 0 to π such that $\varepsilon_{\theta_0} = \varepsilon'_{\theta_0}$; hence, for all possible values of ϕ_0 there is a strain discontinuity along parallel circles at the junction. In practice this discontinuity is eliminated by bending actions at the junction; these provide a small perturbation on the membrane state of stress, and are diffused rapidly into the spherical shells and the support structure.

The problem of the spherical shell of Fig. 6.17 under its own weight is one having axial symmetry. If the shell is subjected to a sideways acceleration, such as would occur during an earth tremor, for example, the axial symmetry is lost. Suppose all parts of the spherical shell are subjected to

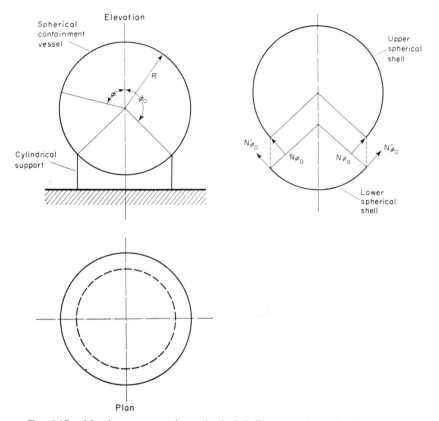

FIG. 6.17. Membrane stresses in a spherical shell supported on a horizontal ring.

the same lateral acceleration g', directed along the axis $\theta = 0$ in our general co-ordinate system, Fig. 6.18. The loading per unit area of the middle surface is then

$$w \, (\text{say}) = \rho g' t \tag{6.76}$$

in the direction $\theta = 0$. The pressures q_θ, q_ϕ, q_n then become

$$q_\theta = -w \sin \theta$$

$$q_\phi = w \cos \phi \cos \theta \tag{6.77}$$

$$q_n = w \sin \phi \cos \theta$$

We take the solutions for N_θ, N_ϕ, $\bar{N}_{\theta\phi}$ in the forms

$$N_\theta = N'_\theta \cos\theta$$
$$N_\phi = N'_\phi \cos\theta \qquad (6.78)$$
$$\bar{N}_{\theta\phi} = \bar{N}'_{\theta\phi} \sin\theta$$

where N'_θ, N'_ϕ, $\bar{N}'_{\theta\phi}$ are functions of ϕ only. Equations (6.64) then become

$$N'_\theta - \bar{N}'_{\theta\phi}\cos\phi - \frac{d}{d\phi}(\bar{N}'_{\theta\phi}\sin\phi) = -wR\sin\phi$$

$$N'_\theta\cos\phi - \frac{d}{d\phi}(N'_\phi\sin\phi) - \bar{N}'_{\theta\phi} = wR\cos\phi\sin\phi \qquad (6.79)$$

$$N'_\theta + N'_\phi = wR\sin\phi$$

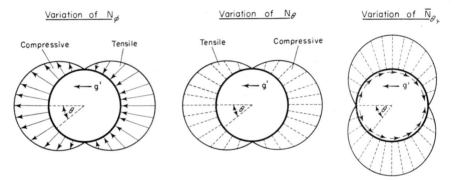

FIG. 6.18.   Variation of N_ϕ, N_θ and $\bar{N}_{\theta\phi}$ at the supports of a spherical shell suffering lateral acceleration.

The values of the internal loads are easily deduced; for the upper part of the shell of Fig. 6.17 ($\phi < \phi_0$), we have finally

$$N_\theta = \frac{wR}{\sin^3\phi}[2 - 2\cos\phi - \sin^2\phi\cos^2\phi]\cos\theta$$

$$N_\phi = -\frac{wR}{\sin^3\phi}[2 - 2\cos\phi - \sin^2\phi]\cos\theta \qquad (6.80)$$

$$\bar{N}_{\theta\phi} = \frac{wR}{\sin^3\phi}[2 - 2\cos\phi - \cos\phi\sin^2\phi]\sin\theta$$

The variation of the internal forces for ϕ in the range $\pi/2$ to π is of the form shown in Fig. 6.18.

6.4. FLAT PLATES

(i) *General*

The most extreme case of a shell is that of a flat plate. We need not therefore consider the linear-elastic bending of flat plates *ab initio*, but introduce into the general shell equations the " flatness " of the plate. In the case of a flat plate the principal curvatures k_1, k_2 become zero, and any mutually perpendicular co-ordinate lines may be taken in the middle surface of the plate. In the case of rectangular or square plates it is convenient to use Cartesian co-ordinate axes parallel to the sides of the plate; we put

$$\xi_1 = x_1, \quad \xi_2 = x_2$$

where x_1, x_2 are axes along adjacent edges, Fig. 6.19. Then

$$\delta s_1 = \delta x_1, \quad \delta s_2 = \delta x_2$$

so that

$$f_1 = f_2 = 1$$

Then, we have

$$\varepsilon_1 = \frac{\partial u_1}{\partial x_1}, \qquad \varepsilon_2 = \frac{\partial u_2}{\partial x_2}, \qquad \varepsilon_{12} = \frac{\partial u_1}{\partial x_2} + \frac{\partial u_2}{\partial x_1}$$

$$\beta_1 = -\frac{\partial^2 u_n}{\partial x_1^2}, \quad \beta_2 = -\frac{\partial^2 u_n}{\partial x_2^2}, \quad \beta_{12} = -\frac{\partial^2 u_n}{\partial x_1 \partial x_2} \tag{6.81}$$

The internal loads become

$$N_1 = \frac{Et}{1-v^2}\left(\frac{\partial u_1}{\partial x_1} + v\frac{\partial u_2}{\partial x_2}\right)$$

$$N_2 = \frac{Et}{1-v^2}\left(\frac{\partial u_2}{\partial x_2} + v\frac{\partial u_1}{\partial x_1}\right)$$

$$\overline{N}_{12} = \frac{Et}{2(1+v)}\left(\frac{\partial u_1}{\partial x_2} + \frac{\partial u_2}{\partial x_1}\right)$$

$$M_1 = -\frac{Et^3}{12(1-v^2)}\left(\frac{\partial^2 u_n}{\partial x_1^2} + v\frac{\partial^2 u_n}{\partial x_2^2}\right) \tag{6.82}$$

$$M_2 = -\frac{Et^3}{12(1-v^2)}\left(\frac{\partial^2 u_n}{\partial x_2^2} + v\frac{\partial^2 u_n}{\partial x_1^2}\right)$$

$$\overline{M}_{12} = -\frac{Et^3}{12(1+v)}\left(\frac{\partial^2 u_n}{\partial x_1 \partial x_2}\right)$$

The first two of equations (6.24) become the equations of equilibrium of a thin sheet under loads in its own plane; the third equation becomes

$$\frac{\partial^2 M_1}{\partial x_1^2} + 2\frac{\partial^2 \overline{M}_{12}}{\partial x_1\,\partial x_2} + \frac{\partial^2 M_2}{\partial x_2^2} + q_n = 0 \tag{6.83}$$

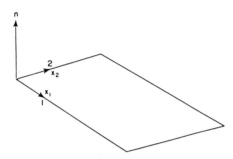

FIG. 6.19. Cartesian co-ordinate system for a rectangular plate.

and on expressing M_1, M_2, $\overline{M}_{12}$ in terms of u_n, we have

$$\nabla^4 u_n = -\frac{12(1-v^2)}{Et^3} q_n \tag{6.84}$$

where

$$\nabla^4 = \frac{\partial^4}{\partial x_1^4} + 2\frac{\partial^4}{\partial x_1^2\,\partial x_2^2} + \frac{\partial^4}{\partial x_2^4}$$

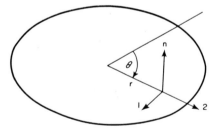

FIG. 6.20. Polar co-ordinate system for a circular plate.

In the case of circular plates it is more convenient to use polar coordinates, with origin at the centre of the plate, Fig. 6.20. We put

$$\xi_1 = \theta, \quad \xi_2 = r$$

Then

$$\delta s_1 = r\,\delta\theta, \quad \delta s_2 = \delta r$$

so that

$$f_1 = r, \quad f_2 = 1$$

The strains then become

$$\varepsilon_\theta = \frac{1}{r}\frac{\partial u_\theta}{\partial \theta} + \frac{u_r}{r}, \qquad \varepsilon_r = \frac{\partial u_r}{\partial r}, \qquad \varepsilon_{\theta r} = \frac{1}{r}\frac{\partial u_r}{\partial \theta} + \frac{\partial u_\theta}{\partial r} - \frac{u_\theta}{r}$$

$$\beta_\theta = -\frac{1}{r^2}\frac{\partial^2 u_n}{\partial \theta^2} - \frac{1}{r}\frac{\partial u_n}{\partial r}, \quad \beta_r = -\frac{\partial^2 u_n}{\partial r^2}, \quad \beta_{\theta r} = -\frac{1}{r}\frac{\partial^2 u_n}{\partial \theta \partial r} + \frac{1}{r^2}\frac{\partial u_n}{\partial \theta}$$

$$(6.85)$$

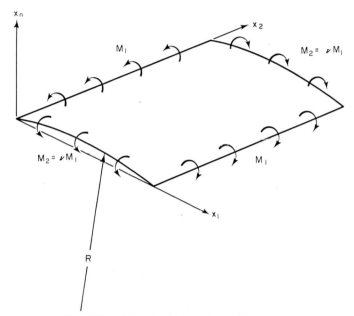

FIG. 6.21.   Plate bent to a cylindrical surface.

The third of equations (6.24) becomes

$$\nabla^4 u_n = -\frac{12(1-v^2)}{Et^3} q_n \qquad (6.86)$$

where

$$\nabla^4 = (\nabla^2)^2 = \left(\frac{\partial^2}{\partial r^2} + \frac{1}{r}\frac{\partial}{\partial r} + \frac{1}{r^2}\frac{\partial^2}{\partial \theta^2}\right)^2$$

Two simple cases of bending of flat plates are of some interest. First, if a rectangular plate, Fig. 6.21, is bent into a cylindrical surface of radius of curvature R in the $x_1 x_n$-plane, say, then

$$\frac{\partial^2 u_n}{\partial x_1^2} = -\frac{1}{R}, \quad \frac{\partial^2 u_n}{\partial x_2^2} = 0, \quad \frac{\partial^2 u_n}{\partial x_1 \partial x_2} = 0$$

and the couples on the edges of the plate become

$$M_1 = \frac{Et^3}{12(1-v^2)R}, \quad M_2 = \frac{vEt^3}{12(1-v^2)R}, \quad \overline{M}_{12} = 0$$

so that

$$M_2 = vM_1$$

Then bending actions are required on all four edges of the plate to produce a cylindrical surface. Second, if a plate is bent into equal curvatures $(1/R)$, say, in all directions of the middle surface, in any two mutually perpendicular directions x_1, x_2, say, we have

$$\frac{\partial^2 u_n}{\partial x_1^2} = \frac{\partial^2 u_n}{\partial x_2^2} = -\frac{1}{R}, \quad \frac{\partial^2 u_n}{\partial x_1 \partial x_2} = 0$$

so that

$$M_1 = M_2 = Et^3/12(1+v)R$$

In such a case the plate is subjected to the same bending moment in all directions.

The equations (6.84) and (6.86) governing small elastic bending deflexions have been solved for a wide range of problems; the bending of rectangular, circular and triangular plates (as well as other shapes) has been studied for concentrated and distributed lateral loads. Some problems can be solved by the direct solution of the general equations, while others can be dealt with more easily by approximate methods.

(ii) Simply-supported Rectangular Plate

In the case of a simply-supported rectangular plate the deflected form of the plate may be taken in the form

$$u_n = \sum_{p_1=1}^{\infty} \sum_{p_2=1}^{\infty} U_{p_1 p_2} \sin\frac{p_1 \pi x_1}{L_1} \sin\frac{p_2 \pi x_2}{L_2}$$

which satisfies the conditions of simple-support on the edges $x_1 = 0$, $x_1 = L_1$, $x_2 = 0$, $x_2 = L_2$, Fig. 6.22. Consider the particular case when the lateral load intensity q_n is defined by

$$q_n = q_0 \sin\frac{\pi x_1}{L_1} \sin\frac{\pi x_2}{L_2}$$

that is, a peak value at the centre of q_0, and zero on the supported edges; such a distribution represents the first term in any Fourier expansion of a more general value of q_n. The lateral deflexion then takes the form

$$u_n = U_{11} \sin\frac{\pi x_1}{L_1} \sin\frac{\pi x_2}{L_2}$$

and on substituting this value of u_n into equation (6.86) we have

$$U_{11} = \frac{12q_0(1-v^2)}{\pi^4 E l^3} \frac{L_1^4 L_2^4}{(L_2^2 + L_1^2)^2} \tag{6.87}$$

The total reactive forces on the supported edges are now calculable; along the edges, the shearing forces vary sinusoidally. The sum of the distributed forces on the edges is greater than the total lateral load due to q_n, and we deduce that concentrated forces F must be applied at the corners of the plate in the same direction as the force q_n. The forces F are necessary to hold down the corners of the plate. In the case of a square plate for which $L_1 = L_2 = L$ (say),

$$F = \tfrac{1}{8}(1-v)\frac{4q_0 L^2}{\pi^2}$$

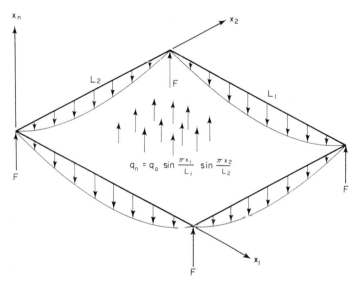

FIG. 6.22. Concentrated forces at the corners of a square plate carrying lateral load.

The total lateral load on a square plate due to q_n is

$$\frac{4q_0 L^2}{\pi^2}$$

so that the ratio of F to the total lateral load is

$$\tfrac{1}{8}(1-v)$$

which is of the order of 10 per cent.

(iii) *Bending of Grillages*

In many practical problems a form of the simple plate-bending theory can be applied to intersecting systems of beams, or grillages; these may be considered to form an anisotropic plate. The simplest type of grillage is a regular rectangular one, in which a system of beams running parallel to the x_1-axis is rigidly connected with a system running parallel to the x_2-axis, Fig. 6.23. We imagine there are a large number of beams in each direction. If a unit length is taken along the x_2-axis, then this length cuts beams running in the x_1-direction; suppose these beams have bending stiffness B_1 per unit length, and torsional stiffness B_{12} per unit length; similarly the beams running parallel to the x_2-axis have bending stiffness B_2 per unit length, and torsional stiffness B_{21} per unit length. An elemental rectangle of the middle surface of the grillage can then be considered as formed of a number of intersecting beams; statical equilibrium is ensured under a lateral load of intensity q_n if

$$q_n = \left(\frac{\partial^2 M_1}{\partial x_1^2} + \frac{\partial^2 M_{12}}{\partial x_1 \partial x_2} + \frac{\partial^2 M_{21}}{\partial x_1 \partial x_2} + \frac{\partial^2 M_2}{\partial x_2^2} \right)$$

where M_1, M_2, M_{12}, M_{21} have the same meanings as in plate theory. For the bending and twisting of the beams

$$M_1 = -B_1 \frac{\partial^2 u_n}{\partial x_1^2}, \qquad M_2 = -B_2 \frac{\partial^2 u_n}{\partial x_2^2}$$

$$M_{12} = -B_{12} \frac{\partial^2 u_n}{\partial x_1 \partial x_2}, \qquad M_{21} = -B_{21} \frac{\partial^2 u_n}{\partial x_1 \partial x_2} \qquad (6.88)$$

where u_n is the lateral deflexion of the middle surface parallel to the x_n-axis. Then

$$q_n = B_1 \frac{\partial^4 u_n}{\partial x_1^4} + (B_{12} + B_{21}) \frac{\partial^4 u_n}{\partial x_1^2 \partial x_2^2} + B_2 \frac{\partial^4 u_n}{\partial x_2^4} \qquad (6.89)$$

In practical applications the rectangular grillage is used in some reactors to support the graphite core of the reactor. The grillage is supported on a circular boundary, Fig. 6.24; as in the case of a square plate, the reactions on the boundary due to a uniformly distributed load on the grillage may be intense along the diagonals of the grillage.

(iv) *Membrane Actions in Thin Plates*

In discussing shells we presented a general theory of linear-elastic behaviour, and considered as special cases those problems in which stiffness of a shell is derived solely from membrane actions. An important property of a curved plate, or shell, is that it can be designed in many cases so that the internal

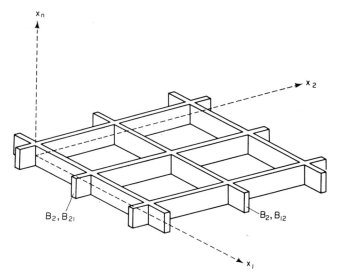

FIG. 6.23. Rectangular grillage of beams.

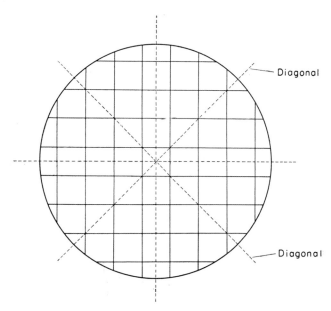

FIG. 6.24. Square grillage with circular boundary, of the type used to support the core of a nuclear reactor.

loading actions are predominantly of the membrane type. For such shells membrane stresses can be calculated with reasonable accuracy on linear-elastic theory. In the case of flat plates, on the other hand, the state of membrane stress is accurately calculated by our general theory only provided the plate remains flat; where the plate is under the action of bending forces the calculation of membrane stresses must be based on large deflexion, and therefore non-linear, considerations.

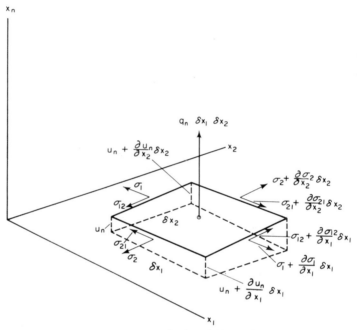

FIG. 6.25.   Membrane stresses in the middle surface of a flat plate.

When a flat plate is extremely thin, much of its resistance to lateral loading is derived from a membrane action in the middle surface. Again, when the deflexions in bending become large, membrane stresses are induced in the middle surface. We consider the middle surface of the plate, originally in the $x_1 x_2$-plane; any point P of the middle surface is displaced amounts u_1, u_2, u_n parallel to the axes x_1, x_2, x_n, respectively, Fig. 6.25; the intensity of loading parallel to the x_n-axis is q_n. If the deflexions u_1, u_2, u_n are small, the strains in the middle surface are

$$\varepsilon_1 = \frac{\partial u_1}{\partial x_1} + \frac{1}{2}\left(\frac{\partial u_n}{\partial x_1}\right)^2, \quad \varepsilon_2 = \frac{\partial u_2}{\partial x_2} + \frac{1}{2}\left(\frac{\partial u_n}{\partial x_2}\right)^2, \quad \varepsilon_{12} = \frac{\partial u_1}{\partial x_2} + \frac{\partial u_2}{\partial x_1} + \frac{\partial u_n}{\partial x_1}\frac{\partial u_n}{\partial x_2} \quad (6.90)$$

when second-order terms are included; second-order terms were previously ignored. We suppose that only membrane stresses are set up in the middle surface, and that there are no bending couples; the plate is assumed sufficiently thin for the membrane stresses to be uniform over the thickness. Then, if t is the thickness of the plate, for lateral equilibrium of the middle surface

$$\frac{q_n}{t} = -\sigma_1 \frac{\partial^2 u_n}{\partial x_1^2} - \sigma_2 \frac{\partial^2 u_n}{\partial x_2^2} - (\sigma_{12}+\sigma_{21})\frac{\partial^2 u_n}{\partial x_1 \partial x_2}$$

For rotational equilibrium about an axis parallel to the x_n-axis, we have $\sigma_{12} = \sigma_{21}$, so that

$$\frac{q_n}{t} = -\sigma_1 \frac{\partial^2 u_n}{\partial x_1^2} - \sigma_2 \frac{\partial^2 u_n}{\partial x_2^2} - 2\sigma_{12}\frac{\partial^2 u_n}{\partial x_1 \partial x_2} \tag{6.91}$$

Again, for equilibrium in the $x_1 x_2$-plane,

$$\frac{\partial \sigma_1}{\partial x_1} + \frac{\partial \sigma_{12}}{\partial x_2} = 0, \quad \frac{\partial \sigma_2}{\partial x_2} + \frac{\partial \sigma_{12}}{\partial x_1} = 0 \tag{6.92}$$

If the material remains elastic

$$\varepsilon_1 = \frac{1}{E}(\sigma_1 - v\sigma_2), \quad \varepsilon_2 = \frac{1}{E}(\sigma_2 - v\sigma_1), \quad \varepsilon_{12} = \frac{2}{E}(1+v)\sigma_{12} \tag{6.93}$$

In the nine equations (6.90), (6.91), (6.92) and (6.93) there are nine unknowns

$$\sigma_1, \sigma_2, \sigma_{12}, \quad \varepsilon_1, \varepsilon_2, \varepsilon_{12}, \quad u_1, u_2, u_n$$

if the value of q_n is given; in theory, the nine unknowns are soluble, therefore. In practice this calculation is a difficult one; however, the stage of bending of a flat plate at which membrane stresses become significant can be estimated fairly easily. Consider, for example, a square plate of side L, Fig. 6.26, and suppose first that the plate is stretched as a membrane, that is, without bending stiffness; suppose the edges of the membrane are held rigidly and that the lateral deflexion at any point is

$$u_n = U \sin \frac{\pi x_1}{L_1} \sin \frac{\pi x_2}{L_2}$$

The length of the stretched middle surface along the line $x_2 = \frac{1}{2}L$ is given approximately by

$$s = L + \int_0^L \frac{1}{2}\left(\frac{\partial u_n}{\partial x_1}\right)^2 dx_1$$

On substituting for u_n, the stretching of the middle surface becomes

$$s - L = \int_0^L \frac{1}{2}\left(\frac{\partial u_n}{\partial x_1}\right)^2 dx_1 = \frac{\pi^2 U^2}{4L}$$

The average strain along the line $x_2 = \frac{1}{2}L$ is then

$$\frac{s-L}{L} = \frac{\pi^2}{4}\left(\frac{U}{L}\right)^2 = \varepsilon_m, \quad \text{(say)} \tag{6.94}$$

Now suppose the plate is bent into the form

$$u_n = U \sin\frac{\pi x_1}{L_1} \sin\frac{\pi x_2}{L_2}$$

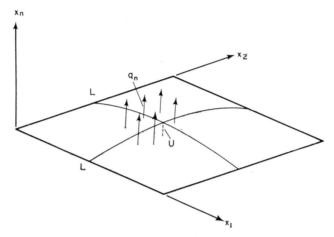

Fig. 6.26.   Comparison of membrane and bending strains in a thin plate.

The bending strain in the x_1-direction at the outer fibres of the centre of the plate is of the order

$$\varepsilon_b(\text{say}) = \frac{1}{2}t\frac{\partial^2 u_n}{\partial x_1^2} = \frac{\pi^2 U t}{2L^2} \tag{6.95}$$

where t is the thickness of the plate. Then

$$\frac{\varepsilon_m}{\varepsilon_b} = \frac{U}{2t} \tag{6.96}$$

and ε_m, ε_b are of the same order when u_n is of order $2t$. In this analysis we have assumed that the edges of the plate are held rigidly in the membrane action; the analysis gives some indication of the importance of membrane action in cases where the edges of a plate are held rigidly. In other cases where the edges are not held rigidly, the importance of membrane actions is usually of the same order.

   A number of approximate attempts have been made to include membrane effects in the theory of bending of plates; in the case of a simply supported square plate of side L, Timoshenko* derives the lateral load q_n for a central deflexion U in the form

$$q_n = \frac{Et^3 U}{0 \cdot 0468 L^4} \left[1 + 1 \cdot 45 \left(\frac{U}{t} \right)^2 \right] \tag{6.97}$$

The deflexion U is then a non-linear function of q_n.

6.5. BUCKLING OF SHELLS AND PLATES

(i) *General*

We have considered so far the linear-elastic behaviour of shells and plates. The essential feature of linear behaviour is that the deformations are infinitesimally small; equilibrium considerations can then be based on the undistorted geometry of the shell. When distortions of the shell are relatively large any accurate treatment of load equilibrium must be based on the distorted form of the shell; the resulting analysis is non-linear since there is no longer a simple proportional relation between external loads and deformations. Such problems fall into the class of instability, or buckling, problems. We shall restrict our discussion to the *elastic* buckling of shells and plates. A general theory of the buckling of shells is not presented; this is so because the buckling characteristics of any shell problem are not necessarily the same as those of any other shell problem; a thin flat plate is usually in a condition of stable equilibrium after buckling, for example, whereas a spherical shell under external pressure is in an unstable condition after buckling. We begin with a discussion of the elastic buckling of thin flat plates; the elastic buckling of thin shells is discussed only briefly, the limitations of present methods of analysis being indicated.

(ii) *Buckling of Thin Rectangular Flat Plates*

In many practical applications thin flat plates carry loads which induce direct and shearing stresses in the middle surface of the plate. Typical problems of this type are the component plates of a box-girder; under certain circumstances the stresses in the middle surface may become critical, and the plate is prone to buckling by bending; thus lateral bending distortions occur without the direct application of lateral bending loads. Consider, for example, a rectangular flat plate, Fig. 6.27; suppose at a point (x_1, x_2) of the middle surface of the plate the direct and shearing stresses before buckling are σ_1, σ_2, σ_{12}. Now consider equilibrium of an element of the middle surface in a buckled mode in which u_n is the lateral deflexion of the middle surface parallel to the x_n-axis. If the plate had no

* See bibliography on p. 188.

bending stiffness the buckled form of the plate could be held in equilibrium if a lateral load of intensity

$$(q_n)_1 = -\sigma_1 t \frac{\partial^2 u_n}{\partial x_1^2} - \sigma_2 t \frac{\partial^2 u_n}{\partial x_2^2} - 2\sigma_{12} t \frac{\partial^2 u_n}{\partial x_1 \, \partial x_2}$$

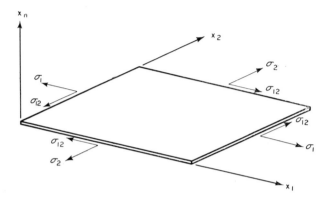

FIG. 6.27.   Buckling of flat plates under the action of stresses in the middle surface.

were applied to the plate; in discussing linear-elastic bending of a thin plate we found that for small deflexions u_n, the lateral load $(q_n)_2$ corresponding to any deflected form is

$$(q_n)_2 = \frac{Et^3}{12(1-v^2)} (\nabla^4 u_n)$$

Now consider a superposition of the two cases: the resultant lateral load is then

$$(q_n)_1 + (q_n)_2$$

Then no resultant lateral load is required when

$$(q_n)_1 + (q_n)_2 = 0$$

that is, when

$$\nabla^4 u_n = \frac{12(1-v^2)}{Et^2} \left[\sigma_1 \frac{\partial^2 u_n}{\partial x_1^2} + 2\sigma_{12} \frac{\partial^2 u_n}{\partial x_1 \, \partial x_2} + \sigma_2 \frac{\partial^2 u_n}{\partial x_2^2} \right] \qquad (6.98)$$

This equation governs initial elastic buckling of thin rectangular flat plates.

The simplest plate-buckling problem is that of a rectangular plate of sides L, b, the edges $x_1 = 0$, $x_1 = L$ carrying uniform compressive stress σ, Fig. 6.28. If all the edges are simply supported, the value of u_n may be taken in the form

$$u_n = \sum_{p_1=1}^{\infty} \sum_{p_2=1}^{\infty} U_{p_1 p_2} \sin \frac{p_1 \pi x_1}{L} \sin \frac{p_2 \pi x_2}{b}$$

On substituting into equation (6.98) we have, for buckling in the p_1p_2-th mode,

$$\sigma_{cr} = \frac{\pi^2 EL^2t^2}{12(1-v^2)p_1^2}\left(\frac{p_1^2}{L^2} + \frac{p_2^2}{b^2}\right)^2$$

This always has a minimum value when $p_2 = 1$, giving

$$\sigma_{cr} = \frac{\pi^2 Et^2}{12(1-v^2)b^2}\left(\frac{p_1 b}{L} + \frac{L}{p_1 b}\right)^2 \tag{6.99}$$

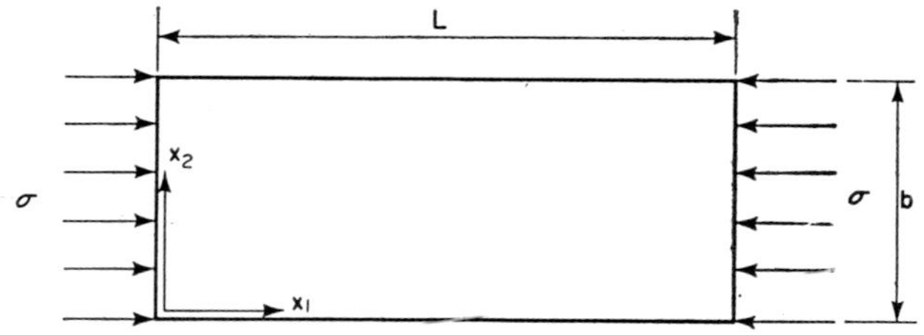

FIG. 6.28. Buckling of a uniformly compressed flat plate.

The variation of σ_{cr} for different values of p_1 and L/b is shown in Fig. 6.29; for each value of p_1, the critical stress is a minimum when

$$p_1 = \frac{L}{b}$$

The minimum buckling stress is then

$$\sigma_{min} = \frac{4\pi^2}{12(1-v^2)}\cdot\left(\frac{t}{b}\right)^2 \tag{6.100}$$

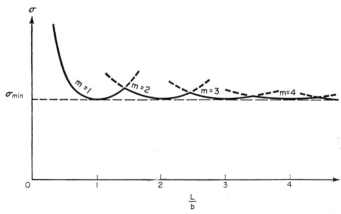

FIG. 6.29. Variation of buckling stress for different lengths of a uniformly compressed simply supported flat plate.

which is independent of the length L of the plate; σ_{min} is known as the *local buckling* stress. The plate buckles in such a way that p_1, which must always be an integer, is approximately equal to L/b.

Many other loading conditions of simply supported plates have been studied; for any other type of edge loading, the critical stress can always be given in the form

$$\sigma_{cr} = C \frac{\pi^2 E}{12(1-v^2)} \left(\frac{t}{b}\right)^2 \qquad (6.101)$$

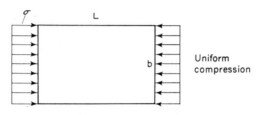

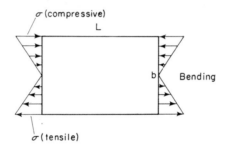

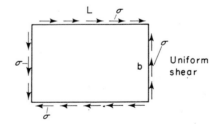

Fig. 6.30. Plates under compressive, bending and shearing stresses.

where σ_{cr} is the stress at some point of the edge, and C depends on the edge loading and boundary conditions. The cases of bending and uniform shearing stress are shown in Fig. 6.30; exact solutions to these problems are not available, but approximate solutions can be found to any required degree of accuracy.

(iii) *Post-buckling Behaviour of Flat Plates*

In the case of a very thin flat plate, initial elastic buckling is not followed by an immediate collapse of the plate. In Fig. 6.31 is shown a very thin square plate, simply supported on all four edges; two opposite edges are compressed between rigid platens, while the unloaded edges are free to expand laterally. In the early stages of loading there is a uniform com-pressive stress σ over the loaded edges; if σ is less than σ_{cr}, the initial elastic buckling stress, then the plate remains flat. When the edge compressive stress attains the value σ_{cr}, then small lateral displacements take place. If

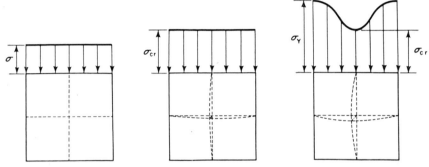

FIG. 6.31.   Buckling of a square plate loaded " rigidly " on two opposite edges.

the edges are further compressed by rigid platens, large lateral displacements occur at the centre of the plate, and the distribution of stress over the loaded edge becomes non-uniform. At the centre of the plate, the mean stress over the thickness remains approximately at the critical value σ_{cr}; at the sup-ported edges there is little or no buckling, and this region can carry stresses greater than σ_{cr}. However, when the longitudinal stress at the edge of the plate reaches the yield stress, σ_y, of the material, the plate can carry no further compressive load; the average stress over the breadth of the plate is then taken as the maximum stress, σ_{max}, carried by the plate. If the distribution of compressive stress over the breadth of the plate is determined by the values of σ_{cr} and σ_y, then we may write

$$\sigma_{max} = f(\sigma_{cr}, \sigma_y)$$

where f is a function of σ_{cr} and σ_y. Then we have that

$$\frac{\sigma_{max}}{\sigma_y} = F\left(\frac{\sigma_{cr}}{\sigma_y}\right) \tag{6.102}$$

The initial buckling stress may be written

$$\sigma_{cr} = \frac{C\pi^2 E}{12(1-v^2)}\left(\frac{t}{b}\right)^2$$

Then
$$\sqrt{\left(\frac{\sigma_y}{\sigma_{cr}}\right)} \propto \frac{b}{t} \qquad (6.103)$$

This parameter is used rather than σ_{cr}/σ_y; tests on single flat plates in compression for a number of metals give results of the type shown in Fig. 6.32, in which (σ_{max}/σ_y) is plotted against $\sqrt{(\sigma_y/\sigma_{cr})}$. If complete collapse occurred when the initial elastic buckling stress were reached, then $\sigma_{max} = \sigma_{cr}$, which is shown by one of the broken lines in Fig. 6.32; if failure occurs due to the yielding of the material, $\sigma_{max} = \sigma_y$, which is shown by another broken line in Fig. 6.32. In fact test results fall below the point (1, 1) in Fig. 6.32, but above the line $\sigma_{max} = \sigma_{cr}$, as $\sqrt{(\sigma_y/\sigma_{cr})}$ (and hence b/t) increases.

A post-buckling problem of another type exists in the web-plates of deep girder beams; the cantilever beam of Fig. 6.33 consists of a deep web-plate, of uniform thickness t and depth D, attached to flanges. The cantilever carries an end load F, which we assume is distributed uniformly over the web-plate in the form of a shearing stress of magnitude

$$F/Dt$$

Before the onset of buckling, the web-plate near the free end of the cantilever is in a condition of uniform shear; for an element of the web-plate inclined at 45° to the longitudinal axis of the cantilever, there are equal and opposite tensile and compressive stresses of the same magnitude, F/Dt. When the web-plate buckles in shear we may assume that buckling occurs in the direction of the compressive stress at 45° to the axis of the cantilever; the web-plate therefore gives no support in this direction after the onset of buckling. However, the tensile stress at 45° to the axis of the cantilever remains operative. The loss of the compressive stress means a transference of the load to the vertical stringers. The ultimate load on the web-plate is reached when the tensile stress in the web-plate reaches the yield stress σ_y. Examination of the equilibrium of a triangular element at the end of the web-plate shows that, at the ultimate load-carrying capacity of the web,

$$F/Dt = \tfrac{1}{2}\sigma_y$$

so that
$$F_{max} = \tfrac{1}{2}\sigma_y \, Dt$$

In this analysis it is assumed, of course, that failure in the flanges or vertical stringers does not occur.

(iv) Buckling of Shells

The analysis of shell-buckling problems—as opposed to flat plates—presents rather more formidable problems; many theoretical treatments of shell-buckling problems have been made, but the amount of experimental

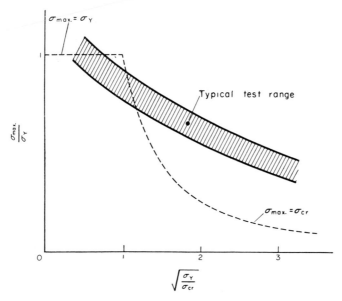

FIG. 6.32.   Results of post-buckling tests on simply supported plates.

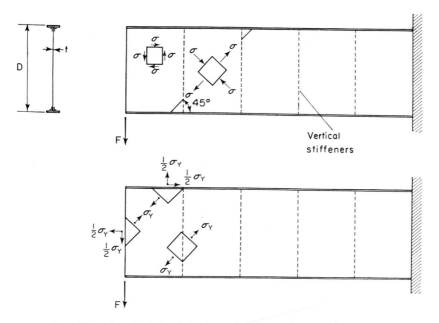

FIG. 6.33.   Post-buckling behaviour of a deep web-girder cantilever.

work is very limited. We consider, as a simple example of the elastic buckling of shells, a circular cylindrical shell under a uniform compressive stress σ, Fig. 6.34. Initially the cylinder distorts uniformly under membrane stresses σ, and before the onset of buckling the membrane strains are

$$\varepsilon_\theta = \frac{v\sigma}{E}, \quad \varepsilon_\phi = -\frac{\sigma}{E}, \quad \varepsilon_{12} = 0$$

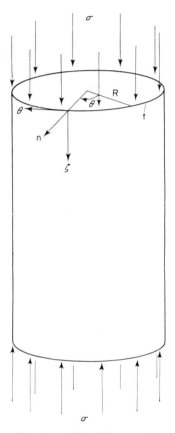

Fig. 6.34. Cylinder under uniform axial compression.

There are no bending strains initially. The initial radial displacement at any point of the middle surface is

$$(u_n)_0 = v\sigma R/E$$

Suppose the middle surface now suffers a small further distortion, due to buckling; for simplicity we shall assume that all deformations are axially symmetric. Then we are concerned with two further displacements u_ζ and u_n. Imagine an element of the middle surface, Fig. 6.35, initially of length $R\delta\zeta$ and breadth $R\delta\theta$; suppose this element is completely disconnected from all other parts of the shell. Then to maintain this element in equilibrium in the displaced form with normal displacement u_n, we require a normal force on the element of areal intensity

$$\frac{\sigma t}{R^2}\frac{d^2 u_n}{d\zeta^2}$$

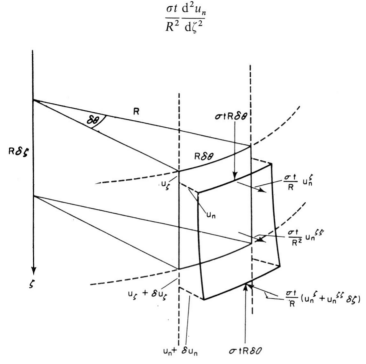

FIG. 6.35. Axially symmetric buckling of a uniformly compressed cylindrical shell.

To connect the element with adjacent parts of the shell we need to add a further normal force of intensity

$$q_n = \frac{Et}{(1-v^2)R^2}\left[\mu\frac{d^4 u_n}{d\zeta^4}+(1-v^2)u_n\right]$$

No resultant lateral force is required if the sum of these two forces is zero, i.e. if

$$\frac{d^4 u_n}{d\zeta^4}+\frac{(1-v^2)\sigma}{\mu E}\frac{d^2 u_n}{d\zeta^2}+\frac{1-v^2}{\mu}u_n=0 \qquad (6.104)$$

If the length of the shell is L, we may take the displacement in the form

$$u_n = U \sin \frac{p\pi R\zeta}{L}$$

Equation (6.104) then gives

$$\sigma = E\left(\frac{L}{p\pi R}\right) + \frac{\mu}{1-v^2}\left(\frac{p\pi R}{L}\right)^2$$

This has a minimum value when

$$\frac{p\pi R}{L} = \sqrt[4]{\left(\frac{1-v_2}{\mu}\right)}$$

and then

$$\sigma_{min} = \frac{Et}{R\sqrt{[3(1-v^2)]}} \qquad (6.105)$$

This minimum value of σ represents the buckling stress of a long cylinder.

Tests on circular cylinders under uniform axial compression give results appreciably below the theoretical stress of equation (6.105). The scatter of test results is very considerable; experimental work on a number of materials

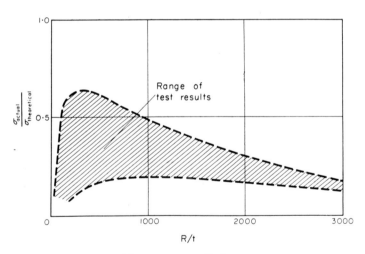

FIG. 6.36. Results of buckling tests on cylinders under uniform axial compression.

gives the scatter indicated in Fig. 6.36. All the test results are appreciably below the theoretical buckling stress; this is understandable for the smaller (R/t) ratios, where the shells are so thick that material failure occurs. However, the discrepancy is also very wide at the higher (R/t) ratios—for the thinner shells. This discrepancy is due to the fact that immediately after initial buckling, a perfect shell is in a condition of unstable equilibrium; Fig. 6.37 indicates the form of the variation of end-compressive stress with shortening of the shell; initially the shell shortens in a linear manner, due to axial compression; if the shell is a perfect one, the linear shortening continues up to a point A where the elastic buckling stress is reached. At this stage the condition of equilibrium is an unstable one, and if, for example, the shortening is maintained constant, the end-compressive stress can be

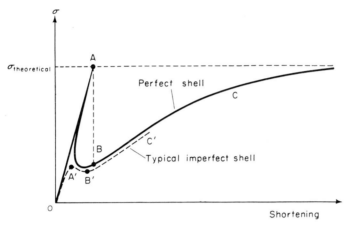

FIG. 6.37. Post-buckling behaviour of a cylinder under uniform axial compression.

reduced appreciably to the point B. The condition of equilibrium at B is stable, and the shell can now withstand further increases of compressive stress, giving the curve BC. The behaviour of a typical imperfect shell is shown by the curve $OA'B'C'$ in Fig. 6.37; the point A is never reached, and there is a more gradual transition from linear behaviour to buckling; the point A' may correspond to a maximum stress considerably below that of A.

A similar situation holds in many other shell buckling problems for which initial buckling occurs under conditions of unstable equilibrium. In the case of a thin spherical shell under uniform external pressure, for example, the theoretical buckling pressure q_n is

$$q_n = \frac{2Et^2}{R^2\sqrt{[3(1-v^2)]}} \tag{6.106}$$

Since the shell is unstable at this pressure, there is little chance of attaining this pressure experimentally for imperfect shells, and the highest pressures reached in practice are of the order $0\cdot 3q_n$.

6.6. SHORT BIBLIOGRAPHY ON SHELL THEORY

As mentioned earlier, the general linear-elastic theory presented in this chapter is that due to Novozhilov. Fuller discussions of practical problems can be found in the books by Flügge, and by Timoshenko and Woinowsky-Krieger. Many references to papers on shell theory can be found in the books by these authors. The following is a short list of books dealing with the main problems of shells and plates:

V. V. NOVOZHILOV, *The Theory of Thin Shells* (English translation). Noordhoff, Groningen (1959).

A. L. GOL'DENVEIZER, *The Theory of Elastic Thin Shells* (English translation). Pergamon Press, (1961).

W. FLÜGGE, *Stresses in Shells*. Springer-Verlag, Berlin (1960).

W. FLÜGGE, *Statik und Dynamik der Schalen*. Springer, Berlin (1934).

S. P. TIMOSHENKO, S. WOINOWSKY-KRIEGER, *Theory of Plates and Shells*, McGraw-Hill, New York (1959).

V. Z. VLASOV, *General Theory of Shells*, Moscow (1949).

A. E. GREEN, W. ZERNA, *Theoretical Elasticity*. Oxford (1954).

C. B. BIEZENO, R. GRAMMEL, *Engineering Dynamics* (English translation). Blackie, London (1956).

K. GIRKMANN, *Flachentragwerke*. Vienna (1959).

R. M. KENEDI (Editor), *Symposium on Nuclear Reactor Containment Buildings and Pressure Vessels*. Butterworth (1960).

W. T. KOITER (Editor), *Symposium on the Theory of Thin Elastic Shells*. North-Holland, Amsterdam (1960).

CHAPTER 7

THE MATRIX PROGRESSION METHOD IN STRUCTURAL ANALYSIS

H. Tottenham

7.1. INTRODUCTION

The "matrix progression method" is a technique of structural analysis especially designed for application to complex structures composed of several shell or plate elements. It can be applied to all structures in which the problem of analysis can be reduced to finding the variation of internal forces and displacements in the direction of one co-ordinate line only. Such structures will be termed "unidirectional". A structure may be unidirectional in itself, as for example in a beam or a plane frame, it may be unidirectional owing to the loading system, as for example would be a uniform circular plate under an axisymmetrical load, or it may be treated as unidirectional by expressing its applied loads, internal forces, and displacements in the form of a suitable Fourier (or other) series in the direction of one or more co-ordinate lines—an example of this would be a multi-bay cylindrical shell roof simply supported at the ends. Several examples of unidirectional structures are illustrated in Fig. 7.1.

The analysis of complex shell structures involves a considerable amount of numerical computation whatever method is used. The purpose of the matrix progression method is to make the analysis as simple and systematic as possible. By using matrix algebra the calculations are readily planned. Further, most high-speed digital computers have "interpretive schemes" or libraries of subroutines which make the programming of calculations written in matrix form a simple task even for those not well acquainted with such machines. It is now more economical to programme most shell calculations and have the computations carried out on a high-speed computer than for the engineer to have the calculations carried out in the normal manner. Even if calculations are to be carried out on a desk machine, it is usually easier to prepare them in a matrix form than in the more cumbersome conventional notations. It is with these factors in mind that the matrix progression method has been devised.

The basis of the method is a special form of solution of the basic differ-

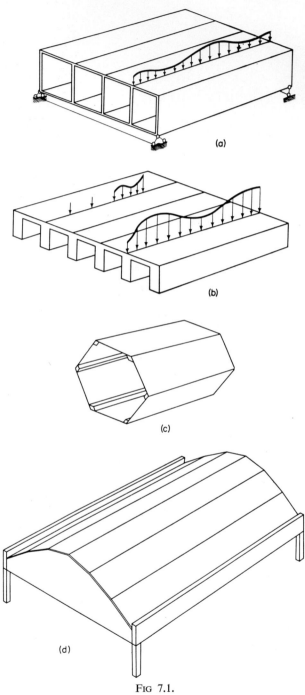

FIG 7.1.

ential equation governing the stress and displacement condition in a structure. This solution is in two parts, corresponding to the complementary function and the particular integral, the first part of which depends only on the boundary conditions at one edge and the second part of which depends only on the load. By using a solution in this form we can write the solution for an element of the structure in general terms and add in the effects of applied loads as and when they occur. The essential features of the method are best brought out by considering a simple concrete example. Such an example will also serve to introduce the terminology.

7.2. GENERAL OUTLINE OF METHOD

Let us consider, then, a simple two-span beam, each span having uniform cross-section and being subjected to uniformly distributed loads as in Fig. 7.2. In the analysis of an elastic beam it is necessary to consider four factors; namely

(1) the normal displacement w;
(2) the rotation of the normal ψ;
(3) the bending moment M;
(4) the normal shear force S.

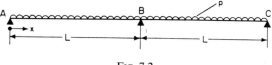

FIG 7.2.

The collection of displacements and internal forces will be termed the " actions ". The column matrix $\mathbf{Z}$ containing these actions will be termed the " action matrix ".

$$\mathbf{Z} = \begin{bmatrix} w \\ \psi \\ M \\ S \end{bmatrix}$$

Starting at one end of the structure, say the left-hand end A, the " initial boundary conditions " are

$$w_0 = M_0 = 0, \quad x = 0$$

and there are two unknown actions ψ_0 and S_0 at this end. The action matrix at A is therefore

$$\mathbf{Z}_0 = \begin{bmatrix} w_0 \\ \psi_0 \\ M_0 \\ S_0 \end{bmatrix} = \begin{bmatrix} 0 & 0 \\ 1 & 0 \\ 0 & 0 \\ 0 & 1 \end{bmatrix} \begin{bmatrix} \psi_0 \\ S_0 \end{bmatrix} = \mathbf{K}_A \bar{\mathbf{Z}}_0 \tag{7.1}$$

The matrix $\mathbf{K}_A$ is termed the initial boundary restraint matrix. The expression for $\mathbf{Z}_0$ is written in this form to enable the more general case of an elastic support at A to be treated in the same manner. For example, if the end of the beam at A were to be held in an elastic medium we would have the forces and displacements at A related by

$$\begin{bmatrix} M_0 \\ S_0 \end{bmatrix} = \begin{bmatrix} C_{11} & C_{12} \\ C_{21} & C_{22} \end{bmatrix} \begin{bmatrix} w_0 \\ \psi_0 \end{bmatrix}$$

where the coefficients C_{ik} are defined by the elastic properties of the support. This would then give

$$\mathbf{Z}_0 = \begin{bmatrix} 1 & 0 \\ 0 & 1 \\ C_{11} & C_{12} \\ C_{21} & C_{22} \end{bmatrix} \begin{bmatrix} w_0 \\ \psi_0 \end{bmatrix}$$

Again we have a boundary restraint matrix and a matrix containing two unknown actions. In any structure it is always possible to express all the relevant actions at an edge in terms of a boundary restraint matrix and an action matrix containing only one half of those actions. Furthermore, the reduced action matrix $\mathbf{Z}_0$ will contain one action, and only one action, corresponding to each degree of freedom. Thus in the case of an elastic beam the reduced action matrix will always contain *either w_0 or S_0 and either ψ_0 or M_0*.

The solution used in the matrix progression method gives the actions $\mathbf{Z}(x)$ at any section x in the first span AB in the form

$$\mathbf{Z}(x) = \mathbf{G}_1(x)\mathbf{Z}_0 + \bar{\mathbf{Z}}_0(x) \tag{7.2}$$

In this the matrix $\mathbf{G}_1(x)$ which is termed the " action distribution matrix ", gives the actions at x due to the actions imposed on the beam at A, that is, $\mathbf{Z}_0$. The matrix $\bar{\mathbf{Z}}_0(x)$ gives the actions due to the imposed loads and is termed the " loading solution matrix ". At $x = 0$ these matrices become the identity matrix $\mathbf{I}$ and a null matrix $\mathbf{0}$, respectively.

The derivation of these two matrices will be considered later. They are, in fact,

$$G_1(x) = \begin{bmatrix} 1 & x & -\dfrac{x^2}{2EI_1} & -\dfrac{x^3}{6EI_1} \\ 0 & 1 & -\dfrac{x}{EI_1} & -\dfrac{x^2}{2EI_1} \\ 0 & 0 & 1 & x \\ 0 & 0 & 0 & 1 \end{bmatrix}, \qquad \tilde{Z}_0(x) = \dfrac{p_1}{24EI_1} \begin{bmatrix} x^4 \\ 4x^3 \\ -12EI_1 x^2 \\ -24EI_1 x \end{bmatrix}$$

Using expression (7.1) we now have

$$Z(x) = G_1(x)K_A \bar{Z}_0 + \tilde{Z}_0(x) \tag{7.3}$$

Thus all the actions are given in terms of the two unknowns $\bar{Z}_0$.

At the right-hand edge of this member, $x = L_1$, i.e. support B, we have the actions

$$Z(L_1) = G_1(L_1)K_A \bar{Z}_0 + \tilde{Z}_0(L_1)$$

Also at B will be some reaction R, at present of unknown magnitude. This may be considered as a discontinuity in S, and thus in Z of magnitude ΔZ, where

$$\Delta Z = \begin{bmatrix} 0 \\ 0 \\ 0 \\ R \end{bmatrix}$$

The actions at the right-hand side of B are thus

$$Z_B = Z(L_1) + \Delta Z$$

These actions are the initial boundary actions for the span BC, so that taking B as a new origin for x we can say that in BC the actions are

$$Z(x) = G_2(x)Z_B + \tilde{Z}_B(x)$$

The matrices G_2 and $\tilde{Z}_B$ will be of similar form to G_1 and $\tilde{Z}_0$, but with I_2 and p_2 in place of I_1 and p_1.

Substituting for Z_B in this we have

$$Z(x) = G_2(x)[G_1(L_1)K_A \bar{Z}_0 + \tilde{Z}_0(L_1) + \Delta Z] + \tilde{Z}_B(x) \tag{7.4}$$

Equations (7.3) and (7.4) thus express all the actions in the two spans in terms of the three unknown factors ψ_0, S_0 and R. Equations for these three factors may be obtained from the condition at B and C. Thus at B the normal displacement w is zero. In order to separate out the action w from the others, we introduce the "isolation matrix".

$$\mathbf{I}_w = [1 \quad 0 \quad 0 \quad 0]$$

We can then write

$$\mathbf{I}_w \mathbf{Z}(L_1) = 0$$

or

$$\mathbf{I}_w[\mathbf{G}_1(L_1)\mathbf{K}_A\bar{\mathbf{Z}}_0 + \tilde{\mathbf{Z}}_0(L_1)] = 0 \tag{7.5}$$

At the support C we have the final boundary conditions

$$w_C = M_C = 0, \quad x = L_2$$

or

$$\begin{bmatrix} 1 & 0 & 0 & 0 \\ 0 & 0 & 1 & 0 \end{bmatrix} \mathbf{Z}(L_2) = \mathbf{I}_c\mathbf{Z}(L_2) = \begin{bmatrix} 0 \\ 0 \end{bmatrix} \tag{7.6}$$

Equations (7.5) and (7.6) give three conditions for the determination of ψ_0, S_0 and R. When these have been found the results may be substituted back in (7.3) and (7.4) to obtain the actions at any section.

Had the support C been of an elastic medium, the final boundary conditions would have been in the form

$$\begin{bmatrix} M_C \\ S_C \end{bmatrix} = \begin{bmatrix} C_{11} & C_{12} \\ C_{21} & C_{22} \end{bmatrix} \begin{bmatrix} w_C \\ \psi_C \end{bmatrix}$$

and we would have

$$\begin{bmatrix} C_{11} & C_{12} & -1 & 0 \\ C_{21} & C_{22} & 0 & -1 \end{bmatrix} \begin{bmatrix} w_C \\ \psi_C \\ M_C \\ S_C \end{bmatrix} = \mathbf{K}_C\mathbf{Z}_C = \begin{bmatrix} 0 \\ 0 \end{bmatrix}$$

In this $\mathbf{K}_C$ is termed the "final boundary restraint" matrix.

We will now extend our notation so that $\mathbf{G}_a(x)$ is the action distribution matrix giving the values of the actions at any section x in terms of the values of the actions at $x = a$, i.e.

$$\mathbf{Z}(x) = \mathbf{G}_a(x)\mathbf{Z}(a) \tag{7.7}$$

We will also denote by $\tilde{\mathbf{Z}}_a(x)$ the loading solution matrix giving the actions at x due to the applied loads and having all elements zero at $x = a$. It is easily seen that

$$\mathbf{G}_a(x) = \mathbf{G}_0(x-a), \qquad \tilde{\mathbf{Z}}_a(x) = \tilde{\mathbf{Z}}_0(x-a) \qquad (7.8)$$

The following relationships are also readily obtained

$$\mathbf{G}_a(b)\mathbf{G}_0(c) = \mathbf{G}_a(b+c) = \mathbf{G}_0(b+c-a) = \mathbf{G}_0(b)\mathbf{G}_a(c) \qquad (7.9)$$

$$\mathbf{G}_a(a) = \mathbf{I}, \quad \mathbf{G}_0^{-1}(x) = \mathbf{G}_0(-x)$$

and

$$\tilde{\mathbf{Z}}_0(x) = \tilde{\mathbf{Z}}_a(x) + \mathbf{G}_a(x)\tilde{\mathbf{Z}}_0(a) \qquad (7.10)$$

Let us now return to the two-span beam and put $I_1 = I_2 = I$, $p_1 = p_2 = p$, and $L_1 = L_2 = C$. We then have, as before, in span AB

$$\mathbf{Z}(x) = \mathbf{G}_0(x)\mathbf{K}_A\overline{\mathbf{Z}}_0 + \tilde{\mathbf{Z}}_0(x) \qquad (7.11)$$

and at B

$$\mathbf{Z}(L) = \mathbf{G}_0(L)\mathbf{K}_A\overline{\mathbf{Z}}_0 + \tilde{\mathbf{Z}}_0(L)$$

At the right-hand side of B

$$\mathbf{Z}_B = \mathbf{Z}(L) + \Delta\mathbf{Z}$$

Keeping now the origin at A, we have in span BC

$$\mathbf{Z}(x) = \mathbf{G}_L(x)\mathbf{Z}_B + \tilde{\mathbf{Z}}_L(x)$$

$$= \mathbf{G}_L(x)[\mathbf{G}_0(L)\mathbf{K}_A\overline{\mathbf{Z}}_0 + \tilde{\mathbf{Z}}_0(L)] + \tilde{\mathbf{Z}}_L(x) + \mathbf{G}_L(x)\Delta\mathbf{Z}$$

From (7.9) and (7.10),

$$\mathbf{G}_L(x)\mathbf{G}_0(L) = \mathbf{G}_0(x+L-L) = \mathbf{G}_0(x)$$

$$\mathbf{G}_L(x)\tilde{\mathbf{Z}}_0(L) + \tilde{\mathbf{Z}}_L(x) = \tilde{\mathbf{Z}}_0(x)$$

whence

$$\mathbf{Z}(x) = \mathbf{G}_0(x)\mathbf{K}_A\overline{\mathbf{Z}}_0 + \tilde{\mathbf{Z}}_0(x) + \mathbf{G}_L(x)\Delta\mathbf{Z} \qquad (7.12)$$

We see now that equation (7.12) is of similar form to equation (7.11) and all we have had to do is add in the effect of the reaction R (i.e. $\Delta\mathbf{Z}$) at $x = C$ by means of the term $\mathbf{G}_L(x)\Delta\mathbf{Z}$. We will return to this feature later, meanwhile we will continue with the solution of our problem.

At C, $x = 2L$, we have

$$\mathbf{Z}_C = \mathbf{G}_0(2L)\mathbf{K}_A\overline{\mathbf{Z}}_0 + \tilde{\mathbf{Z}}_0(2L) + \mathbf{G}_L(2L)\Delta\mathbf{Z}$$

$$= \mathbf{G}_0(2L)\mathbf{K}_A\overline{\mathbf{Z}}_0 + \tilde{\mathbf{Z}}_0(2L) + \mathbf{G}_0(L)\Delta\mathbf{Z}$$

The equations for finding $\Delta\mathbf{Z}$ and $\overline{\mathbf{Z}}_0$ are

$$\mathbf{I}_w\mathbf{Z}(L) = 0, \quad \mathbf{I}_C\mathbf{Z}_C = \begin{bmatrix} 0 \\ 0 \end{bmatrix}$$

These give

$$[L \quad -L^3/6EI] \begin{bmatrix} \psi_0 \\ S_0 \end{bmatrix} + \frac{pL^4}{24EI} = 0$$

and

$$\begin{bmatrix} 2L & -8L^3/6EI \\ 0 & 2L \end{bmatrix} \begin{bmatrix} \psi_0 \\ S_0 \end{bmatrix} + \begin{bmatrix} -L^3/6EI \\ L \end{bmatrix} \left[R + \frac{p}{24} \begin{vmatrix} 16L^4 \\ \hline EI \\ -48L^2 \end{vmatrix} \right] = \begin{bmatrix} 0 \\ 0 \end{bmatrix}$$

Whence

$$\psi_0 = +\frac{1}{48}\frac{pL^3}{EI}, \quad S_0 = +\frac{3}{8}pL, \quad R = +\frac{10}{8}pL$$

We have just seen that the effect of the unknown reaction could be added to the general expression. Let us look, therefore, at a beam to which concentrated loads in the form of bending moments or normal loads are applied. Let us take a beam MN, with the origin of the beam at M. Let $\mathbf{Z}_M$ be the actions at M, and let there be an applied moment M_1, and applied load P_1 at $x = x_1$. In the region $0 < x < x_1$ the actions are simply

$$\mathbf{Z}(x) = \mathbf{G}_0(x)\mathbf{Z}_M$$

and at $x = x_1$ the actions are $\mathbf{G}_0(x_1)\mathbf{Z}_M$. At the right-hand side of x_1 the actions are

$$\mathbf{Z}(x_1+) = \mathbf{Z}(x_1) + \Delta\mathbf{Z}$$

where

$$\Delta\mathbf{Z} = \begin{bmatrix} 0 \\ 0 \\ M_1 \\ P_1 \end{bmatrix}$$

there being no change in w or ψ at x_1. At any point $x > x_1$

$$\mathbf{Z}(x) = \mathbf{G}_{x_1}(x)\mathbf{Z}(x_1+)$$
$$= \mathbf{G}_{x_1}(x)[\mathbf{Z}(x_1) + \Delta\mathbf{Z}]$$
$$= \mathbf{G}_0(x)\mathbf{Z}_M + \mathbf{G}_{x_1}(x)\Delta\mathbf{Z}$$

Thus if there are concentrated actions on the beam it is merely necessary to include these in the same manner as the initial boundary conditions. That is to say, the effect of the concentrated action can be found using the same distribution matrix as for the initial boundary actions. It should be noted that effects of artificially introduced displacements—for example due to prestressing or temperature variations—can be included in the same way as concentrated loads. Also if there are a series of concentrated actions $\Delta Z_1, \Delta Z_2 \ldots \Delta Z_n$ at $x = x_1, x_2 \ldots x_n$, then the actions at any section will be

$$\mathbf{Z}(x) = \mathbf{G}_0(x)\mathbf{Z}_m + \mathbf{G}_{x_1}(x)\,\Delta\mathbf{Z}_1 + \mathbf{G}_{x_2}(x)\,\Delta\mathbf{Z}_2 + \ldots \mathbf{G}_{xn}(x)\,\Delta\mathbf{Z}_n$$

where each influence matrix $\mathbf{G}_{xj}(x)$ only applies for $x > x_j$. In order to keep our notation consistent, we use a unit step matrix $\mathbf{H}_{an}$ which has the properties

$$\mathbf{H}_{a_n} = \mathbf{O} \quad x < a_n$$

$$\mathbf{H}_{a_n} = \mathbf{I} \quad x \geqslant a_n$$

With this, the above expression becomes

$$\mathbf{Z}(x) = \mathbf{G}_0(x)\mathbf{Z}_m + \sum_n \mathbf{H}_{x_n}\mathbf{G}_{x_n}(x)\,\Delta\mathbf{Z}_{x_n} \tag{7.13}$$

Let us now look at a beam with a uniformly distributed load between $x = x_1$ and $x = x_2$. As before we have

$$x_1 > x > x_0 \qquad \mathbf{Z} = \mathbf{G}_0(x)\mathbf{Z}_0$$

$$x = x_1 \qquad \mathbf{Z}_{x_1} = \mathbf{G}_0(x_1)\mathbf{Z}_0$$

$$x_2 > x > x_1 \qquad \mathbf{Z} = \mathbf{G}_{x_1}\mathbf{Z}_{x1} + \tilde{\mathbf{Z}}_{x_1}(x)$$

$$= \mathbf{G}_{x_1}(x)\mathbf{G}_0(x_1)\mathbf{Z}_0 + \tilde{\mathbf{Z}}_{x_1}(x)$$

$$= \mathbf{G}_0(x)\mathbf{Z}_0 + \tilde{\mathbf{Z}}_{x_1}(x)$$

At $\qquad x = x_2 \qquad \mathbf{Z}(x_2) = \mathbf{G}_0(x_2)\mathbf{Z}_0 + \tilde{\mathbf{Z}}_{x_1}(x_2)$

$$x > x_2 \qquad \mathbf{Z}(x_2) = \mathbf{G}_{x_2}(x)\mathbf{Z}(x_2)$$

$$= \mathbf{G}_{x_2}(x)\mathbf{G}_0(x_2)\mathbf{Z}_0 + \mathbf{G}_{x_2}(x)\tilde{\mathbf{Z}}_{x_1}(x_2)$$

$$= \mathbf{G}_0(x)\mathbf{Z}_0 + \mathbf{G}_{x_2}(x)\tilde{\mathbf{Z}}_{x_1}(x_2) \tag{7.14}$$

$$= \mathbf{G}_0(x)\mathbf{Z}_0 + \mathbf{G}_0(x - x_2)\tilde{\mathbf{Z}}_0(x_2 - x_1) \tag{7.14a}$$

Alternatively, we can apply a load, equal in magnitude but in the opposite direction, to the beam in the region $x > x_2$, and continue the original load for all $x > x_1$. We would then have

$$x_1 > x > 0 \qquad \mathbf{Z} = \mathbf{G}_0(x)\mathbf{Z}_0$$

$$x_2 > x > x_1 \qquad \mathbf{Z} = \mathbf{G}_0(x)\mathbf{Z}_0 + \tilde{\mathbf{Z}}_{x_1}(x)$$

$$x > x_2 \qquad \mathbf{Z} = \mathbf{G}_0(x)\mathbf{Z}_0 + \tilde{\mathbf{Z}}_{x_1}(x) - \tilde{\mathbf{Z}}_{x_2}(x)$$

Using the step matrix these expressions may be written

$$\mathbf{Z} = \mathbf{G}_0(x)\mathbf{Z}_0 + \mathbf{H}_{x_1}\check{\mathbf{Z}}_{x1}(x) - \mathbf{H}_{x_2}\check{\mathbf{Z}}_{x_2}(x) \tag{7.15}$$

A series of distributed loads can be treated in the same manner.

There remains one further feature which should be considered before we proceed to more complex problems. Let us take a beam AB with some distributed load $p(x)$, and let some point C in the span be held in an elastic medium. We will take the elastic coefficients at C to be such that the forces applied to the medium are related to the displacements of the medium by

$$\begin{bmatrix} M_C \\ S_C \end{bmatrix} = \begin{bmatrix} C_{11} & C_{12} \\ C_{21} & C_{22} \end{bmatrix} \begin{bmatrix} w_C \\ \psi_C \end{bmatrix}$$

If now the actions to the left of C are

$$\mathbf{Z}(C) = \mathbf{G}_0(C)\mathbf{Z}_0 + \check{\mathbf{Z}}(C)$$

to the right of C they will be

$$\mathbf{Z}(C+) = \mathbf{Z}(C) + \Delta \mathbf{Z}_C$$

where

$$\Delta \mathbf{Z}_C = \begin{bmatrix} 0 \\ 0 \\ M_C \\ S_C \end{bmatrix}$$

Now

$$\mathbf{Z}(C) + \Delta \mathbf{Z}_C = \begin{bmatrix} w_C \\ \psi_C \\ M_C \\ S_C \end{bmatrix} + \begin{bmatrix} 0 & 0 & 0 & 0 \\ 0 & 0 & 0 & 0 \\ C_{11} & C_{12} & 0 & 0 \\ C_{21} & C_{22} & 0 & 0 \end{bmatrix} \begin{bmatrix} w_C \\ \psi_C \\ M_C \\ S_C \end{bmatrix} = \mathbf{Z}(C) + \bar{\mathbf{R}}_C \mathbf{Z}(C)$$

$$= \begin{bmatrix} 1 & 0 & 0 & 0 \\ 0 & 1 & 0 & 0 \\ C_{11} & C_{12} & 1 & 0 \\ C_{21} & C_{22} & 0 & 1 \end{bmatrix} \begin{bmatrix} w_C \\ \psi_C \\ M_C \\ S_C \end{bmatrix} = \mathbf{R}_C \mathbf{Z}(C)$$

In this $\mathbf{R}_C$ is the elastic restraint matrix at C. We now see that if all the actions to the left of C are given in terms of two unknowns (the reduced boundary action matrix), so also will be the actions to the right of C, i.e. *an elastic restraint introduces no further unknowns.*

In the simple case of a beam it is easy to obtain the loading solution matrix. In other structures it may not be as easy to find this matrix as we must have all the actions zero at one section. However, if we have a particular integral corresponding to the load, but not giving the necessary initial boundary conditions, we can construct the required solution. Let $P(x)$ be any particular integral for the problem, and $\mathbf{P}(x)$ the corresponding action matrix, then at $x = a$ the actions would be $\mathbf{P}(a)$. If we now apply a set of actions equal to $-\mathbf{P}(a)$ at $x = a$ the actions at any section will be

$$\tilde{\mathbf{Z}}_a(x) = \mathbf{P}(x) - \mathbf{G}_a(x)\mathbf{P}(a)$$

The value of the actions at $x = a$ is

$$\tilde{\mathbf{Z}}_a(a) = \mathbf{P}(a) - \mathbf{I}(\mathbf{P}a) = 0$$

Thus the required loading solution matrix is

$$\tilde{\mathbf{Z}}_a(x) = \mathbf{P}(x) - \mathbf{G}_a(x)\mathbf{P}(a)$$

As an example let us consider the " beam on an elastic foundation " equation:

$$\frac{d^4 w}{dx^4} + 4k^4 w = \frac{p(x)}{EI}$$

and let us take a uniform load for $x > a$. For $x < a$ there is no loading solution matrix. A particular solution for $x > a$ is readily seen to be

$$w = \frac{p}{4k^4 EI}$$

for which the action matrix $\mathbf{P}$ is

$$\mathbf{P} = \frac{p}{4k^4 EI} \begin{bmatrix} 1 \\ 0 \\ 0 \\ 0 \end{bmatrix}$$

Since this is not zero at $x = a$, we apply a concentrated action $-\mathbf{P}$ (that is a dislocation in w) at this section and obtain

$$\tilde{\mathbf{Z}} = \mathbf{P} - \mathbf{G}_a(x)\mathbf{P}$$

for the loading solution matrix in the region $x > a$. In this $\mathbf{G}_a(x)$ is, of course, the action distribution matrix associated with the beam on an elastic foundation.

So far we have only considered a simple structure in which the basic equation is the same for all parts. Let us look now at a more complex structure. Again as we are only examining the technique we will take a structure in the form of a beam of span $2L$, simply supported at each end, under a uniformly distributed load, and having the region $L < x < 2L$ supported on an elastic base. We now have two different differential equations for the deflexions in the two halves of the beam, i.e.

$$0 < x < L \qquad \frac{d^4w}{dx^4} = \frac{p}{EI}$$

$$L < x < 2L \qquad \frac{d^4w}{dx^4} + 4k^2w = \frac{p}{EI}$$

In both parts the actions are w, ψ, M and S. We will assume that we know the action distribution matrices $G_0^1(x)$ and $G_0^2(x)$ corresponding to the two equations, and the loading solution matrices $\tilde{Z}^1(x)$ and $\tilde{Z}^2(x)$ corresponding to a uniformly distribution load. We now start at one end, as before, and can say that the initial boundary values of the actions are

$$\mathbf{Z}_0 = \mathbf{K}_A \bar{\mathbf{Z}}_0$$

In the part of the beam $0 < x < L$ the actions are

$$\mathbf{Z}(x) = \mathbf{G}_0^1(x)\mathbf{Z}_0 + \tilde{\mathbf{Z}}_0^1(x)$$

and at the junction with the elastic base, $x = L$, they are

$$\mathbf{Z}_L = \mathbf{G}_0^1(L)\mathbf{Z}_0 + \tilde{\mathbf{Z}}_0^1(L)$$

Now these actions are the initial boundary actions for the part of the beam resting on the elastic foundation, and in this part of the beam (i.e. $L < x < 2L$)

$$\mathbf{Z}(x) = \mathbf{G}_L^2(x)\mathbf{Z}_L + \tilde{\mathbf{Z}}_L^2(x)$$

Substituting for $\mathbf{Z}(L)$ we then have

$$\mathbf{Z}(x) = \mathbf{G}_L^2(x)[\mathbf{G}_0^1(L)\mathbf{K}_A\bar{\mathbf{Z}}_0 + \tilde{\mathbf{Z}}_0^1(L)] + \tilde{\mathbf{Z}}_L^2(x)$$
$$= \mathbf{G}_0^2(x-L)[\mathbf{G}_0^1(L)\mathbf{K}_A\bar{\mathbf{Z}}_0 + \tilde{\mathbf{Z}}_0^1(L)] + \tilde{\mathbf{Z}}_0^2(x-L)$$

At the right-hand end of the beam $(x = 2L)$

$$\mathbf{Z}(2L) = \mathbf{G}_0^2(L)[\mathbf{G}_0^1(L)\mathbf{K}_A\bar{\mathbf{Z}}_0 + \tilde{\mathbf{Z}}_0^1(L)] + \tilde{\mathbf{Z}}_0^2(L)$$

and as before the value of $\mathbf{Z}_0$ can be found from the condition

$$I_C Z(2L) = \begin{bmatrix} 0 \\ 0 \end{bmatrix}$$

We note that the change in the form of the structure (i.e. from simple span to beam on an elastic foundation) does not introduce any further unknowns. All beam problems, being defined by a fourth-order differential equation, have four relevant actions and have a *basic indeterminacy factor of two*. The indeterminacy factor is increased by one for each condition imposed between the ends. Thus if at some section there is a hinge the condition $M = 0$ is imposed, if at a section the displacement w_1 is prescribed, the condition $w = w_1$ is imposed, etc. The indeterminacy factor is the basic indeterminacy factor plus the number of imposed conditions. At each point where a condition is imposed, there is a discontinuity of unknown magnitude in the complimentary action (i.e. if w is prescribed there is a discontinuity in S, etc.). These rules apply to all single chain structures.

Let us see now what happens if there is a branch chain in the structure. For this we will group the actions into two sets: those involving displacements $\mathbf{U}$, and those involving forces $\mathbf{Y}$, and put the total actions $\mathbf{Z}$ in the form

$$\mathbf{Z} = \begin{bmatrix} \mathbf{U} \\ \mathbf{Y} \end{bmatrix}$$

Let the structure be composed of three elements AB, BC, and BD. Then starting at A the actions are

$$\mathbf{Z}_A = \mathbf{K}_A \mathbf{Z}_A$$

In AB the actions are

$$\mathbf{Z}(x) = \mathbf{G}_0^1 \mathbf{Z}_A + \tilde{\mathbf{Z}}_0^1(x)$$

(The superfixes 1, 2 and 3 will relate to the three elements AB, BC and BD.)
At the junction B the actions are

$$\mathbf{Z}_B = \mathbf{G}_0^1(AB)\mathbf{Z}_A + \tilde{\mathbf{Z}}_0^1(AB)$$

Now the displacements at B will be, in the absence of any imposed conditions, common to all elements, so that, keeping the same co-ordinate system,

$$\mathbf{U}_B^1 = \mathbf{U}_B^2 = \mathbf{U}_B^3$$

We can isolate the displacements by means of the isolation matrix of order $n \times 2n$

$$\mathbf{I}_U = \begin{bmatrix} \mathbf{I} & \mathbf{O} \end{bmatrix}$$

where $\mathbf{O}$ is a null matrix. With this

$$\mathbf{U}_B = \mathbf{I}_U \mathbf{Z}_B$$

For equilibrium at B

$$Y_B^1 = Y_B^2 + Y_B^3$$

or using the isolation matrix

$$I_y = [\,O \quad I\,]$$
$$I_y Z_B^1 = I_y Z_B^2 + I_y Z_B^3$$

Let us take the action Y_B^3 as being a further set of unknown quantities then

$$I_y Z_B^2 = I_y Z_B^1 - Y_B^3$$

The actions Z_B^2 are then

$$Z_B^2 = \begin{bmatrix} U_B \\ I_y Z_B - Y_B \end{bmatrix} = \begin{bmatrix} I_U Z_B^1 \\ I_y Z_B^1 \end{bmatrix} - \begin{bmatrix} O \\ Y_B^3 \end{bmatrix}$$
$$= Z_B^1 - I_y^* Y_B^3$$

where

$$I_y^* = \begin{bmatrix} O \\ I \end{bmatrix}$$

and the actions Z_B^3 are

$$Z_B^3 = \begin{bmatrix} U_B \\ Y_B^3 \end{bmatrix} = I_u^* I_C Z_B^1 + I_y^* Y_B^3$$

where

$$I_u^* = \begin{bmatrix} I \\ O \end{bmatrix}$$

It is generally necessary to use new co-ordinate systems in branches 2 and 3, let O^2 and O^3 be the matrices transforming the actions Z into the new sets of coordinates. Then at the origin of branch 2 in its co-ordinate system

$$Z_0^2 = O^2[Z_B^1 - I_y^* Y_B^3]$$

and in branch 3

$$Z_0^3 = O^3[I_U^* I_U Z_B^1 + I_y^* Y_B]$$

Thus all the sets of actions are stated in terms of the initial set of actions Z_A and the unknowns Y_0^3. Two sets of equations for determining these can be found from the conditions at the ends C and D. If there are further branches the same technique can be applied and there will be a further set of unknowns Y at each branch.

We may also note that if a branch returns to the main line, we still get a set of equations to help determine the unknowns in the branch, namely the condition that the displacements in the branch and the main line are equal. If the return junction is the end of the structure, we have two sets of conditions, namely equality of displacements and equilibrium of forces. In appropriate co-ordinates these may be written

$$U_{\text{branch}} = U_{\text{main line}}$$
$$Y_{\text{branch}} + Y_{\text{main line}} = O$$

We can thus formulate a general rule for finding the indeterminacy of a structure. If the basic equations are of order n, there will be n relevant actions and the basic indeterminacy factor is $n/2$. To this must be added one further indeterminacy for every imposed condition plus $n/2$ further indeterminates for every branch in the structure—whether the branch returns to the main structure or not. A loop structure, such as four plates forming a box section, must be considered as a main line with a return branch. The addition of a fifth plate in these circumstances does not increase the indeterminacy unless it forms a two-cell box structure.

7.3. ILLUSTRATIVE EXAMPLES

Two examples will not only illustrate the application of the matrix progression method, but will also show the different means whereby the distribution matrix $G(x)$ can be formed.

Example 1. A circular cylindrical storage vessel, fig 7·3, has a radius of 20 ft. and is 15 ft. high. The wall thickness is 6 in. over the lower 7 ft. 6 in. and 3 in. over the top 7 ft. 6 in. The base of the wall is seated in a groove which restrains radial movement but allows rotation of the wall section. At the top of the wall is a 3-in.-thick spherical shell with a radius of curvature of 50 ft. The actions in the structure due to hydrostatic loading will be found.

Considering first the cylindrical tank, we know that the differential equation for the radial displacement is

$$\frac{d^4 w}{dx^4} + 4\alpha^4 w = -\frac{p}{ED}$$

where
$$\alpha^4 = \frac{3(1-\sigma^2)}{R^2 t^2}, \quad D = \frac{t^3}{12(1-\sigma^2)}$$

Also the actions are related to w by

$$\psi = \frac{dw}{dx}, \quad M_x = -ED\frac{d^2 w}{dx^2}, \quad Q_x = -ED\frac{d^3 w}{dx^3}$$

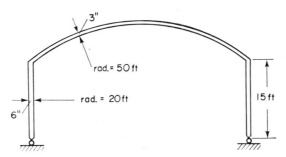

FIG. 7.3. Diagram for Example 1.

The solution, w_3, of the differential equation (a) such that

$$\frac{d^3w_3}{dx^3} = 1, \quad w_3 = \frac{dw_3}{dx} = \frac{d^2w_3}{dx^2} = 0 \text{ at } x = 0$$

is given by

$$w_3 = \sum_{\lambda=1}^{4} \frac{\exp(\lambda_s x)}{P_1(\lambda)_s}$$

where λ_s are the roots of the differential equation and

$$P_1(\lambda_s) = \frac{\partial}{\partial \lambda} P(\lambda)\big|_{\lambda=\lambda s}$$

$P(\lambda)$ being the characteristic polynomial. In this case:

$$w_3 = \sum \frac{\exp(\lambda_s x)}{4\lambda^3} \quad \begin{matrix} \lambda_{1,2} = & \alpha(1 \pm i) \\ \lambda_{3,4} = & -\alpha(1 \pm i) \end{matrix}$$

giving

$$w_3 = \frac{1}{4\alpha^3}(\cosh \alpha x \sin \alpha x - \sinh \alpha x \cos \alpha x)$$

The solutions such that

$$\frac{d^i w_j}{dx^i} = \begin{matrix} 1 & i = j \\ 0 & i \neq j \end{matrix}$$

are related by

$$\frac{dw_3}{dx} = w_2$$

$$\frac{dw_2}{dx} = w_1$$

$$\frac{dw_1}{dx} = w_0$$

$$\frac{dw_0}{dx} = -\alpha^4 w_3$$

giving

$$w_2 = \frac{1}{2\alpha^2} \sinh \alpha x \sin \alpha x$$

$$w_1 = \frac{1}{2\alpha}(\cosh \alpha x \sin \alpha x + \sinh \alpha x \cos \alpha x)$$

$$w_0 = \cosh \alpha x \cos \alpha x$$

The influence distribution matrix is thus

$$
\begin{bmatrix}
w_0 & w_1 & w_2 & w_3 \\
-4\alpha^4 w_3 & w_0 & w_1 & w_2 \\
-4\alpha^4 w_2 & -4\alpha^4 w_3 & w_0 & w_1 \\
-4\alpha^4 w_1 & -4\alpha^4 w_2 & -4\alpha^4 w_3 & w_0
\end{bmatrix}
$$

The actions are given by

$$
\mathbf{Z} =
\begin{bmatrix} Ew \\ E\psi \\ Mx \\ Qx \end{bmatrix}
=
\begin{bmatrix}
1 & \cdot & \cdot & \cdot \\
\cdot & 1 & \cdot & \cdot \\
\cdot & \cdot & -D & \cdot \\
\cdot & \cdot & \cdot & -D
\end{bmatrix}
\begin{bmatrix} Ew \\ Ew' \\ Ew'' \\ Ew''' \end{bmatrix}
= \mathbf{BW}
$$

and thus at any section, due to the actions $\mathbf{Z}_0$ at $x = 0$

$$
\mathbf{Z} = \mathbf{BW}(x)\, \mathbf{B}^{-1}\, \mathbf{Z}_0
$$

As a particular integral we can use

$$
E\tilde{w} = \frac{p(h-x)}{D}
$$

giving

$$
\tilde{\mathbf{W}}(0) = \frac{p}{D}
\begin{bmatrix} h \\ r \\ 0 \\ 0 \end{bmatrix}
= \tilde{\mathbf{Z}}_0
$$

at $x = 0$.

whence

$$
\mathbf{Z} = \mathbf{BW}(x)\mathbf{B}^{-1}(\mathbf{Z}_0 - \tilde{\mathbf{Z}}_0) + \tilde{\mathbf{Z}}(x)
$$

where

$$
\tilde{\mathbf{Z}} = \frac{p}{D}
\begin{bmatrix} h-x \\ -1 \\ 0 \\ 0 \end{bmatrix}
$$

At $x = 0$ the boundary conditions are $w = M_x = 0$, and thus

$$\mathbf{Z}_0 = \begin{bmatrix} 0 & 0 \\ 1 & 0 \\ 0 & 0 \\ 0 & 1 \end{bmatrix} \begin{bmatrix} E\psi_0 \\ Q_0 \end{bmatrix} = \mathbf{K}_0 \mathbf{Z}_0$$

At $x = 7{\cdot}5\,\text{ft}$.

$$\mathbf{Z}(7{\cdot}5) = \mathbf{BW}(7{\cdot}5)\mathbf{B}^{-1}(\mathbf{Z}_0 - \tilde{\mathbf{Z}}_0) + \tilde{\mathbf{Z}}(7{\cdot}5)$$

These are the actions at the origin of the second portion of the cylinder, for which, in the same way

$$\mathbf{Z}_1(7{\cdot}5) = \mathbf{B}_1 \mathbf{W}_1(7{\cdot}5)\mathbf{B}_1^{-1}(\mathbf{Z}(7{\cdot}5) - \tilde{\mathbf{Z}}_{10}) + \tilde{\mathbf{Z}}_1(7{\cdot}5)$$

the suffix 1 denoting the matrix appropriate to the top half of the cylinder.

The displacements at the edge of a shallow spherical shell are related to the displacements by

$$\begin{bmatrix} Ew \\ E\psi \end{bmatrix} = \begin{bmatrix} \delta_{11} & \delta_{12} \\ \delta_{21} & \delta_{22} \end{bmatrix} \begin{bmatrix} M \\ Q \end{bmatrix} = \mathbf{\Delta} \begin{bmatrix} M \\ Q \end{bmatrix}$$

where

$$\delta_{11} = -\frac{a^2 t^2}{6}\sin\phi, \quad \delta_{12} = \frac{Rat^2 \sin^2 \phi}{6}$$

$$\delta_{21} = \frac{ta}{\sqrt{3}}, \quad \delta_{22} = \frac{a^2 t^2 \sin\phi}{6}$$

$$a^4 = 3(1 - \sigma^2)R^2/t^2$$

Now

$$\begin{bmatrix} Ew \\ E\psi \end{bmatrix} = \begin{bmatrix} 1 & 0 & 0 & 0 \\ 0 & 1 & 0 & 0 \end{bmatrix} \mathbf{Z} = \mathbf{I}_1 \mathbf{Z}$$

$$\begin{bmatrix} M_x \\ Q_2 \end{bmatrix} = \begin{bmatrix} 0 & 0 & 1 & 0 \\ 0 & 0 & 0 & 1 \end{bmatrix} \mathbf{Z} = \mathbf{I}_2 \mathbf{Z}$$

giving, at $x = 7{\cdot}5$

$$\mathbf{I}_1 \mathbf{Z} = \mathbf{\Delta I}_2 \mathbf{Z}$$

or

$$[\mathbf{I}_1 - \mathbf{\Delta I}_2]\mathbf{Z}(7{\cdot}5) = 0$$

This gives two equations for $\mathbf{Z}_0$, with which all the actions can then be obtained.

Example 2. A cylindrical shell is simply supported at the ends. The shell has an internal angle of ϕ and has a radial live load in the form $P\cos\pi x/L$ along a generator angle θ from the edge (Fig. 7.4).

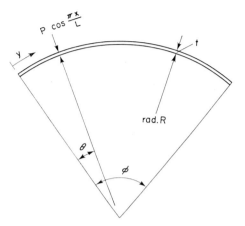

FIG. 7.4. Diagram for Example 2.

The equations of equilibrium are

$$\frac{\partial T_2}{\partial y} + \frac{\partial S}{\partial x} = 0$$

$$\frac{\partial S}{\partial y} + \frac{\partial T_1}{\partial x} = 0$$

$$\frac{\partial M_{12}}{\partial y} + \frac{\partial M_1}{\partial x} + N_1 = 0$$

$$\frac{\partial M_2}{\partial y} + \frac{\partial M_{12}}{\partial x} + N_2 = 0$$

$$\frac{\partial N_2}{\partial y} + \frac{\partial N_1}{\partial x} - \frac{T_2}{R} = 0$$

The forces are related to the displacements by

$$\varepsilon_1 = \frac{\partial u}{\partial x} = \frac{1}{Et}(T_1 - \sigma T_2) \qquad x_1 = \frac{\partial^2 w}{\partial x^2} = \frac{1}{ED}(M_1 - \sigma M_2)$$

$$\varepsilon_2 = \frac{\partial v}{\partial y} + \frac{w}{R} = \frac{1}{Et}(T_2 - \sigma T_1) \qquad x_2 = \frac{\partial^2 w}{\partial y^2} = \frac{1}{ED}(M_2 - \sigma M_1)$$

$$\psi = \frac{\partial u}{\partial y} + \frac{\partial v}{\partial x} = \frac{2(1+\sigma)S}{Et} \qquad \psi_{12} = \frac{\partial^2 w}{\partial x \, \partial y} = \frac{1+\sigma}{ED} M_{12}$$

The rotation of the tangent is defined by

$$\psi_2 = \frac{\partial w}{\partial y}$$

For the Kirchhoff boundary condition we need

$$R = N_2 + \frac{\partial M_{12}}{\partial x}$$

Expressing w, ψ, M_1, M_2, T_1, T_2, N_2 and v in the form $w\cos \pi x/L$, etc., and the actions u, S, M_{12} and N_1 in the form $u\sin \pi x/L$, etc., we have, denoting derivatives d/dy by ψ', and putting $n/L = \alpha$:

$$\psi = w'$$

$$M_2 = D\psi' - \sigma\alpha^2 w$$

$$M_1 = -(1-\sigma^2)\alpha^2 Dw + \sigma D M_2$$

$$M_{12} = -(1-\sigma)\alpha D\psi$$

$$N_2 = -M_2' + \alpha^2(1-\sigma)D\psi$$

$$R_2 = -M_2' + 2\alpha^2(1-\sigma)D\psi$$

$$N_1 = -(1-\sigma)\alpha^2 Dw + \sigma M_2$$

$$T_2 = R[\alpha^2 M_2 + N_2' - (1-\sigma)\alpha'' Dw]$$

$$S = -\frac{1}{\alpha}T_2'$$

$$T_1 = \frac{1}{\alpha}S$$

$$u = \frac{1}{\alpha Et}\left(\frac{1}{\alpha}S' - \sigma T_2\right)$$

$$v = \frac{1}{\alpha}\left[u' - \frac{2(1-\sigma)}{Et}S\right]$$

$$w = R\left[(1-\sigma^2)\frac{T}{Et} - v' - \sigma\alpha u\right]$$

or

$$\frac{d}{dy}\begin{bmatrix} Ew \\ E\psi \\ M_2 \\ R_2 \\ T_2 \\ S \\ Eu \\ Ev \end{bmatrix} = \begin{bmatrix} 0 & 1 & 0 & 0 & 0 & 0 & 0 & 0 \\ \sigma\alpha^2 & 0 & 1 & 0 & 0 & 0 & 0 & 0 \\ 0 & (1-\sigma)\alpha^2 D & 0 & -1 & 0 & 0 & 0 & 0 \\ (1-\sigma)\alpha^2 D & 0 & \alpha^2 D & 0 & 1/R & 0 & 0 & 0 \\ 0 & 0 & 0 & 0 & 0 & -\alpha & 0 & 0 \\ 0 & 0 & 0 & 0 & \sigma\alpha & 0 & \alpha^2 t & 0 \\ 0 & 0 & 0 & 0 & 0 & 2(1+\sigma)R & 0 & \alpha \\ -1/R & 0 & 0 & 0 & (1-\sigma^2)R/t & 0 & \sigma\alpha & 0 \end{bmatrix}\begin{bmatrix} Ew \\ E\psi \\ M_2 \\ R_2 \\ T_2 \\ S \\ Eu \\ Ev \end{bmatrix}$$

or

$$\frac{d}{dy}\mathbf{Z} = \mathbf{AZ}$$

The actions at any section $y < R\phi$ are then

$$\mathbf{Z}(y) = \exp\left[\int_0^y A\,dy\right]\mathbf{Z}_0$$

$$= \mathbf{G}(y)\mathbf{Z}_0 \tag{a}$$

where

$$\mathbf{G}(y) = \exp[\mathbf{A}y] = \mathbf{I} + \mathbf{A}y + \mathbf{A}^2\frac{y^2}{2!} + \mathbf{A}^3\frac{y^3}{3!} + \cdots$$

Now at $y = 0$, $M_2 = R_2 = T_2 = S = 0$, or

$$\mathbf{Z}_0 = \begin{bmatrix} 1 & 0 & 0 & 0 \\ 0 & 1 & 0 & 0 \\ 0 & 0 & 0 & 0 \\ 0 & 0 & 0 & 0 \\ 0 & 0 & 0 & 0 \\ 0 & 0 & 0 & 0 \\ 0 & 0 & 1 & 0 \\ 0 & 0 & 0 & 1 \end{bmatrix}\begin{bmatrix} Ew \\ E\psi \\ Eu \\ Ev \end{bmatrix}_0 = \mathbf{I}_1\overline{\mathbf{Z}}_0$$

At $y = R\theta$ there is a step in R_2 of magnitude P whence for $y > R\theta$

$$\mathbf{Z}(y) = \mathbf{G}(y)\mathbf{I}_1\overline{\mathbf{Z}}_0 + \mathbf{G}(y - R\theta)\Delta\mathbf{Z} \tag{b}$$

and

$$\Delta\mathbf{Z} = \text{Col}\,[0,0,0,P,0,0,0,0,]$$

At the edge $y = R\phi$, the forces M_2, T_2, R_2 and S are zero, or:

$$\mathbf{I}_2\mathbf{Z}(R\phi) = \mathbf{O}$$

where

$$\mathbf{I}_2 = \begin{bmatrix} 0 & 0 & 1 & 0 & 0 & 0 & 0 & 0 \\ 0 & 0 & 0 & 1 & 0 & 0 & 0 & 0 \\ 0 & 0 & 0 & 0 & 1 & 0 & 0 & 0 \\ 0 & 0 & 0 & 0 & 0 & 1 & 0 & 0 \end{bmatrix}$$

whence

$$\mathbf{I}_2\mathbf{G}(R\phi)\mathbf{I}_1\overline{\mathbf{Z}}_0 + \mathbf{I}_2\mathbf{G}[R(\phi - \theta)]\,\Delta\mathbf{Z} = \mathbf{O}$$

and thus

$$\overline{\mathbf{Z}}_0 = [\mathbf{I}_2\mathbf{G}(R\phi)\mathbf{I}_1]^{-1}\mathbf{I}_2\mathbf{G}[R(\phi - \theta)]\,\Delta\mathbf{Z}$$

the actions at any section can now be found from (a) and (b) above.

FURTHER READING

H. Tottenham, *A New Method of Analysis of Thin-Walled Spatial Structures.* Timber Development Association, London (1958).

H. Tottenham, The Linear Analysis of Thin-Walled Spatial Structures. *Symposium on the Use of Computers in Structural Engineering. Southampton University* (1959).

F. A. Leckie and L. Pestel, Fundamentals of Transfer Matrices. *International J. Mech. Sci.*, Nov. 137–154 (1960).

CHAPTER 8

THERMAL STRESSES

J. S. Przemieniecki

NOTATION

(Note: Bold-face type is used to denote matrices)

x_1, x_2, x_3 = rectangular co-ordinates.

x, y, z = set of mutually orthogonal axes in the middle surface of shells or plates.

u_1, u_2, u_3 = displacements in x_1, x_2 and x_3 directions, respectively.

u, v, w = displacements in x, y and z directions, respectively.

n_i = direction cosine of an outward drawn normal and the ith axis ($i = 1, 2, 3$).

e_{ij} = total strain ($i, j = 1, 2, 3$).

ε_{ij} = elastic strain.

η_{ij} = temperature strain (thermal dilatation).

α = coefficient of thermal expansion.

δ_{ij} = Kronecker delta.

$G = E/2(1+v)$, modulus of rigidity.

E = Young's modulus.

v = Poisson's ratio.

σ_{ij} = stress ($i, j = 1, 2, 3$).

$s = \sigma_{11} + \sigma_{22} + \sigma_{33}$.

$e = e_{11} + e_{22} + e_{33}$.

ω_i = body force in the ith direction

$\bar{\omega}_i$ = fictitious body force used in Duhamel's analogy.

X_i = component of surface force per unit area ($i = 1, 2, 3$).

Φ = thermoelastic displacement potential.

F = Airy stress function.

F_h, F_p = homogeneous and particular solutions for the Airy stress function.

N_1, N_2, N_x, N_y = direct stress resultants.

Q, N_{xy} = shear resultants.

M_1, M_2, M_x, M_y = stress couples.

M_{xy} = twisting couple.

T = temperature distribution.

T_m = mean temperature.

ΔT = temperature "gradient," defined by equation (8.74).

T^* = self-equilibrating temperature distribution.

d = shell (or plate) thickness.

D = $Ed^3/12(1-v^2)$, flexural stiffness of shells or plates.

R_1, R_2 = principal radii of curvature.

λ = R_2/R_1.

ϕ = angle between the normal to the middle surface and the axis of symmetry (axi-symmetrical shells).

$$U = \left(u + \frac{dw}{d\phi}\right) \times \frac{1}{R_1}.$$

$V = R_2 Q.$

μ, k, k_i = constants.

I = moment of inertia.

δW^* = increment of complementary work of external forces.

$\delta U_i^* = \int_v \varepsilon\,\delta\sigma\,dV$, increment in complementary strain energy.

$\delta U_e^* = -\delta W^*$, increment in the complementary potential of external forces.

$\delta U_d^* = \delta U_i^* + \int_v \alpha T\delta s\,dV$, increment in the complementary potential energy of total deformation.

$\delta s = \delta\sigma_{11} + \delta\sigma_{22} + \delta\sigma_{33}.$

$\bar{\sigma}$ = stresses due to a unit load.

$\mathbf{s}$ = internal load distribution matrix.

$\mathbf{b}_0$ = distribution matrix for basic system.

$\mathbf{b}_1$ = distribution matrix for self-equilibrating stress systems.

$\mathbf{X}$ = self-equilibrating loads.

u_r = displacement in the rth direction.

$\mathbf{v}$ = generalized displacements.

$\overline{\mathbf{S}}$ = internal load distribution due to a unit load.

$\mathbf{f}$ = flexibility matrix.

$\mathbf{H}$ = generalized thermal deformations.

$\nabla^2 \equiv \dfrac{\partial^2}{\partial x_1^2} + \dfrac{\partial^2}{\partial x_2^2} + \dfrac{\partial^2}{\partial x_3^2}, \left(\text{or } \dfrac{\partial^2}{\partial x_1^2} + \dfrac{\partial^2}{\partial x_2^2}\right)$, Laplace operator.

$\nabla^4 \equiv \dfrac{\partial^4}{\partial x_1^4} + 2\dfrac{\partial^4}{\partial x_1^2\,\partial x_2^2} + \dfrac{\partial^4}{\partial x_2^4}$, biharmonic operator.

$\nabla_e^2 \equiv \dfrac{\partial^2}{\partial x^2} + \dfrac{\partial^2}{\partial y^2}.$

$\nabla_k^2 \equiv \dfrac{\partial^2}{\partial x^2} + \lambda\dfrac{\partial^2}{\partial y^2}.$

$$L(\ ) \equiv \frac{d^2(\ )}{d\phi^2} + \left[\frac{R_1}{R_2}\frac{d}{d\phi}\left(\frac{R_2}{R_1}\right) + \cot\phi\right]\frac{d(\ )}{d\phi} - \frac{R_1^2}{R_2^2}\cot^2\phi(\ ).$$

8.1. INTRODUCTION

THE determination of thermal stresses plays an important part in the design of nuclear reactors, gas and steam turbines, heat exchangers, supersonic aircraft and many other types of structures operating at elevated temperatures. Thermal stress calculations are generally based on linear elasticity and this serves as a first step indicating whether further computations will be required to allow for non-linear effects caused by plastic flow and creep. Thermal stresses are produced either by a non-uniform temperature distribution, which gives rise to non-uniform expansions and volumetric changes in different parts of the structure, or by external restraints restricting free expansion of the boundaries. Furthermore, thermal stresses can also be induced by a uniform temperature rise in a composite structure consisting of materials having different coefficients of expansion.

In general, thermal stress problems can be treated as quasi-static, since even under varying temperature distribution the thermal inertia effects can be entirely neglected and the problem can be considered as static. When investigating thermal strain effects the analysis should be based on thermo-dynamic considerations, which, strictly speaking, should include coupling effects between temperature and thermoelastic deformations. Although these coupling effects are of some interest in the study of basic physical laws in thermoelasticity, they need not be considered in ordinary engineering applications.

Thermal stresses in an unrestrained structure are self-equilibrating, that is on any *overall* cross-section thermal stresses produce zero resultant direct and shear loads and zero bending moment. Thus they are analogous to residual stresses; the only difference is that whereas the residual stresses need no external " stimuli " the thermal stresses in a homogeneous body can only be maintained by the non-uniform temperature field and, if the elastic limit has not been exceeded, they disappear completely once the temperature field becomes uniform. Before the residual stresses can be produced by temperature changes, it is necessary that non-uniform *plastic* deformations occur in different parts of the body. These stresses are usually produced during quenching operations involving cooling from a high temperature. If the deformations arising during the cooling period are within the *elastic limit* of the material, then no residual stresses are present after temperature equilibrium is reached. Thus the method of cooling (rate of cooling) and the stress–strain characteristics at elevated temperatures influence the magnitude and distribution of the residual stresses produced by temperature changes.

The introduction of thermal effects into the theory of elasticity dates back to the first half of the last century when Duhamel[1-3] presented his papers which discussed the generalization of the fundamental theorems of elasticity to include thermal strains and stresses caused by non-uniform temperature distributions in an elastic body. The theory thus arrived at has not been developed very much because of its limited application to practical problems. However, the recent advances in nuclear and chemical engineering, such as gas turbines, missiles and supersonic aircraft, have stimulated further interest in thermoelasticity and have led to extensive theoretical and experimental studies of thermal stress problems.

The maximum power of a nuclear reactor is determined by the rate at which heat can be removed from the fuel elements. Heat is conducted from the fuel through the solid components of the reactor to a surface along which the flowing coolant receives heat by convection. Moreover, heat is not only generated within the fuel elements but it is also produced from the slowing down of neutrons and beta-particles and the absorption of various gamma-radiations in the reactor core and structure. The resulting heat source distribution combined with the heat removal by the coolant produce a non-uniform temperature distribution which causes thermal stresses. Particularly severe thermal stresses can arise also due to accidental causes in the reactor operation when sudden temperature increases (thermal shock) can be experienced on some parts of the reactor structure.

In producing power by heat engines the heat cycle efficiency increases with the absolute temperature. This can be seen directly from the formula for the efficiency of conversion of heat into work in an ideal engine, operating between two absolute temperatures $T_1 > T_2$:

$$\text{Carnot efficiency} = 1 - \frac{T_2}{T_1}$$

Thus an increase in T_1 produces an appreciable gain in efficiency but at the same time it entails higher thermal stresses and higher creep rates.

In chemical engineering many processes can be accelerated and carried out more efficiently by increasing the temperature and pressure. Hence, in designing vessels in which a high temperature is needed for chemical reactions, thermal stresses must be included in the design calculations and combined with stresses due to pressure and any other loading to ensure adequate strength and life.

Aircraft structures designed for supersonic flight are subjected to aerodynamic heating. The air surrounding the aircraft in flight is progressively slowed down through the boundary layer and this process generates heat and consequently all external surfaces on the aircraft are heated. This leads to non-uniform transient temperatures which produce transient thermal stresses in the structure.

In this chapter an attempt has been made to present some of the fundamental principles of thermoelasticity and to show some typical methods employed for the solution of thermal stress problems in structures subjected to " temperature loading ". In discussing the methods of solution the main emphasis has been on the practical applications rather than on the mathematical rigour of the solution. Only first-order terms have been included. If required, more refined calculations can be found in the numerous papers, now available, in the technical literature on this subject. This chapter can therefore be regarded as a general introduction to the theory of thermoelasticity.

8.2. GENERAL THEOREMS[4-7]

(i) Strain–Displacement Equations

The deformed shape of an elastic body subjected to " temperature loading " can be described by the three displacements

$$u_1 = u_1(x_1, x_2, x_3)$$
$$u_2 = u_2(x_1, x_2, x_3) \tag{8.1}$$
$$u_3 = u_3(x_1, x_2, x_3)$$

or using tensor notation

$$u_i = u_i(x_1, x_2, x_3); \quad i = 1, 2, 3 \tag{8.1a}$$

where the suffices 1, 2 and 3 denote the directions of a set of rectangular axes.

The strains in the body can be expressed in terms of the partial derivatives with respect to the three chosen directions. The direct strains are given by

$$e_{11} = \frac{\partial u_1}{\partial x_1}$$

$$e_{22} = \frac{\partial u_2}{\partial x_2} \tag{8.2}$$

$$e_{33} = \frac{\partial u_3}{\partial x_3}$$

while the shear strains by

$$e_{12} = e_{21} = \tfrac{1}{2}\left(\frac{\partial u_2}{\partial x_1} + \frac{\partial u_1}{\partial x_2}\right)$$

$$e_{23} = e_{32} = \tfrac{1}{2}\left(\frac{\partial u_3}{\partial x_2} + \frac{\partial u_2}{\partial x_3}\right) \tag{8.3}$$

$$e_{31} = e_{13} = \tfrac{1}{2}\left(\frac{\partial u_1}{\partial x_3} + \frac{\partial u_3}{\partial x_1}\right)$$

The general expression for strains can therefore be written in tensor notation as

$$e_{ij} = e_{ji} = \tfrac{1}{2}\left(\frac{\partial u_j}{\partial x_i} + \frac{\partial u_i}{\partial x_j}\right); \quad (i,j = 1,2,3) \tag{8.4}$$

The above expressions for strains are valid only if the deformations are small. For large deformations higher-order non-linear terms must be included, but this would be outside the scope of this chapter which deals basically with the linearized theory of thermoelasticity.

(ii) Stress–Strain Equations: Hooke's Law

If a body is subjected to a change in temperature T, then an element of length dl will expand to a new length $(1+\alpha T)dl$, and if the expansion of each element is unrestricted then no thermal stresses will be induced. For an isotropic and homogeneous body the coefficient of expansion α is independent of the direction of dl and the position of the element, and it is usually assumed that the coefficient of expansion and the elastic constants are independent of temperature. The variation of α with temperature, however, can be included without much difficulty, since the temperature loading enters various equations of elasticity as a product αT and therefore it is possible to modify this product by taking appropriate values of the coefficient of expansion.

In composite structures, variations in αT are caused not only by the temperature variation but also by the variation of α, if the materials used have different coefficients of expansion. Thus even if the temperature increase is uniform, there may be stresses set up by non-uniform expansions. Sometimes these stresses are referred to as *temperature stresses* to distinguish them from *thermal stresses* which are caused by a non-uniform temperature distribution.

With these assumptions an infinitely small parallelepiped subjected to a change in temperature will still retain its rectangular orientation, since the expansion of the element will be the same in all directions. The temperature strains (thermal dilatations) in the element are therefore given by

$$\eta_{11} = \eta_{22} = \eta_{33} = \alpha T$$

and
$$\eta_{12} = \eta_{21} = \eta_{23} = \eta_{32} = \eta_{31} = \eta_{13} = 0 \tag{8.5}$$

or alternatively
$$\eta_{ij} = \alpha T \delta_{ij} \tag{8.5a}$$

where δ_{ij} is the Kronecker delta given by

$$\delta_{ij} = 1; \quad i = j \tag{8.6}$$
$$= 0; \quad i \neq j$$

In general, the change in volume of the element will not be allowed to take place freely and the thermal stresses σ_{ij} will be induced which will give rise to additional (elastic) strains ε_{ij}. These elastic strains are related to the stresses σ_{ij} through the generalized Hooke's law for three-dimensional elasticity:

$$\varepsilon_{11} = \frac{1}{2G}\left(\sigma_{11} - \frac{v}{1+v}s\right); \quad \varepsilon_{12} = \frac{1}{2G}\sigma_{12}$$

$$\varepsilon_{22} = \frac{1}{2G}\left(\sigma_{22} - \frac{v}{1+v}s\right); \quad \varepsilon_{23} = \frac{1}{2G}\sigma_{23}$$

$$\varepsilon_{33} = \frac{1}{2G}\left(\sigma_{33} - \frac{v}{1+v}s\right); \quad \varepsilon_{31} = \frac{1}{2G}\sigma_{31} \tag{8.7}$$

or

$$\varepsilon_{ij} = \frac{1}{2G}\left(\sigma_{ij} - \frac{v}{1+v}s\delta_{ij}\right) \tag{8.7a}$$

where

$$G = \frac{E}{2(1+v)} \tag{8.8}$$

denotes the modulus of rigidity, E is Young's modulus, v is Poisson's ratio and s is the sum of the three direct stresses, i.e.

$$s = \sigma_{11} + \sigma_{22} + \sigma_{33} \tag{8.9}$$

The total strains consist of the sum of the temperature strains (thermal dilatations) and the elastic strains arising from the thermal stresses, i.e.

$$e_{ij} = \varepsilon_{ij} + \eta_{ij}$$

$$= \varepsilon_{ij} + \alpha T \delta_{ij} \tag{8.10}$$

Hence using equations (8.5), (8.7) and (8.10)

$$e_{11} = \frac{1}{2G}\left(\sigma_{11} - \frac{v}{1+v}s\right) + \alpha T; \quad e_{12} = \frac{1}{2G}\sigma_{12}$$

$$e_{22} = \frac{1}{2G}\left(\sigma_{22} - \frac{v}{1+v}s\right) + \alpha T; \quad e_{23} = \frac{1}{2G}\sigma_{23}$$

$$e_{33} = \frac{1}{2G}\left(\sigma_{33} - \frac{v}{1+v}s\right) + \alpha T; \quad e_{31} = \frac{1}{2G}\sigma_{31} \tag{8.11}$$

or

$$e_{ij} = \frac{1}{2G}\left(\sigma_{ij} - \frac{v}{1+v}s\delta_{ij}\right) + \alpha T \delta_{ij} \tag{8.11a}$$

Sometimes it is necessary to have expressions for the stresses in terms of strains. Solving therefore equations (8.11) for σ_{ij}

$$\sigma_{11} = 2G\left[e_{11} + \frac{v}{1-2v}e - \frac{(1+v)}{(1-2v)}\alpha T\right]; \quad \sigma_{12} = 2Ge_{12}$$

$$\sigma_{22} = 2G\left[e_{22} + \frac{v}{1-2v}e - \frac{1+v}{1-2v}\alpha T\right]; \quad \sigma_{23} = 2Ge_{23}$$

$$\sigma_{33} = 2G\left[e_{33} + \frac{v}{1-2v}e - \frac{1+v}{1-2v}\alpha T\right]; \quad \sigma_{31} = 2Ge_{31} \qquad (8.12)$$

or

$$\sigma_{ij} = 2G\left[e_{ij} + \frac{v}{1-2v}e\,\delta_{ij} - \frac{1+v}{1-2v}\alpha T\delta_{ij}\right] \qquad (8.12a)$$

where

$$e = e_{11} + e_{22} + e_{33}$$

$$= \frac{1-2v}{1+v}\frac{s}{2G} + 3\alpha T \qquad (8.13)$$

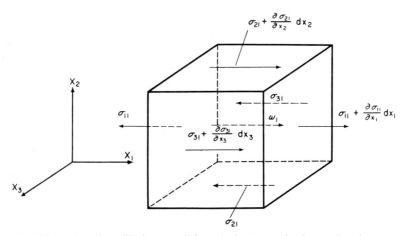

Fig. 8.1.   Internal equilibrium conditions (only stresses in the x_1-direction are shown).

(iii) *Differential Equations of Equilibrium: Boundary Conditions*

Taking moments of forces acting on a small rectangular parallelepiped (see Fig. 8.1) it can be shown that

$$\sigma_{12} = \sigma_{21}; \quad \sigma_{23} = \sigma_{32} \quad \text{and} \quad \sigma_{31} = \sigma_{13} \qquad (8.14)$$

or

$$\sigma_{ij} = \sigma_{ji}; \quad (i, j = 1, 2, 3) \qquad (8.14a)$$

which is in agreement with the strain equation (8.4).

The equations of equilibrium in terms of stresses are obtained by resolving all the forces acting on the element in x_1, x_2 and x_3 directions, respectively. After dividing by dx_1, dx_2, dx_3 and proceeding to the limit by shrinking the element down to the point (x_1, x_2, x_3), the following equations are obtained:

$$\frac{\partial \sigma_{11}}{\partial x_1} + \frac{\partial \sigma_{12}}{\partial x_2} + \frac{\partial \sigma_{13}}{\partial x_3} + \omega_1 = 0$$

$$\frac{\partial \sigma_{21}}{\partial x_1} + \frac{\partial \sigma_{22}}{\partial x_2} + \frac{\partial \sigma_{23}}{\partial x_3} + \omega_2 = 0$$

$$\frac{\partial \sigma_{31}}{\partial x_1} + \frac{\partial \sigma_{32}}{\partial x_2} + \frac{\partial \sigma_{33}}{\partial x_3} + \omega_3 = 0 \tag{8.15}$$

or

$$\sum_j \frac{\partial \sigma_{ij}}{\partial x_j} + \omega_i = 0 \tag{8.15a}$$

where ω_i's are the body forces acting on the element.

If the stress–strain and strain–displacement relations [equations (8.12), (8.2) and (8.3)] are substituted into equations (8.15) it can then be shown that

$$\nabla^2 u_1 + \frac{1}{1-2v}\frac{\partial e}{\partial x_1} - \frac{2(1+v)}{1-2v}\alpha\frac{\partial T}{\partial x_1} + \frac{\omega_1}{G} = 0$$

$$\nabla^2 u_2 + \frac{1}{1-2v}\frac{\partial e}{\partial x_2} - \frac{2(1+v)}{1-2v}\alpha\frac{\partial T}{\partial x_2} + \frac{\omega_2}{G} = 0$$

$$\nabla^2 u_3 + \frac{1}{1-2v}\frac{\partial e}{\partial x_3} - \frac{2(1+v)}{1-2v}\alpha\frac{\partial T}{\partial x_3} + \frac{\omega_3}{G} = 0 \tag{8.16}$$

or

$$\nabla^2 u_i + \frac{1}{1-2v}\frac{\partial e}{\partial x_i} - \frac{2(1+v)}{1-2v}\alpha\frac{\partial T}{\partial x_i} + \frac{\omega_i}{G} = 0 \tag{8.16a}$$

where

$$\nabla^2 \equiv \frac{\partial^2}{\partial x_1^2} + \frac{\partial^2}{\partial x_2^2} + \frac{\partial^2}{\partial x_3^2} \tag{8.17}$$

Equations (8.16) are the differential equations of equilibrium in terms of displacements containing only the three unknown displacements u_1, u_2, and u_3.

Equations (8.15) must be satisfied at all points of the body. The stresses vary throughout the body and at the surface they must be in equilibrium with the external forces applied on the surface of the body. Denoting by X_i the components of the surface forces per unit area, it can be shown that

$$\sigma_{11}n_1 + \sigma_{12}n_2 + \sigma_{13}n_3 = X_1$$

$$\sigma_{21}n_1 + \sigma_{22}n_2 + \sigma_{23}n_3 = X_2 \tag{8.18}$$

$$\sigma_{31}n_1 + \sigma_{32}n_2 + \sigma_{33}n_3 = X_3$$

where n_1, n_2, and n_3 are the direction cosines of an outward drawn normal to the surface of the body. In tensor notation equation (8.18) becomes simply

$$\sum_j \sigma_{ij} n_j = X_i; \quad (i, j = 1, 2, 3) \tag{8.18a}$$

(iv) *Compatibility Equations*

The strains and displacements in an elastic and homogeneous body must vary continuously and this imposes the condition that the derivatives of strains and displacements must be continuous. Mathematically this implies that the order of differentiation can be reversed; for example

$$\frac{\partial^2}{\partial x_i \partial x_j} = \frac{\partial^2}{\partial x_j \partial x_i}; \quad \frac{\partial^3}{\partial x_i^2 \partial x_j} = \frac{\partial^3}{\partial x_j \partial x_i^2}, \quad \text{etc.} \tag{8.19}$$

Using, therefore, the strain–displacement equations (8.2) and (8.3) and the condition of derivative continuity, equation (8.19), the following six differential equations are obtained:

$$\frac{\partial^2 e_{11}}{\partial x_2^2} + \frac{\partial^2 e_{22}}{\partial x_1^2} = 2\frac{\partial^2 e_{12}}{\partial x_1 \partial x_2}; \quad \frac{\partial^2 e_{11}}{\partial x_2 \partial x_3} = \frac{\partial}{\partial x_1}\left(-\frac{\partial e_{23}}{\partial x_1} + \frac{\partial e_{31}}{\partial x_2} + \frac{\partial e_{12}}{\partial x_3} \right)$$

$$\frac{\partial^2 e_{22}}{\partial x_3^2} + \frac{\partial^2 e_{33}}{\partial x_2^2} = 2\frac{\partial^2 e_{23}}{\partial x_2 \partial x_3}; \quad \frac{\partial^2 e_{22}}{\partial x_3 \partial x_1} = \frac{\partial}{\partial x_2}\left(\frac{\partial e_{23}}{\partial x_1} - \frac{\partial e_{31}}{\partial x_2} + \frac{\partial e_{12}}{\partial x_3} \right) \tag{8.20}$$

$$\frac{\partial^2 e_{33}}{\partial x_1^2} + \frac{\partial^2 e_{11}}{\partial x_3^2} = 2\frac{\partial^2 e_{31}}{\partial x_3 \partial x_1}; \quad \frac{\partial^2 e_{33}}{\partial x_1 \partial x_2} = \frac{\partial}{\partial x_3}\left(\frac{\partial e_{23}}{\partial x_1} + \frac{\partial e_{31}}{\partial x_2} - \frac{\partial e_{12}}{\partial x_3} \right)$$

Equations (8.20) are the compatibility equations in terms of strain components.

Alternatively equations (8.20) can be written as

$$\frac{\partial^2 e_{ij}}{\partial x_k \partial x_l} + \frac{\partial^2 e_{kl}}{\partial x_i \partial x_j} - \frac{\partial^2 e_{jl}}{\partial x_i \partial x_k} - \frac{\partial^2 e_{ik}}{\partial x_j \partial x_l} = 0; \quad (i, j, k, l = 1, 2, 3) \tag{8.20a}$$

The compatibility equations in terms of stress components are obtained by substituting into equations (8.20) the strain components from (8.11) and then using equations of equilibrium (8.15). Thus from the first compatibility equation

$$\frac{1}{2G}\left(\nabla^2 s - \nabla^2 \sigma_{11} - \frac{\partial^2 s}{\partial x_1^2} \right) - \frac{v}{2G(1+v)}\left(\nabla^2 s - \frac{\partial^2 s}{\partial x_1^2} \right) + \alpha\left(\nabla^2 T - \frac{\partial^2 T}{\partial x_1^2} \right)$$

$$= \frac{1}{2G}\left(\frac{\partial \omega_1}{\partial x_1} - \frac{\partial \omega_2}{\partial x_2} - \frac{\partial \omega_3}{\partial x_3} \right) \tag{8.21}$$

while the other two equations are obtained by changing suffixes. Adding together the three equations of the type (8.21)

$$\frac{(1-v)}{2G(1+v)}\nabla^2 s + 2\alpha\nabla^2 T = \frac{1}{2G}\left(\frac{\partial\omega_1}{\partial x_1} + \frac{\partial\omega_2}{\partial x_2} + \frac{\partial\omega_3}{\partial x_3}\right) \qquad (8.22)$$

Substituting now this expression for $\nabla^2 s$ into the three equations of the type (8.21) and assuming that the body forces are zero it follows that

$$\frac{1}{2G}\nabla^2\sigma_{11} + \frac{1}{2G(1+v)}\frac{\partial^2 s}{\partial x_1^2} + \frac{(1+v)}{(1-v)}\alpha\nabla^2 T + \alpha\frac{\partial^2 T}{\partial x_1^2} = 0$$

$$\frac{1}{2G}\nabla^2\sigma_{22} + \frac{1}{2G(1+v)}\frac{\partial^2 s}{\partial x_2^2} + \frac{(1+v)}{(1-v)}\alpha\nabla^2 T + \alpha\frac{\partial^2 T}{\partial x_2^2} = 0$$

$$\frac{1}{2G}\nabla^2\sigma_{33} + \frac{1}{2G(1+v)}\frac{\partial^2 s}{\partial x_3^2} + \frac{(1+v)}{(1-v)}\alpha\nabla^2 T + \alpha\frac{\partial^2 T}{\partial x_3^2} = 0 \qquad (8.23)$$

or

$$\frac{1}{2G}\nabla^2\sigma_{ii} + \frac{1}{2G(1+v)}\frac{\partial^2 s}{\partial x_i^2} + \frac{(1+v)}{(1-v)}\alpha\nabla^2 T + \alpha\frac{\partial^2 T}{\partial x_i^2} = 0 \qquad (8.23a)$$

In the same manner the remaining three compatibility equations in terms of strains can be transformed. Assuming again that $\omega_i = 0$,

$$\nabla^2\sigma_{12} + \frac{1}{(1+v)}\frac{\partial^2 s}{\partial x_1\,\partial x_2} + 2G\alpha\frac{\partial^2 T}{\partial x_1\,\partial x_2} = 0$$

$$\nabla^2\sigma_{23} + \frac{1}{(1+v)}\frac{\partial^2 s}{\partial x_2\,\partial x_3} + 2G\alpha\frac{\partial^2 T}{\partial x_2\,\partial x_3} = 0$$

$$\nabla^2\sigma_{31} + \frac{1}{(1+v)}\frac{\partial^2 s}{\partial x_3\,\partial x_1} + 2G\alpha\frac{\partial^2 T}{\partial x_3\,\partial x_1} = 0 \qquad (8.24)$$

or

$$\nabla^2\sigma_{ij} + \frac{1}{(1+v)}\frac{\partial^2 s}{\partial x_i\,\partial x_j} + 2G\alpha\frac{\partial^2 T}{\partial x_i\,\partial x_j} = 0 \qquad (8.24a)$$

$$(i \neq j)$$

(v) *Thermoelastic Displacement Potential*

The equations derived in Sections (i) to (iv) are equally valid for the case where $T \equiv 0$ and then they become the well-known basic equations of the theory of elasticity. In finding the complete solution to any thermoelastic problem we must also take into consideration the boundary conditions on the surface of the body. The boundary conditions can be either prescribed displacements or prescribed stresses. In what follows a particular solution to the equations of equilibrium in terms of displacements [equations (8.16)] will be derived and then by the superposition of possible solutions with

$T \equiv 0$ the required boundary conditions will be satisfied; the latter being, of course, the fundamental problem of the theory of elasticity.

To find a particular solution to equations (8.16) a continuous function Φ is introduced, the derivatives of which give directly the displacements

$$u_i = \frac{\partial \Phi}{\partial x_i}; \quad (i = 1, 2, 3) \tag{8.25}$$

The function Φ can thus be described as the thermoelastic displacement potential.

Substituting equation (8.25) into the equations of equilibrium expressed in terms of the displacements (equations (8.16)) it follows that

$$\frac{1-v}{1-2v} \frac{\partial^2 \nabla \Phi}{\partial x_i} - \frac{1+v}{1-2v} \alpha \frac{\partial T}{\partial x_i} = 0 \tag{8.26}$$

This equation can now be integrated directly and it leads to Poisson's equation

$$\nabla^2 \Phi = \frac{1+v}{1-v} \alpha T \tag{8.27}$$

Assuming that the particular solution of equation (8.27) has been found, the thermal stresses and strains can be calculated from the second derivatives of Φ. Substituting equation (8.25) into (8.4) the expressions for the strains become,

$$e_{11} = \frac{\partial^2 \Phi}{\partial x_1^2}; \quad e_{12} = \frac{\partial^2 \Phi}{\partial x_1 \partial x_2}$$

$$e_{22} = \frac{\partial^2 \Phi}{\partial x_2^2}; \quad e_{23} = \frac{\partial^2 \Phi}{\partial x_2 \partial x_3}$$

$$e_{33} = \frac{\partial^2 \Phi}{\partial x_3^2}; \quad e_{31} = \frac{\partial^2 \Phi}{\partial x_3 \partial x_1} \tag{8.28}$$

or

$$e_{ij} = \frac{\partial^2 \Phi}{\partial x_i \partial x_j} \tag{8.29}$$

while the stresses follow directly from equations (8.12) which become

$$\sigma_{11} = -2G\left(\frac{\partial^2 \Phi}{\partial x_2^2} + \frac{\partial^2 \Phi}{\partial x_3^2}\right); \quad \sigma_{12} = 2G\frac{\partial^2 \Phi}{\partial x_1 \partial x_2}$$

$$\sigma_{22} = -2G\left(\frac{\partial^2 \Phi}{\partial x_3^2} + \frac{\partial^2 \Phi}{\partial x_1^2}\right); \quad \sigma_{23} = 2G\frac{\partial^2 \Phi}{\partial x_2 \partial x_3}$$

$$\sigma_{33} = -2G\left(\frac{\partial^2 \Phi}{\partial x_1^2} + \frac{\partial^2 \Phi}{\partial x_2^2}\right); \quad \sigma_{31} = 2G\frac{\partial^2 \Phi}{\partial x_3 \partial x_1} \tag{8.30}$$

or
$$\sigma_{ij} = 2G\left(\frac{\partial^2 \Phi}{\partial x_i \partial x_j} - \nabla^2 \Phi \, \delta_{ij}\right) \tag{8.30a}$$

In general, the particular solution to equation (8.27) will not satisfy the prescribed boundary conditions at the surface. It is then necessary to derive a complete solution by combining the particular solution for thermoelastic displacement potential Φ with the general solution for the displacements in an elastic body in which $T \equiv 0$ in order to satisfy the required boundary conditions on displacements and/or stresses.

8.3. STRESS-FREE TEMPERATURE DISTRIBUTION

In this section a special temperature distribution will be considered which does not produce any thermal stresses in a three-dimensional body. Assuming that the body is isotropic, as in the previous sections, the thermal expansion of each element in the body will be uniform in all directions. Thus if the thermal expansion is unhindered, then each element would expand into a similar one without any angular distortions. Because no elastic strains are present it follows therefore that

$$\varepsilon_{ij} = 0; \quad (i,j = 1,2,3) \tag{8.31}$$

and hence $\quad e_{11} = e_{22} = e_{33} = \alpha T \quad$ and $\quad e_{12} = e_{23} = e_{31} = 0 \tag{8.32}$

Substituting these strains into the compatibility equations in terms of strains, equations (8.20), the following equations are obtained

$$\frac{\partial^2 T}{\partial x_1^2} + \frac{\partial^2 T}{\partial x_2^2} = 0; \qquad \frac{\partial^2 T}{\partial x_1 \partial x_2} = 0$$

$$\frac{\partial^2 T}{\partial x_2^2} + \frac{\partial^2 T}{\partial x_3^2} = 0; \qquad \frac{\partial^2 T}{\partial x_2 \partial x_3} = 0 \tag{8.33}$$

$$\frac{\partial^2 T}{\partial x_3^2} + \frac{\partial^2 T}{\partial x_1^2} = 0; \qquad \frac{\partial^2 T}{\partial x_3 \partial x_1} = 0$$

The above system of equations possesses a unique solution

$$T = C_0 + C_1 x_1 + C_2 x_2 + C_3 x_3 \tag{8.34}$$

with arbitrary coefficients C_k ($k = 0, 1, 2$ and 3). Equation (8.34) represents a linear temperature distribution in a three-dimensional body. No thermal stresses are induced by such a distribution but thermal deformations are present. If the thermal deformations are prevented by some external restraint, e.g. surrounding structure, then thermal stresses would be induced. Thus in an unrestrained three-dimensional body, thermal stresses are caused only by non-linear temperature distributions.

8.4. MAGNITUDE OF THERMAL STRESSES

For linear thermoelasticity the maximum total direct strains (elastic strain and thermal expansion) can be assumed to be proportional to the maximum temperature change T, i.e.

$$e_{ii} = k_i \alpha T; \quad (i = 1, 2, 3) \tag{8.35}$$

Hence $k_i = 1$ corresponds to unrestrained expansion due to the temperature change T, while $k_i = 0$ represents a complete restriction of thermal expansion. In actual problems, however, k_i will have some intermediate value between 0 and 1. In the regions of low temperature the same argument can be applied provided a negative temperature change is used.

Substituting equation (8.35) into (8.12a) it follows that

$$
\begin{aligned}
\sigma_{ii} &= 2G\alpha T \left\{ k_i + \frac{v}{1-2v}(k_1 + k_2 + k_3) - \frac{(1+v)}{(1-2v)} \right\} \\
&= -\frac{\alpha ET}{(1-2v)(1+v)} \{(1+v) - (1-2v)k_i - v(k_1 + k_2 + k_3)\}
\end{aligned} \tag{8.36}
$$

For complete restraint against thermal expansion $k_1 = k_2 = k_3 = 0$ and hence the maximum thermal stresses become

$$\sigma_{11} = \sigma_{22} = \sigma_{33} = -\frac{\alpha ET}{(1-2v)} \tag{8.37}$$

For complete restraint in the x_1 and x_2 directions $k_1 = k_2 = 0$. If in addition $\sigma_{33} = 0$, as in two-dimensional problems, then from equation (8.36)

$$k_3 = (1+v)/(1-v) \tag{8.38}$$

and the maximum thermal stresses become

$$\sigma_{11} = \sigma_{22} = -\frac{\alpha ET}{(1-v)} \tag{8.39}$$

If only $k_1 = 0$ and $\sigma_{22} = \sigma_{33} = 0$ (one-dimensional problems), then

$$k_2 = k_3 = (1+v) \tag{8.40}$$

and the maximum thermal stress becomes

$$\sigma_{11} = -\alpha ET \tag{8.41}$$

Equations (8.37), (8.39) and (8.41) represent maximum thermal stresses attainable in three-, two- and one-dimensional problems, respectively. These simple equations are extremely useful when assessing the magnitude of thermal stresses; in many cases this is all that need be considered. If the maximum thermal stresses are small compared with other stresses then there is obviously no need to employ more refined methods for thermal stress calculations, as the simple formulae given by the equations (8.37), (8.39) and (8.41) are sufficiently accurate for engineering purposes. The negative sign in these formulae indicates that compressive stresses are induced in regions of high temperatures (positive temperature changes).

8.5. DUHAMEL'S ANALOGY[1]

Duhamel's analogy can be of some importance in the solution of thermo-elastic problems. This analogy establishes a correspondence between a thermal stress problem for a given elastic body and a fictitious stress problem for the same body at a uniform temperature. For a formal proof of Duhamel's analogy, Ref. 8 should be consulted.

This analogy allows us to reformulate any thermal stress problem in terms of a body and surface stress problem which leads to identical strains. If an elastic body, which is initially at a uniform temperature, has its temperature increased non-uniformly to $T(x_1, x_2, x_3)$, then the thermal stresses which would arise are equal to the stresses calculated on the same body at a uniform temperature as follows:

(1) Apply to each element of volume throughout the body, a body force having the components per unit volume given by

$$\bar{\omega}_i = -\frac{\alpha E}{(1-2v)}\frac{\partial T_i}{\partial x_i}; \quad (i = 1, 2, 3) \tag{8.42}$$

(2) Apply at every point on the surface a normal force per unit area given by

$$X = \frac{\alpha E T}{(1-2v)} \tag{8.43}$$

(3) Solve for the elastic stresses σ_{ij} in this hypothetical elasticity problem and then add to each direct stress σ_{ii} the stress

$$\sigma = \frac{\alpha E T}{(1-2v)} \tag{8.44}$$

to obtain the required thermal stresses due to the non-uniform temperature distribution T.

In this analysis the body forces $\bar{\omega}_i$ are hypothetical and should not be confused with true body forces which might actually be applied on the body. The stresses due to the true body forces can be determined separately and then superposed on the thermal stresses.

For convenience Duhamel's analogy is also presented in Table 8.1, where suffices I and II refer to the actual and hypothetical (analogous) bodies, respectively.

It may appear that the solutions to many thermal stress problems would already have been obtained in elasticity theory. Unfortunately, this is not so, because only few elasticity problems with body forces have been solved, and those which have been solved are of little interest. This means that most thermal stress problems must be solved directly without the help of Duhamel's thermoelastic analogy.

TABLE 8.1.   DUHAMEL'S ANALOGY

	Body I (actual)	Body II (hypothetical)
Temperature	$T^{\mathrm{I}} \not\equiv 0$	$T^{\mathrm{II}} \equiv 0$
Body force distribution	$\omega_i{}^{\mathrm{I}} \not\equiv 0$	$\omega_i{}^{\mathrm{II}} = \omega_i{}^{\mathrm{I}} - \dfrac{\alpha E}{(1-2\nu)}\dfrac{\partial T^{\mathrm{I}}}{\partial x_i}$
Surface forces	$X_i{}^{\mathrm{I}} \not\equiv 0$	$X_i{}^{\mathrm{II}} = X_i{}^{\mathrm{I}} + \dfrac{\alpha E T^{\mathrm{I}}}{(1-2\nu)} n_i$
Stresses	$\sigma_{ij}{}^{\mathrm{I}} \not\equiv 0$	$\sigma_{ij}{}^{\mathrm{II}} = \sigma_{ij}{}^{\mathrm{I}} + \dfrac{\alpha E T^{\mathrm{I}}}{(1-2\nu)} \delta_{ij}$
Strains	$\varepsilon_{ij}{}^{\mathrm{I}} \not\equiv 0$	$\varepsilon_{ij}{}^{\mathrm{II}} = \varepsilon_{ij}{}^{\mathrm{I}}$

(Note: n_i's denote here direction cosines of a normal at the surface.)

8.6.   TWO-DIMENSIONAL STRESS DISTRIBUTIONS

(i) *Plane Stress Problems*

In the analysis of thin plates it may be assumed that the stress components do not vary through the thickness. Furthermore, it could be assumed tentatively that $\sigma_{33} = \sigma_{23} = \sigma_{13} = 0$ not only at the surfaces but also within the plate. It can be shown, however, that these assumptions do not in fact satisfy all the conditions of compatibility but are sufficiently accurate if the plate is thin. The stress distributions based on these assumptions are described as plane stress distributions.

The three-dimensional equations derived in Sections 8.2(i) to (v) can be modified using the above assumptions for the plane stress. A summary of these plane stress equations is given below.

Strain–displacement equations. The same as for the three-dimensional distribution.

Stress–strain equations

$$e_{11} = \frac{1}{E}(\sigma_{11} - v\sigma_{22}) + \alpha T; \qquad\qquad e_{12} = \frac{1}{2G}\sigma_{12}$$

$$e_{22} = \frac{1}{E}(\sigma_{22} - v\sigma_{11}) + \alpha T; \qquad\qquad e_{23} = 0$$

$$e_{33} = \frac{-v}{E}(\sigma_{11} + \sigma_{22}) + \alpha T; \qquad\qquad e_{31} = 0 \qquad (8.45)$$

$$\sigma_{11} = \frac{E}{(1-v^2)}(e_{11} + ve_{22}) - \frac{E}{(1-v)}\alpha T; \quad \sigma_{12} = 2Ge_{12}$$

$$\sigma_{22} = \frac{E}{(1-v^2)}(e_{22} + ve_{11}) - \frac{E}{(1-v)}\alpha T; \quad \sigma_{23} = 0$$

$$\sigma_{33} = 0 \qquad\qquad\qquad ; \quad \sigma_{31} = 0 \qquad (8.46)$$

Differential equations of equilibrium (body forces equal to zero)

$$\frac{\partial \sigma_{11}}{\partial x_1} + \frac{\partial \sigma_{12}}{\partial x_2} = 0$$

$$\frac{\partial \sigma_{21}}{\partial x_1} + \frac{\partial \sigma_{22}}{\partial x_2} = 0 \qquad (8.47)$$

$$(1-v)\nabla^2 u_1 + (1+v)\frac{\partial}{\partial x_1}\left(\frac{\partial u_1}{\partial x_1} + \frac{\partial u_2}{\partial x_2}\right) - 2(1+v)\alpha\frac{\partial T}{\partial x_1} = 0$$

$$(1-v)\nabla^2 u_2 + (1+v)\frac{\partial}{\partial x_2}\left(\frac{\partial u_1}{\partial x_1} + \frac{\partial u_2}{\partial x_2}\right) - 2(1+v)\alpha\frac{\partial T}{\partial x_2} = 0 \qquad (8.48)$$

where
$$\nabla^2 \equiv \frac{\partial^2}{\partial x_1^2} + \frac{\partial^2}{\partial x_2^2} \qquad (8.49)$$

Boundary conditions

$$\sigma_{11} n_1 + \sigma_{12} n_2 = X_1$$

$$\sigma_{21} n_1 + \sigma_{22} n_2 = X_2 \qquad (8.50)$$

Compatibility equations

$$\frac{\partial^2 e_{11}}{\partial x_2^2} + \frac{\partial^2 e_{22}}{\partial x_1^2} = 2\frac{\partial^2 e_{12}}{\partial x_1 \partial x_2} \qquad (8.51)$$

$$\nabla^2(\sigma_{11} + \sigma_{22}) = -\alpha E \nabla^2 T \qquad (8.52)$$

Thermoelastic potential

$$u_1 = \frac{\partial \Phi}{\partial x_1}; \quad u_2 = \frac{\partial \Phi}{\partial x_2} \qquad (8.53)$$

where Φ is determined from

$$\nabla^2\Phi = (1+\nu)\alpha T \tag{8.54}$$

(ii) Solutions of Plane Stress Problems

To solve the equations of equilibrium a stress function F can be introduced such that

$$\sigma_{11} = \frac{\partial^2 F}{\partial x_2^2}; \quad \sigma_{22} = \frac{\partial^2 F}{\partial x_1^2}; \quad \text{and} \quad \sigma_{12} = -\frac{\partial^2 F}{\partial x_1 \partial x_2} \tag{8.55}$$

The function F is usually known as the Airy stress function. It can be verified easily that F satisfies automatically the two differential equations of equilibrium in terms of stresses. Substituting F into the compatibility equation (8.52) it is found that the stress function must satisfy the biharmonic differential equation

$$\nabla^4 F = -\alpha E \nabla^2 T \tag{8.56}$$

where

$$\nabla^4 = \frac{\partial^4}{\partial x_1^4} + 2\frac{\partial^4}{\partial x_1^2 \partial x_2^2} + \frac{\partial^4}{\partial x_2^4} \tag{8.57}$$

The Airy stress function is a convenient tool for obtaining solutions to two-dimensional problems. Several such solutions are discussed in Section 8.8.

An alternative method, which has found favour on the Continent, is to assume that the Airy stress function is given by the sum of two functions F_h and Φ_p so that

$$F = F_h - 2G\Phi_p \tag{8.58}$$

where Φ_p satisfies the equation

$$\nabla^2(2G\Phi_p) - \alpha ET = 0 \tag{8.59}$$

Substituting equation (8.58) into (8.56) it follows that

$$\nabla^4 F_h = \nabla^4(2G\Phi_p) - \alpha E \nabla^2 T \tag{8.60}$$

Now since

$$2G\nabla^4\Phi_p - \alpha E \nabla^2 T = \nabla^2[2G\nabla^2\Phi_p - \alpha ET] = 0 \tag{8.61}$$

equations (8.60) can be separated into two equations

$$\nabla^4 F_h = 0 \tag{8.62}$$

and

$$2G\nabla^2\Phi_p = \alpha ET \quad \text{or} \quad \nabla^2\Phi_p = (1+\nu)\alpha T \tag{8.63}$$

Since the solution $\nabla^2\Phi_p = 0$ can be included in solutions to the biharmonic equation $\nabla^4 F_h = 0$ only a particular integral is needed for the solution of $\nabla^2\Phi_p = (1+\nu)\alpha T$. It should be noted that Φ_p is a particular integral of the thermoelastic potential obtained from equation (8.54).

Using equations (8.55) the stresses derived from the particular solution Φ_p become

$$\bar{\sigma}_{11} = -2G\frac{\partial^2 \Phi_p}{\partial x_2^2}$$

$$\bar{\sigma}_{22} = -2G\frac{\partial^2 \Phi_p}{\partial x_1^2}$$

$$\bar{\sigma}_{12} = 2G\frac{\partial^2 \Phi_p}{\partial x_1 \partial x_2} \tag{8.64}$$

and these stresses generally violate the required boundary conditions. The satisfaction of all the boundary conditions is achieved by the second part of the solution given by the stresses

$$\bar{\bar{\sigma}}_{11} = \frac{\partial^2 F_h}{\partial x_2^2}$$

$$\bar{\bar{\sigma}}_{22} = \frac{\partial^2 F_h}{\partial x_1^2}$$

$$\bar{\bar{\sigma}}_{12} = -\frac{\partial^2 F_h}{\partial x_1 \partial x_2} \tag{8.65}$$

The true stresses are then calculated from

$$\sigma_{11} = \bar{\sigma}_{11} + \bar{\bar{\sigma}}_{11} = \frac{\partial^2}{\partial x_2^2}(F_h - 2G\Phi_p)$$

$$\sigma_{22} = \bar{\sigma}_{22} + \bar{\bar{\sigma}}_{22} = \frac{\partial^2}{\partial x_1^2}(F_h - 2G\Phi_p)$$

$$\sigma_{12} = \bar{\sigma}_{12} + \bar{\bar{\sigma}}_{12} = -\frac{\partial^2}{\partial x_1 \partial x_2}(F_h - 2G\Phi_p) \tag{8.66}$$

The main advantage of this type of solution lies in the fact that it is sometimes relatively easy to determine the particular solution Φ_p and then remove any superfluous stresses from the boundaries by means of the Airy stress function F_h determined from the biharmonic equation $\nabla^4 F_h = 0$.

(iii) *Plane Strain Problems*

The main assumptions in the plane strain problems are: $e_{33} = e_{23} = e_{13} = 0$ and $\partial/\partial x_3 \equiv 0$. Here again, starting from the fundamental equations of the three-dimensional theory of thermoelasticity, the plane strain formulae can be derived.

It is possible, however, to convert the plane stress into the plane strain distribution. For example, if the Airy stress function F has been found for a plane stress problem it can then be converted into a plane strain solution by dividing F by $(1-v)$. A full discussion of the plane strain problems can be found in Ref. 5.

8.7. ENGINEERS' THEORY FOR DISTRIBUTION OF THERMAL STRESSES[5]

Consider a flat rectangular plate subjected to a temperature distribution which varies only through the thickness of the plate, i.e. the temperature is a function of $x_3 = z$ only. The free expansion of an element in the x_1 and x_2 directions will be completely suppressed by applying stresses obtained from equation (8.39)

$$\sigma_{11} = \sigma_{22} = -\frac{\alpha E T(z)}{(1-v)} \tag{8.39a}$$

The compressive stresses given by (8.39a) must be applied on the boundaries of the plate. The thermal stresses in the plate free from external stresses are obtained by superposing on the stresses (8.39a) the stresses due to application of equal and opposite stresses applied at the edges. These stresses produce, away from the edges, a mean tensile stress and a bending stress given by

$$\sigma_{\text{mean}} = \frac{1}{d} \int_{-d/2}^{d/2} \frac{\alpha E T}{(1-v)} \, dz \tag{8.67}$$

and

$$\sigma_{\text{bending}} = \frac{z}{I} \int_{-d/2}^{d/2} \frac{\alpha E T}{(1-v)} z \, dz$$

$$= \frac{12}{d^2}\left(\frac{z}{d}\right) \int_{-d/2}^{d/2} \frac{\alpha E}{(1-v)} Tz \, dz \tag{8.68}$$

where

$$I = \frac{d^3}{12}; \quad \text{(moment of inertia per unit length)} \tag{8.69}$$

and z is measured from the middle surface of the plate and d is the plate thickness.

Adding now equations (8.39a), (8.67) and (8.68) the following equation is obtained

$$\sigma_{11} = \sigma_{22} = \frac{\alpha E}{(1-v)}\left\{-T + \frac{1}{d}\int_{-d/2}^{d/2} T\,dz + \frac{12z}{d^2 d}\int_{-d/2}^{d/2} Tz\,dz\right\} \tag{8.70}$$

The temperature distribution through the thickness of a plate (or a thin shell) can be separated into linear and " self-equilibrating " temperature distributions, i.e.

$$T = T_m + \Delta T \frac{z}{d} + T^*(z) \tag{8.71}$$

where T_m is the mean temperature, ΔT is the linear temperature " gradient "‡ and T^* is the self-equilibrating temperature distribution for which

$$\int_{-d/2}^{d/2} T^* dz = \int_{-d/2}^{d/2} T^* z\, dz = 0 \tag{8.72}$$

Thus only the first two terms on the right-hand side of equation (8.71) contribute to the overall deformation of the plate whereas the T^* distribution, being self-equilibrating, produces zero resultant deformations. T_m and ΔT terms produce thermal stresses in the presence of edge restraints. Stresses due to T^*, on the other hand, are not affected by the edge restraints and they occur even if all the edges are completely free.

Using equations (8.71) and (8.72) it follows that

$$T_m = \frac{1}{d} \int_{-d/2}^{d/2} T\, dz \tag{8.73}$$

and

$$\Delta T = \frac{12}{d^2} \int_{-d/2}^{d/2} Tz\, dz \tag{8.74}$$

Substituting equations (8.71), (8.73) and (8.74) into (8.70)

$$\sigma_{11} = \sigma_{22} = -\frac{\alpha E}{(1-v)} T^* \tag{8.75}$$

which implies that the thermal stresses in an unrestrained plate are proportional to the self-equilibrating temperature distribution T^*.

Similar argument can be applied to a long beam with the temperature varying through the depth of beam and constant temperatures along the length. The equivalent formula to equation (8.70) for a singly symmetric beam takes the form

$$\sigma = \alpha E \left\{ -T(z) + \frac{1}{A} \int T(z)\, b(z)\, dz + \frac{z}{I_{xx}} \int T(z)\, zb(z)\, dz \right\} \tag{8.76}$$

where A = cross-sectional area of beam;
$\quad\quad b(z)$ = width of beam web or flange;
$\quad\quad I_{xx}$ = moment of inertia about the x-axis through centroid of cross-section, the x-axis being one of the principal axes of the section.

‡ For simplicity of presentation, ΔT is defined as a temperature gradient (in °C); however the actual temperature gradient is given by $\Delta T/d$.

Equations (8.70) and (8.76) are extremely useful for approximate engineering calculations to determine thermal stresses in plates and beams. In fact these equations can be regarded as being equivalent to a stress distribution in beams based on the Engineers' Theory of Bending.

8.8. PLATES

(i) Two-dimensional Stress Distribution (Plane Stress Problems)

Various methods have been employed for the solution of flat plates subjected to arbitrary temperature distributions in the plane of the plate. Methods used for plane stress problems will be summarized briefly together with a few remarks on their practical application.

(a) *Eigenfunction solution.* The general solution of the biharmonic equation for the Airy stress function can be divided into two parts

$$F = F_h + F_p \tag{8.77}$$

where F_h is the solution of the homogeneous equation (complementary functions) and F_p is a particular integral of the inhomogeneous equation. Now since $\nabla^4 F_p + \alpha E \nabla^2 T = 0$ can also be represented as $\nabla^2(\nabla^2 F_p + \alpha E T) = 0$, F_p can be any particular integral of the Poisson's equation:

$$\nabla^2 F_p = -\alpha E T \tag{8.78}$$

The particular integral (or particular solution) of this equation can be written in the form

$$F_p = -\frac{\alpha E}{2\pi} \int\!\!\int T(\xi_1, \xi_2) \log\left[(x_1 - \xi_1)^2 + (x_2 - \xi_2)^2\right]^{\frac{1}{2}} d\xi_1 \, d\xi_2 \tag{8.79}$$

where the integration limits for ξ_1 and ξ_2 extend over the entire region of the plate. Although this expression yields a closed-form solution for the particular integral the actual integration may be very difficult to perform unless T is of a particularly convenient form. If necessary, however, it is always possible to carry out this integration numerically.

The solutions to the biharmonic equation $\nabla^4 F_h = 0$ are known. These are usually presented in the form

$$F_h = \sum_m \sum_n a_{mn} F_m(x_1) F_n(x_2) \tag{8.80}$$

where $F_m(x_1)$ and $F_n(x_2)$ are functions of x_1 and x_2. The main difficulty with this type of solution is the satisfaction of the boundary conditions through the arbitrary coefficients a_{mn}. Unfortunately there are no exact methods of determining these coefficients, except in very special cases. In practice, therefore, these coefficients are estimated by a least squares or collocation method.

(b) *Complex variable solution.*[10] In this method, developed originally by Muskhelishvili,[10] a complicated geometric shape can be transformed into a simpler configuration by suitable conformal mapping technique. This simpler configuration may be more amenable to analytical solutions using complex variables. For example, the case of a circular plate with an eccentric hole may be transformed into a circular plate with a concentric hole.

(c) *Fourier integral technique.*[11,12] This is essentially similar to the series solution in terms of the eigenfunctions of the biharmonic equation, except that instead of the infinite summation, Fourier integrals are used. This method has been used by Horvay[11] to study thermal stresses in rectangular strips.

(d) *Single product solution.*[13] Here the Airy stress function is assumed to be given by $F = f(x)g(y)$ where $f(x)$ is the stress function representing the thermal stress distribution σ_∞ in an infinitely long plate and $g(y)$ is obtained using the principle of minimum complementary energy. The main limitation to this method is the fact that since only a single product function is used, it cannot give good approximation, particularly if the temperature distribution varies in two directions.

(e) *Self-equilibrating polynomials.*[14-16] Singer et al.[14] calculated thermal stresses in plates by reducing the problem to that of determining the end effects of the self-equilibrating thermal stresses σ_∞ applied at the short sides of the plate and then solving the resulting end traction problem by the method of self-equilibrating orthogonal polynomials derived by Horvay.[15] This method, however, is only applicable to plates with aspect ratios greater than two and with temperature distributions restricted necessarily to one direction.

(f) *Collocation solution.*[17] In this method the biharmonic equation is satisfied everywhere in x but at only a finite number of values of y. Thus if in a rectangular plate n stations are taken along y, i.e. $y_1, y_2, y_3 \ldots y_n$, then the stress function is assumed to be of the form

$$F = \sum_{j=1}^{} P_j(y)\phi_j(x) \qquad (8.81)$$

where $P_j(y)$ is a polynomial associated with the jth station and satisfying the following condition:

$$P_j(y_j) = 1;$$

$$P_j(y_i) = 0; \quad j \neq i \qquad (8.82)$$

In addition we must ensure that $P_j(y)$ must satisfy the boundary conditions of zero stress and this leads to

$$P_j(\pm 1) = \frac{d}{dy} P(\pm 1) = 0 \qquad (8.83)$$

where the boundaries for y have been assumed as $y = \pm 1$. Polynomials having this property can be expressed as

$$P_j(y) = \frac{(y^2 - 1)^2}{(y_j - 1)^2} \frac{\prod\limits_{i \neq j}(y - y_i)}{\prod\limits_{i \neq j}(y_j - y_i)} ; \quad y_j \neq \pm 1 \tag{8.84}$$

where $\prod\limits_{i \neq j}$ is the product for all the values of i except $i = j$. Substituting now equation (8.84) into equations (8.80) and (8.56) a set of simultaneous fourth-order ordinary differential equations in $\phi_j(x)$ is obtained.

The serious disadvantage of this type of collocation method is that the solution to the simultaneous equations may involve considerable amount of computing work.

(g) *Normal modes of vibration.*[18] It may be expected that the boundary conditions rather than the exact adherence to the differential equation have the most powerful effect in defining specific stress distribution in any two-dimensional elasticity problem. Consequently, better results may be obtained by methods in which the boundary conditions are satisfied exactly, while adherence to the differential equations is achieved only at a finite number of points depending on the number of terms in the solution.

Such a solution can be derived from the governing differential equation by expressing the Airy stress function and the Laplacian of the temperature distribution as a generalized Fourier series in terms of the characteristic functions representing normal modes of vibration of a clamped–clamped beam. The problem is then reduced to the solution of a set of simultaneous linear equations for the unknown coefficients in the stress function. Since these equations are extremely well conditioned, they are particularly suitable for iterative solutions and, in general, one or two iterations are usually sufficient for engineering calculations. The overall accuracy depends on the number of coefficients evaluated and on the form of the temperature distribution; violent variations in the temperature distribution naturally require a greater number of terms in the expansions. The solution is approximate in the sense that in any practical problem a finite aggregate of terms is used and, consequently, the differential equation is satisfied only approximately. All boundary conditions, on the other hand, are satisfied exactly.

The thermal stresses are obtained in terms of the characteristic functions and their derivatives. Since these functions have recently been tabulated,[19] the practical application of this method presents no difficulty. Furthermore, tables are available for setting up the simultaneous equations for the coefficients in the Airy stress function.[18]

(ii) Bending of Plates

The self-equilibrating temperature component T^* of the distribution through the plate thickness gives rise to thermal stresses, given by equation

(8.75), which fall to zero in a narrow "boundary layer" along the edges. These stresses can be considered separately and then superimposed on any other stresses. The remaining two temperature components T_m and ΔT produce thermal stresses only if the edges are restrained against thermal deformations.[20]

Fig. 8.2 shows the overall thermal deformations on a rectangular panel with free edges; it also illustrates how the thermal stresses arise in a panel

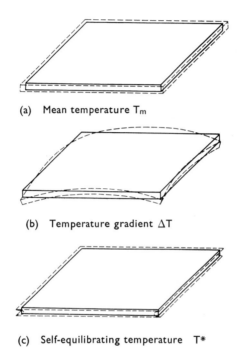

(a)   Mean temperature T_m

(b)   Temperature gradient ΔT

(c)   Self-equilibrating temperature T^*

FIG. 8.2.   Deformation of flat plates due to $T = T_m + \Delta T \, z/d + T^*$;   all edges unrestrained.

as the result of edge restraint from the surrounding structure. The mean temperature T_m induces thermal stresses only if one or more edges are restrained against expansion in the plane of the plate. In such cases compressive or tensile stresses are induced if the plate is, respectively, heated or cooled more rapidly than its surrounding structure.

The effect of the temperature gradient ΔT is to produce a uniform curvature in the plate and therefore in the absence of any edge restraints the plate bends into a spherical surface. If there are restraints along the edges, preventing them from leaving the plane of the supports, then the temperature gradient ΔT produces reactions along the boundaries and bending stresses in the plate.

The large deflexion theory of plates subjected to thermal loading indicates that, in general, there is coupling between the membrane stresses in the middle plane of the plate and the bending stresses. The basic differential equations for the general case are as follows:[21,22]

$$\nabla^4 F = -\alpha E \nabla^2 T_m + E\left\{\left(\frac{\partial^2 w}{\partial x\,\partial y}\right)^2 - \frac{\partial^2 w}{\partial x^2}\frac{\partial^2 w}{\partial y^2}\right\} \tag{8.85}$$

$$D\nabla^4 w = -\frac{\alpha E d^2}{12(1-v)}\nabla^2(\Delta T) + d\left\{\frac{\partial^2 F}{\partial y^2}\frac{\partial^2 w}{\partial x^2} - 2\frac{\partial^2 F}{\partial x\,\partial y}\frac{\partial^2 w}{\partial x\,\partial y} + \frac{\partial^2 F}{\partial x^2}\frac{\partial^2 w}{\partial y^2}\right\} \tag{8.86}$$

$$D = Ed^3/12(1-v^2) \tag{8.87}$$

where the x and y coordinates refer to any set of mutually perpendicular axes in the plane of the plate. The resulting stresses are determined from the solutions for the Airy stress function F and the transverse deflexion w.

If the edges are restrained in the plane of the panel then a strong coupling between the membrane and bending stresses may exist. This has been analysed by Williams,[23,24] who solved the problem of simultaneous loading of pressure and heat on an infinitely long strip with the lengthwise edges either clamped or pin-ended. Parkes[25] analysed the case of flat rectangular plate, subjected to uniform heating with initial eccentricities and with all edges restrained against expansion.

The thermal stresses in rectangular plates due to the temperature gradient ΔT have been determined by Maulbetsch[26] and Timoshenko.[27]

8.9. SHELLS

(i) *Axi-symmetrical Shells*[28-30]

For axi-symmetrical shells in which the shell thickness is constant the governing differential equations can be expressed in terms of two dependent variables U and V. These variables are determined from two differential equations in which the angle ϕ occurs as an independent variable;

$$L(U) - v\frac{R_1}{R_2}U = -\frac{R_1^2}{DR_2}V + G(\phi) \tag{8.88}$$

$$L(V) + v\frac{R_1}{R_2}V = Ed\frac{R_1^2}{R_2}U - H(\phi) \tag{8.89}$$

where

$$L(\ ) \equiv \frac{d^2(\ )}{d\phi^2} + \left[\frac{R_1}{R_2}\frac{d}{d\phi}\left(\frac{R_2}{R_1}\right) + \cot\phi\right]\frac{d(\ )}{d\phi} - \frac{R_1^2}{R_2^2}\cot^2\phi(\ ) \tag{8.90}$$

$$G(\phi) = \frac{R_1(1+v)\alpha}{R_2 d}\left\{(R_1 - R_2)\cot\phi\,\Delta T - \frac{dR_2}{d\phi}\Delta T - R_2\frac{d}{d\phi}(\Delta T)\right\} \tag{8.91}$$

$$H(\phi) = \frac{R_1^2 \, Ed \, \alpha \cot \phi}{R_2} \left(1 - \frac{R_2}{R_1} - \frac{\tan \phi}{R_1} \frac{dR_2}{d\phi} \right) T_m - Ed \, R_1 \, \alpha \frac{d}{d\phi} (T_m) \tag{8.92}$$

while the remaining parameters are defined in Figs. 8.3 and 8.4. In calculating the temperature component ΔT from equation (8.74) z is measured here positive inwards.

The stress-resultants and deformations are given in terms of U and V. Thus the problem of finding thermal stresses and the resulting deformations due to arbitrary axi-symmetrical temperature distributions reduces to the solution of two simultaneous differential equations of the second order in which the "temperature loading" terms occur on the right-hand sides of the equations replacing the ordinary loading terms.

The general solution of equations (8.88) and (8.89) can be separated into the homogeneous solution (complementary functions) and the particular solution (particular integral). The complementary functions are used to satisfy the required boundary conditions while the particular integral depends on the temperature distribution only and is independent of the boundary conditions. If the particular integral happens to satisfy the boundary conditions it would then naturally constitute the exact solution since in such cases the complementary functions must be equal to zero.

The "temperature loading" on the shell is expressed in terms of the mean temperature T_m and the temperature gradient ΔT. If on the other hand the temperature distribution through the thickness of the shell has also a self-equilibrating temperature component T^*, then the thermal stresses due to T^*, by St Venant's principle, will be confined only to the region affected by the self-equilibrating temperature distribution. Thus these stresses can be calculated from equation (8.75) and then superposed on to the stresses obtained from the solution of equations (8.88) and (8.89).

The exact solutions for cylindrical and conical shells[31] are available in terms of trigonometric and modified Bessel functions, respectively. Generally, the exact solutions are unwieldy and it is preferable to use various approximate methods which are usually sufficiently accurate for engineering purposes.

(ii) *Axi-symmetrical Slender Shells*[32-34]

For slender shells of revolution, with constant thickness, it is possible to employ asymptotic integration which leads to an approximate solution of a relatively simple form directly applicable to engineering calculations. The method of asymptotic integration of second-order differential equations with a parameter which is large compared with unity has been discussed by Jeffreys.[34] This parameter in the case of the differential equations for axi-symmetrical shells is given by

$$k^2 = \sqrt{[3(1-v^2)]} \, (R_1^2/dR_2)_{\text{ref}} \tag{8.93}$$

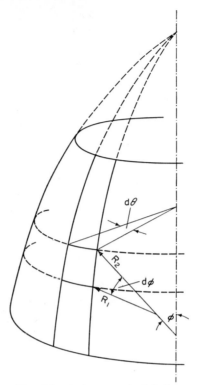

Fig. 8.3.　Axi-symmetrical shell.

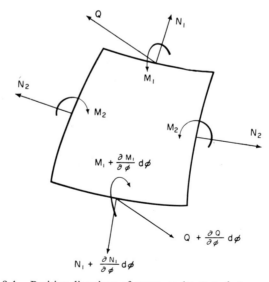

Fig. 8.4.　Positive directions of stress-resultants and stress-couples.

and this is large for slender shells with thin walls. Another assumption which must be introduced in the asymptotic integration is that the radius of curvature R_2 must not be equal to zero and therefore the solution breaks down near a pointed nose of the shell. However, any practical slender shell will usually have a solid nose so that $R_2 \neq 0$ and the asymptotic solution can be used.

It should be emphasized that the asymptotic integration leads to a series solution, in descending powers of k, which is not convergent but the error in using the first n terms of the series instead of an exact solution tends to zero as k tends to infinity. In what follows, only the first-order approximation has been considered, since it appears to be generally satisfactory for engineering purposes.

The results of the asymptotic integration are summarized in Table 8.2, which gives the general solution for the two basic functions U and V. Only simple types of shells have been included for which $R_1 = $ constant, i.e. (i) ogival shells (shells generated by rotating an arc of circle about an axis in the plane containing the circle), (ii) conical shells and (iii) cylindrical shells. The solutions for U and V consist of two parts: (a) complementary functions with four arbitrary constants of integration c_1, c_2, β and δ, and (b) particular integrals $R_2 H(\phi)/EdR_1{}^2$ and $DR_2 G(\phi)/R_1{}^2$ which are known functions depending on the distributions of the mean temperature T_m and the temperature gradient ΔT. In the solution for ogival shells it is necessary to use an integral $\int(1 - \mu \operatorname{cosec} \phi)^{-\frac{1}{2}} d\phi$ which cannot be expressed in terms of known tabulated functions. This integral has therefore been evaluated numerically for a series of values of μ and it is shown in Fig. 8.5.[33]

To determine U and V completely the four arbitrary constants of integration must be evaluated from the boundary conditions on the stresses and/or displacements at the edges of the shell. If the shell consists of n bays reinforced by rings or diaphragms at the joints, then for each bay there will be a separate solution for the functions U and V. Satisfying the boundary conditions at all joints one obtains $4n$ simultaneous linear equations from which the unknown constants of integration can be determined.

The complementary function is predominant only at the edges and usually dies out very rapidly as distance from the edges increases. Therefore, if the boundaries are sufficiently separated, then it is possible to analyse conditions at the outer boundaries independently of each other, so that there will be a separate solution near each boundary. The number of constants in the solution is thus reduced as for each edge only that part of the solution for U and V is considered which decreases towards the other boundary. The boundary conditions are then satisfied approximately since the complementary function, valid at one boundary only, introduces small stresses and displacements at the other boundary, but these are generally negligible if the boundaries are sufficiently separated.

Table 8.2. Asymptotic Solutions for Slender Shells[33]

	Ogival shells	Conical shells	Cylindrical shells
U	$(D \Phi R_2 \sin \phi)^{-1/2} \{ c_1 e^{kF} \cos(kF+\beta) + c_2 e^{-kF} \cos(kF+\delta) \} + \dfrac{R_2}{E\,dR_1^2} H$		
V	$\left(\dfrac{Ed}{\Phi R_2 \sin\phi}\right)^{1/2} \{ c_1 e^{kF} \sin(kF+\beta) - c_2 e^{-kF} \sin(kF+\delta) \} + \dfrac{DR_2}{R_1^2} G$		
Φ	$\dfrac{(1-\mu)^{1/2}}{(1-\mu \operatorname{cosec}\phi)^{1/2}}$	$\left(\dfrac{r_0 \sec\gamma}{s \tan\gamma}\right)^{1/2}$	1
k	$[3(1-\nu^2)]^{1/4} \left[\dfrac{R_1}{(1-\mu)d}\right]^{1/2}$	$[3(1-\nu^2)]^{1/4} \left(\dfrac{R_1^2}{r_0 d \sec\gamma}\right)^{1/2}$	$[3(1-\nu^2)]^{1/4} \left(\dfrac{R_1^2}{R_0 d}\right)^{1/2}$
kF	$[3(1-\nu^2)]^{1/4} \left(\dfrac{R_1}{d}\right)^{1/2} \int (1-\mu \operatorname{cosec}\phi)^{-1/2} \, d\phi$	$2[3(1-\nu^2)]^{1/4} \left(\dfrac{s}{d\tan\gamma'}\right)^{1/2}$	$[3(1-\nu^2)]^{1/4} \dfrac{x}{(R_0 d)^{1/2}}$
R_1	R_1	∞	∞
R_2	$R_1(1-\mu \operatorname{cosec}\phi)$	$s \tan\gamma$	R_0
G	$-\dfrac{R_1}{d}(1+\nu)\alpha \dfrac{d}{d\phi}(\Delta T)$	$-\dfrac{R_1^2}{d}(1+\nu)\alpha \dfrac{d}{ds}(\Delta T)$	$-\dfrac{R_1^2}{d}(1+\nu)\alpha \dfrac{d}{dx}(\Delta T)$
H	$-ER_1 \, d\alpha \dfrac{d}{d\phi}(T_m)$	$-ER_1^2 \, d\alpha \dfrac{d}{ds}(T_m)$	$-ER_1^2 \, d\alpha \dfrac{d}{dx}(T_m)$

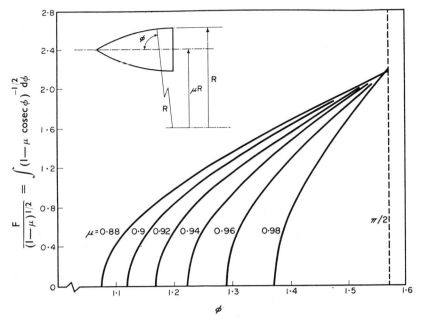

Fig. 8.5. Variation of the function F with ϕ for various values of μ (ogival shells).

The particular integrals given by the asymptotic solutions are also approximate, but in general are sufficiently accurate for engineering applications provided there are no violent changes in temperature distribution. Better approximation can be obtained by using series expansion solutions whose coefficients are determined from the differential equations. These solutions require, however, an appreciable amount of computing compared with the asymptotic solution.

When solutions have been derived for the two basic functions U and V the stress resultants and deformations can be obtained from relatively simple expressions. These are summarized below:

$$N_1 = -\cot\phi \frac{V}{R_2} \tag{8.94}$$

$$N_2 = -\frac{V'}{R_1} \tag{8.95}$$

$$Q = \frac{V}{R_2} \tag{8.96}$$

$$M_1 = -D\left\{\frac{U'}{R_1} + v\frac{\cot\phi}{R_2}U\right\} - \frac{\alpha E}{(1-v)}\frac{d^2}{12}\Delta T \tag{8.97}$$

$$M_2 = -D \left\{ \frac{U \cot \phi}{R_2} + v \frac{U'}{R_1} \right\} - \frac{\alpha E}{(1-v)} \frac{d^2}{12} \Delta T \qquad (8.98)$$

$$w = \frac{R_2 \sin \phi}{Ed} \left\{ \frac{V'}{R_1} + v \cot \phi \frac{V}{R_2} \right\} - \alpha R_2 \sin \phi \, T_m \qquad (8.99)$$

where primes denote derivatives with respect to ϕ, and w is the displacement in the direction at right angle to the axis of symmetry, measured positive inwards.

(iii) *Shallow Shells*[35, 36]

A method for the calculation of stresses and deformations in shallow shells was developed by Ambartsumyan.[35] This method depends on the separation of the Fourier series solution into a portion recognizable as that of a flat plate under the same loading, and the remainder due to the small curvature of the shell. The same method was also applied by Flügge and Conrad[36] who obtained solutions for shallow spherical, cylindrical and hyperboloidal shells under concentrated loading.

A shallow shell can be described by the distance $z(x, y)$ of its middle surface from the x–y plane (see Fig. 8.6). The linearized differential equations for a shallow shell subjected to temperature loading are:

$$\nabla_e^4 w - \frac{1}{DR_2} \nabla_k^2 F = \frac{-(1+v)}{d} \alpha \nabla_e^2 (\Delta T) \qquad (8.100)$$

$$\nabla_e^4 F + \frac{Ed}{R_2} \nabla_k^2 w = -Ed \, \alpha \nabla_e^2 (T_m) \qquad (8.101)$$

where

$\qquad w =$ normal deflexion of shell,

$\qquad F =$ Airy stress function,

$\qquad R_1 =$ radius of curvature in x-direction,

$\qquad R_2 =$ radius of curvature in y-direction,

$$\nabla_e^2 \equiv \frac{\partial^2}{\partial x^2} + \frac{\partial^2}{\partial y^2},$$

$$\nabla_k^2 \equiv \frac{\partial^2}{\partial x^2} + \lambda \frac{\partial^2}{\partial y^2}$$

$$\lambda = R_2/R_1$$

In deriving equations (8.100) and (8.101) it has been assumed that the x and y axes are projections of the lines of principal curvature and that these curvatures are constant. The parameter λ can be either positive or negative. For example, for the shallow sphere $\lambda = 1$, for cylinder $\lambda = 0$ and for hyperboloid $\lambda = -1$.

The stress-resultants are obtained from the Airy stress function as follows

$$N_x = \frac{\partial^2 F}{\partial y^2}; \quad N_y = \frac{\partial^2 F}{\partial x^2} \quad \text{and} \quad N_{xy} = -\frac{\partial^2 F}{\partial x \, \partial y} \tag{8.102}$$

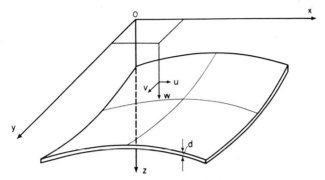

FIG. 8.6.   Shallow shell.

while the moment-resultants and tangential displacements are determined from

$$M_x = -D\left[\frac{\partial^2 w}{\partial x^2} + v\frac{\partial^2 w}{\partial y^2} + \frac{1+v}{d}\alpha \Delta T\right] \tag{8.103}$$

$$M_y = -D\left[\frac{\partial^2 w}{\partial y^2} + v\frac{\partial^2 w}{\partial x^2} + \frac{1+v}{d}\alpha \Delta T\right] \tag{8.104}$$

$$M_{xy} = -D(1-v)\frac{\partial^2 w}{\partial x \, \partial y} \tag{8.105}$$

$$N_{xy} = \frac{Ed}{2(1+v)}\left[\frac{\partial u}{\partial y} + \frac{\partial v}{\partial x}\right] \tag{8.106}$$

$$\frac{\partial u}{\partial x} = \frac{1}{Ed}[N_x - vN_y] + \frac{w}{R_1} + \alpha T_m \tag{8.107}$$

$$\frac{\partial v}{\partial y} = \frac{1}{Ed}[N_y - vN_x] + \frac{w}{R_2} + \alpha T_m \tag{8.108}$$

The temperature loading terms ΔT and T_m are then expanded in double Fourier series and the solutions for F, w, u and v are assumed to be of the same form. By substituting expansions for F and w into the differential equations and then using the orthogonal properties of the Fourier expansions, it is possible to determine explicitly the unknown Fourier coefficients in the expansions. Some advantage may be gained here by separating these coefficients into two parts: the first part represents the solution for a flat plate under the same loading, while the second part represents the terms depending on the curvature, which are more rapidly convergent than the flat-plate solution. Thus the flat-plate solution can be combined with a wide range of shallow-shell solutions.

The solutions derived in terms of the Fourier series are generally incomplete, since not all boundary conditions can be satisfied exactly. This can be corrected by the superposition of complementary functions derived from equations (8.100) and (8.101) with the temperature loading terms equal to zero.

(iv) *Stresses due to Non-symmetrical Temperature Distribution*

When the temperature distribution is not symmetrical, the equations for the deflexions of axi-symmetrical shells become much more complicated, as three deflexions, longitudinal, radial and circumferential, must now be included. The solution of these equations can be extremely laborious and various attempts have been made to simplify the solution by neglecting many of the terms occurring in the differential equations.

An analytical method of calculating thermal stresses in thin-walled circular cylinders due to asymmetric temperature distribution has been given by Payne.[44] Furthermore, he has attempted an alternative solution to the same problem by finite differences. His solution has a practical application in the design of a continuous cylindrical skirt supporting the pressure vessel and reactor core.

8.10. STRAIN ENERGY THEOREMS GENERALIZED FOR THERMAL EFFECTS

Strain energy methods of determining stress distribution in redundant structures can be derived from the fundamental laws of thermodynamics and, in a way, these methods can be regarded as a mathematical link between the classical theory of elasticity and the law of conservation of energy. In modern methods of stress analysis the strain energy as such is very rarely calculated; it is only used indirectly for obtaining compatible load distributions in statically indeterminate structures.

A unified treatment of the theory of thermoelasticity and thermodynamics has been presented by Biot;[37] it includes the general theory of heat conduction, thermal stresses and strains induced by the temperature distribution, coupling effects between temperature and thermoelastic deformations and thermoelastic damping. Although the coupling effects are of some interest in the study of basic physical laws in the theory of thermoelasticity, they need not be considered in ordinary engineering applications.

Strain energy theorems have been generalized in Ref. 38 to include the thermal effects. A detailed discussion of all the energy theorems would undoubtedly necessitate a separate chapter. The principle of virtual forces or virtual complementary work for elastic bodies subjected to thermal effects, however, has found a wide application in thermoelastic problems and therefore only this principle and two other theorems derived directly from it will be discussed in this section.

The Principle of Virtual Forces states that an elastic body is in an elastically compatible state under a given temperature (and load) distribution if for any *virtual* increments of forces and stresses from a position of equilibrium

$$\delta W^* = \delta U_i^* + \int_V \alpha T \delta s \, dV \tag{8.109}$$

where $\delta W^* =$ increment in complementary work of external forces,

$\delta U_i^* = \int_V \varepsilon \, \delta \sigma \, dV$, increment in complementary strain energy,

$\delta s = \delta \sigma_{11} + \delta \sigma_{22} + \delta \sigma_{33}$.

For the formal derivation of this principle Ref. 38 can be consulted. The Principle of Virtual Forces can be used to derive two extremely useful energy theorems: the principle of stationary (minimum) complementary potential energy of total deformation and the unit load theorem.

If the following notation is introduced

$\delta U_e^* = -\delta W^*$,   increment in the complementary potential of the external forces

$\delta U_d^* = \delta U_i^* + \int_V \alpha T \delta s \, dV$, increment in the complementary potential energy of total deformation

then equation (8.109) takes the form

$$\delta(U_d^* + U_e^*) = 0 \tag{8.110}$$

If now the external virtual forces are not varied then $\delta U_e^* = 0$ and equation (8.110) reduces to

$$\delta U_d^* = 0 \tag{8.111}$$

Equation (8.111) is the standard principle of Castigliano of Minimum Strain Energy generalized to include temperature effects. In Ref. 38 this principle is described as the principle of stationary (minimum) value of complementary potential energy of total deformations for internally redundant structures.

To solve an elasticity problem, the equations of equilibrium and compatibility must be satisfied together with the prescribed boundary conditions on stresses and/or displacements. If all the sets of functions which satisfy the equilibrium equations and the required boundary conditions are collected together, then the correct set is found by selecting the set which also satisfies the compatibility equations. This correct set can be found most conveniently by selecting the set which makes the complementary potential energy of total deformations of the body a minimum, since this condition is exactly equivalent to the condition of compatibility of strains.

Another useful theorem is the Unit Load Theorem which can be derived directly from equation (8.109). To demonstrate this theorem it will be assumed that the deformation u_r is required at a given point and direction in an elastic body subjected to a known temperature distribution. The actual total strains in the body are assumed to be known and given by

$$e_{ij} = \varepsilon_{ij} + \alpha T \delta_{ij} \tag{8.10}$$

If a load δP_r is applied in the direction of u_r, then using equation (8.109)

$$\delta W^* = \delta P_r \cdot u_r = \int_V \varepsilon \, \delta \sigma \, \mathrm{d}V + \int_V \alpha T \delta s \, \mathrm{d}V$$

$$= \int_V [\varepsilon_{11} \delta\sigma_{11} + \varepsilon_{22} \delta\sigma_{22} + \varepsilon_{33} \delta\sigma_{33} +$$

$$+ 2(\varepsilon_{12} \delta\sigma_{12} + \varepsilon_{23} \delta\sigma_{23} + \varepsilon_{31} \delta\sigma_{31})] \, \mathrm{d}V +$$

$$+ \int_V \alpha T (\delta\sigma_{11} + \delta\sigma_{22} + \delta\sigma_{33}) \, \mathrm{d}V \tag{8.112}$$

where $\delta\sigma_{11} \ldots \delta\sigma_{12} \ldots$ etc., are the virtual stresses due to δP_r. For linear elasticity $\delta\sigma$'s are proportional to δP_r and hence

$$1 \times u_r = \int [\varepsilon_{11} \bar\sigma_{11} + \varepsilon_{22} \bar\sigma_{22} + \varepsilon_{33} \bar\sigma_{33} + 2(\varepsilon_{12} \bar\sigma_{12} + \varepsilon_{23} \bar\sigma_{23} + \varepsilon_{31} \bar\sigma_{31})] \, \mathrm{d}V +$$

$$+ \int_V \alpha T (\bar\sigma_{11} + \bar\sigma_{22} + \bar\sigma_{33}) \, \mathrm{d}V \tag{8.113}$$

$$= \int [\varepsilon_{11} \bar\sigma_{11} + \varepsilon_{22} \bar\sigma_{22} + \varepsilon_{33} \bar\sigma_{33} + 2(\varepsilon_{12} \bar\sigma_{12} + \varepsilon_{23} \bar\sigma_{23} + \varepsilon_{31} \bar\sigma_{31})] \, \mathrm{d}V$$

where $\bar\sigma_{11} \ldots \bar\sigma_{12} \ldots$ etc., are the stresses due to a unit load in the direction of u_r. Since these stresses were derived from virtual stresses, they need only satisfy the internal equilibrium condition and the external one for $\delta P_r = 1$.

Equation (8.113) represents the Unit Load Theorem, which is particularly useful in solving redundant structures subjected to temperature loading.

8.11. NUMERICAL METHODS

(i) *Matrix Methods*

The introduction of high-speed computing machines has made possible the analysis of highly redundant structures. For such calculations, however, structural problems must be presented in matrix algebra suitable for automatic computation on electronic digital computers and this usually calls for special matrix methods adapted to the type of structure considered. There are already a large number of papers which have led to the present widespread use of matrix methods in structural problems. In particular the work of Langefors[39] on the use of matrix methods should be mentioned. Recently a comprehensive study of two dual matrix methods based on either displacements (Displacement Method) or forces (Force Method) has been presented by Argyris[38] and the latter method is particularly suitable for the analysis of redundant structures subjected to temperature loading.

In the Force Method a simple synthetic stress system—referred to as the basic system—in equilibrium with the applied loading is selected, and then a number of self-equilibrating stress systems are introduced so that when the basic system is combined with the self-equilibrating stress systems the conditions of equilibrium and compatibility are satisfied. These self-equilibrating stress systems may, therefore, be regarded as perturbations of a basic system that is in equilibrium with the applied loading but which does not satisfy the compatibility conditions. The total number of the self-equilibrating stress systems is equal to the degree of redundancy of the complete structure. Thus the internal load distribution in the structure consists of two parts: (a) basic load distribution represented by the matrix $\mathbf{b}_0$, satisfying the external and internal equations of equilibrium, and (b) self-equilibrating load systems, represented by the matrix $\mathbf{b}_1$, which are introduced to satisfy the compatibility conditions. In matrix notation the internal load distribution $\mathbf{S}$ is therefore given by

$$\mathbf{S} = \mathbf{b}_0 + \mathbf{b}_1\,\mathbf{X} \qquad (8.114)$$

where the $\mathbf{X}$-matrix represents the magnitudes of the self-equilibrating systems. For thermal loading only $\mathbf{b}_0 = \mathbf{O}$ and

$$\mathbf{S} = \mathbf{b}_1\,\mathbf{X} \qquad (8.115)$$

It will be now assumed that the generalized displacements under a known thermal loading in the structure are given by the matrix $\mathbf{v} = \{v_a v_b \ldots v_g \ldots v_s\}$. The unit load theorem for a single displacement u_r in matrix notation is derived by replacing the integration in equation (8.113) by a summation, i.e.

$$u_r = \sum_{g=a}^{s} \overline{S}_{r_g} v_g = \overline{\mathbf{S}}'_r \mathbf{v} \qquad (8.116)$$

248   J. S. PRZEMIENIECKI

where the summation extends over all elements in the structure and $\bar{S}_r$ is the
load distribution matrix due a unit load applied in the rth direction.

Applying now the unit load theorem to the self-equilibrating loads, which
naturally produce zero relative displacements, it follows that

$$b_1' v = O \qquad (8.117)$$

The generalized displacements v are given by

$$v = fS + H \qquad (8.118)$$

where f is the flexibility matrix which relates the deformations of the individual *unassembled* elements to their corresponding forces, and H is the
matrix of the thermal deformations of individual elements.

Substituting equations (8.115) and (8.118) into (8.117) it follows that

$$b_1' f b_1 X + b_1' H = O \qquad (8.119)$$

Hence $$X = -(b_1' f b_1)^{-1} b_1' H \qquad (8.120)$$

and $$S = -b_1 (b_1' f b_1)^{-1} b_1' H \qquad (8.121)$$

Thus only very simple algebraic operations on matrices are required to
determine the distribution of loads in redundant structures subjected to
thermal loading.*

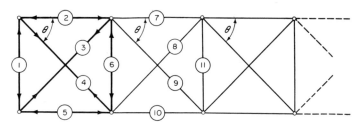

FIG. 8.7.   Typical self-equilibrating load system in a statically indeterminate
framework.

The overlapping between different systems is kept to a minimum by
arranging that these systems affect only a small part of the structure and
this improves the conditioning of the product $(b_1' f b_1)$.   A typical self-
equilibrating load (stress) system for a pin-jointed redundant framework is
shown in Fig. 8.7.   It should be noted that this system gives only a relative
distribution of loads;   the actual loads are obtained by multiplying this
distribution by the appropriate factor in the matrix $\underline{X}$.

Using Fig. 8.7 it follows then, that equation (8.115) for this case becomes,

_____

* Primes are used to indicate matrix transposition, and thus $\bar{S}_j'$ denotes the transpose of $\bar{S}_j$.

$$
\begin{bmatrix} S_1 \\ S_2 \\ S_3 \\ S_4 \\ S_5 \\ S_6 \\ S_7 \\ S_8 \\ S_9 \\ S_{10} \\ S_{11} \\ \cdot \\ \cdot \\ \cdot \end{bmatrix}
=
\begin{bmatrix}
-\sin\theta & 0 & . & . \\
-\cos\theta & 0 & . & . \\
1 & 0 & . & . \\
1 & 0 & . & . \\
-\cos\theta & 0 & . & . \\
-\sin\theta & -\sin\theta & . & . \\
0 & -\cos\theta & . & . \\
0 & 1 & . & . \\
0 & 1 & . & . \\
0 & -\cos\theta & . & . \\
0 & -\sin\theta & . & . \\
0 & 0 & . & . \\
\cdot & \cdot & . & \cdot
\end{bmatrix}
\times
\begin{bmatrix} X_1 \\ X_2 \\ \cdot \\ \cdot \\ \cdot \\ \cdot \\ X_n \end{bmatrix}
\tag{8.122}
$$

where n denotes the degree of redundancy and negative signs are used for compressive loads. The flexibility matrix $\mathbf{f}$ for this case is a diagonal matrix whose elements denote the extentional flexibilities of elements under direct loads, i.e.

$$
\mathbf{f} =
\begin{bmatrix}
\dfrac{l_1}{EA_1} & & & & \mathbf{O} \\
& \dfrac{l_2}{EA_2} & & & \\
& & \ddots & & \\
\mathbf{O} & & & \dfrac{l_i}{EA_{i.}}
\end{bmatrix}
\tag{8.123}
$$

where l_i is the length of the ith member and A_i is its cross-sectional area (assumed constant).

If the temperature of each member is constant along the length, then the thermal deformation matrix $\mathbf{H}$ becomes simply

$$
\mathbf{H} = \{\alpha_1 l_1 T_1, \ \alpha_2 l_2 T_2, \ \ldots \ \alpha_i l_i T_i \ldots\}
\tag{8.124}
$$

where α_i is the coefficient of expansion and T_i is the temperature of the ith member.

Another type of self-equilibrating system is shown in Fig. 8.8, which can be applied in an " egg-box " grillage used in reactors. This system consists basically of shear forces X reacted between the transverse and longitudinal beams. Only bending of beams in the vertical plane is considered; the torsional stiffness of the beams is negligible and bending in the horizontal plane is not involved. The thermal deformation matrix **H** is based here on the temperature gradients through the depth of beams. If the grillage is supported in a redundant manner, then special self-equilibrating systems must also be included to cater for the redundant supports. For a more complete description of the various types of self-equilibrating systems and of the flexibility matrices Refs. 38 and 40 can be consulted.

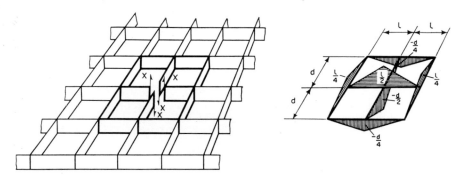

(a) Typical self-equilibrating system   (b) Bending moment distribution

FIG. 8.8. Self-equilibrating systems for bending moments in an " egg-box " grillage.

The Matrix Force Method is probably the most powerful method for the stress analysis of structures with a finite number of redundancies. It is not uncommon nowadays to analyse structures with 100–200 redundancies, a feat which could not possibly be accomplished without the aid of modern electronic digital computers.

(ii) *Finite Difference Methods*

If the exact solution to the differential equations describing the thermo-elastic problem is not possible, then these equations can be replaced by a series of difference equations relating stresses, strains or stress functions at stations removed from each other by finite dimensions. These difference equations lead to numerical solutions that are generally adequate for engineering purposes.

In one-dimensional problems (single independent variable) the finite difference equations are obtained by substituting the finite difference expressions for the derivatives occurring in the ordinary differential equations. The difference equations relate the conditions at one station to those at the adjacent stations. Thus, if the stresses at one station are known, the stresses at other stations can be computed. However, the stresses at any particular station may not be completely known and therefore stresses at other stations must be expressed in terms of the unknown stresses at the reference station. These unknown stresses are then determined from some prescribed boundary conditions. A typical case for a one-dimensional problem has been discussed by Manson in Ref. 41, where he considered thermal stresses in an axi-symmetrical disc subjected to a non-uniform temperature distribution.

The finite difference method can also be used in two-dimensional problems and it is particularly useful when the geometrical boundaries are irregular. For these problems, the partial derivatives are re-written in finite difference form. The satisfaction of boundary conditions, however, may be very difficult in some cases, and because of the large number of equations involved special relaxation procedures may have to be used.[41]

8.12. LOSS OF STIFFNESS CAUSED BY THERMAL STRESSES[42]

Thermal stresses in structures may have an adverse effect on the stiffness and in certain cases could lead to an appreciable increase in deformations due to the external loading. As an example of what is involved one can

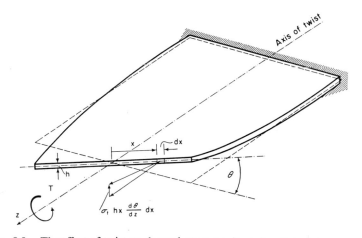

FIG. 8.9. The effect of twist on thermal stress-resultants in a flat plate.

consider a cantilever flat plate with a concentrated torque applied at the tip end of the plate (see Fig. 8.9). The plate is subjected to a non-linear temperature distribution which produces thermal stresses σ_t in the plane of the plate. Because of the twist of the plate under the applied torque, the vectors of the thermal stress-resultants are inclined to the xz-plane. The angle of inclination of the vector at a distance x from the centre of twist is

$$x\frac{d\theta}{dz}$$

and the stress-resultant component perpendicular to the axis of twist is given by

$$h\sigma_t x\frac{d\theta}{dz}dx$$

The total torque on the cross-section due to the axial thermal stresses over the entire section is given by

$$T_t = \frac{d\theta}{dz}\int \sigma_t hx^2 dx \qquad (8.125)$$

The torque T_t must be added to the torque due to the St Venant shear stresses to give the total external torque T. Thus

$$T = GJ\frac{d\theta}{dz}+\frac{d\theta}{dz}\int \sigma_t hx^2 dx \qquad (8.126)$$

where

$$J \simeq \tfrac{1}{3}\int h^3 dx \qquad (8.127)$$

The effective torsional stiffness can then be written as

$$\frac{T}{(d\theta/dz)} = GJ+\int \sigma_t hx^2 dx \qquad (8.128)$$

The integral $\int \sigma_t hx^2 dx$ can be either positive or negative, depending on the stress distribution σ_t. If the edges of the plate are hotter than its centre, then this integral is negative (because of the negative compressive stresses near the edges) and the effective torsional stiffness is reduced. The reduction of the torsional stiffness is similar to the effect of end load in torsional instability of thin-walled struts.

Other examples of the loss of stiffness (not necessarily torsional) caused by thermal stresses could undoubtedly be found on various types of structures subjected to temperature loading. Where deflexions are of paramount importance, it may be necessary in such cases to investigate the possibility of a reduction in stiffness due to thermal stresses caused by non-uniform distribution of temperature.

8.13. THERMAL BUCKLING[43]

Thermal stresses are induced in a flat plate if the temperature gradients are non-uniform or the plate is restrained against expansion at the edges. For temperatures varying across the plate thickness lateral deflexions occur as soon as the heating of the plate begins, but for a non-uniform temperature distribution in the plane of the plate and constant temperatures through the thickness, lateral deflexions do not appear until a certain critical temperature is reached when the plate starts to buckle. This latter phenomenon may be described as thermal buckling of plates under a critical temperature distribution.

Thermal buckling may also occur on other structural components. For example, struts can buckle under thermal loading if the temperature increase is sufficiently high, and the strut ends are restrained against free expansion.

The occurrence of thermal buckling reduces the ability of the structure to carry the applied loads for which it was designed. Even if the thermal stresses do not cause buckling, their coexistence with stresses induced by external loads will result in a decrease of structural performance with respect to these external loads. A typical example of this is the loss of torsional stiffness of plates due to thermal stresses, as shown in Section 8.12.

8.14. METHODS OF ALLEVIATING THERMAL STRESSES

Several typical methods of alleviating thermal effects on structures will be discussed. These methods can broadly be divided into four main groups:

(a) Attenuation of heat input.
(b) Modifications to the thermal characteristics of the structure.
(c) Thermally non-redundant structures.
(d) Choice of materials.

These will now be considered in turn.

(a) *Attenuation of Heat Input*

Thermal stresses naturally depend on the severity of the heat input which leads to non-uniform temperature distributions in the structure. Some reduction in the severity of heating can be achieved by insulation and artificial cooling.

(b) *Modifications to the Thermal Characteristics of the Structure*

The thermal characteristics of any structure subjected to heating can generally be expressed as the Biot number $B = hl/k$, where h is the external heat transfer coefficient, l is the characteristic length in the direction of heat flow and k is the thermal conductivity of the material. The magnitude of thermal stresses increases with an increase in the Biot number and the increase is more pronounced for high values of this number. Therefore some reduction in the magnitude of thermal stresses can be achieved by aiming at small values of the Biot number B, i.e. low values of the surface heat transfer coefficient h and the characteristic length l and a high value of the thermal conductivity k.

For elevated temperature applications we are generally forced to use stainless steels which are poor conductors of heat and this inevitably leads to high values of the Biot number and hence to high thermal stresses. The situation can be greatly improved if the part of the structure exposed to heat is made of a heat-resisting, i.e. low thermal conductivity material, while the non-exposed part is made of a composite material comprising a strength layer of a heat-resisting material and a heat-diffusing layer of a metal or alloy having high thermal conductivity; the two layers are in contact with each other. Thus the effective conductivity of the non-exposed structure can be increased and consequently the temperature gradients and thermal stresses are reduced.

(c) Thermally Non-redundant Structures

The ideal thermally non-redundant structure is one in which the part of the structure at low temperature provides no restraint against thermal expansion of those parts of the structure which are at higher temperatures. Examples of partly or completely thermally non-redundant structures are: statically determinate frameworks, corrugated spar webs on an aircraft wing structure, bellow-type expansion joints on pipes, flexible joints, etc. It should be emphasized that in a great number of cases the adverse thermal effects on structures operating at elevated temperatures can be partially remedied by suitable detail design. However, no generalized suggestions are possible and every scheme must be treated on its own merits in a particular design.

(d) Choice of Materials

Thermal stresses are proportional to the product αE and therefore the materials with low values of the coefficient of expansion α and Young's modulus E will have low thermal stresses. Similarly materials which are good thermal conductors will give rise to smaller temperature gradients and hence low thermal stresses. Furthermore, in materials having high tensile strength a large proportion of the total available stress can be used to accommodate the thermal stress. Therefore to facilitate the choice of materials, a thermal shock resistance parameter may be used as a possible criterion for comparing different materials; it is given by

$$\frac{k\,\sigma_{ult}}{\alpha E}$$

TABLE 8.3. THERMOELASTIC PROPERTIES OF STRUCTURAL MATERIALS AT ROOM TEMPERATURE

Material		Density ρ (lb./ft³)	Specific heat C (CHU/lb. °C)	Conductivity k (CHU/(ft. sec. °C))	Thermal diffusivity κ (in²/sec.)	Coefficient of expansion α (1./°C)	Young's modulus E (lb./in²)	αE (lb./in² °C)	Tensile strength* σ_{ult} (lb./in²)	$\dfrac{k\sigma_{ult}}{\alpha E}$ (CHU/in. sec.)
Metallic	Mild steel	490	0·141	$8·93 \times 10^{-3}$	$18·6 \times 10^{-3}$	12×10^{-6}	30×10^{6}	360	80,000	165×10^{-3}
	12% Cr steel	484	0·115	$3·83 \times 10^{-3}$	$9·22 \times 10^{-3}$	11×10^{-6}	$31·4 \times 10^{6}$	346	157,000	145×10^{-3}
	18% Cr, 8% Ni steel	492	0·120	$2·55 \times 10^{-3}$	$6·22 \times 10^{-3}$	16×10^{-6}	$29·2 \times 10^{6}$	467	130,000	59×10^{-3}
	Titanium alloy	283	0·129	$2·69 \times 10^{-3}$	$10·6 \times 10^{-3}$	$8·5 \times 10^{-6}$	16×10^{6}	136	150,000	248×10^{-3}
	Aluminium alloy	174	0·214	$31·0 \times 10^{-3}$	120×10^{-3}	$22·6 \times 10^{-6}$	$10·2 \times 10^{6}$	230	60,000	675×10^{-3}
	Magnesium alloy	109	0·240	$25·5 \times 10^{-3}$	141×10^{-3}	$26·0 \times 10^{-6}$	$6·5 \times 10^{6}$	169	35,000	441×10^{-3}
	Beryllium	114	0·420	$24·2 \times 10^{-3}$	$76·5 \times 10^{-3}$	$11·5 \times 10^{-6}$	42×10^{6}	482	55,000	230×10^{-3}
Non-metallic	Toughened soda-lime glass	162	0·220	$0·154 \times 10^{-3}$	$0·622 \times 10^{-3}$	$8·7 \times 10^{-6}$	$9·7 \times 10^{6}$	85	~24,000	$3·62 \times 10^{-3}$
	Fused silica	138	0·167	$0·235 \times 10^{-3}$	$1·54 \times 10^{-3}$	$0·54 \times 10^{-6}$	$9·7 \times 10^{6}$	5·2	~10,000	$37·7 \times 10^{-3}$
	Concrete (1:2:4)	143	0·230	$0·148 \times 10^{-3}$	$0·65 \times 10^{-3}$	12×10^{-6}	3×10^{6}	36	~300	$·103 \times 10^{-3}$
	Silicon nitride (ceramic)	137	0·140	$0·249 \times 10^{-3}$	$1·87 \times 10^{-3}$	$2·5 \times 10^{-6}$	9×10^{6}	22·5	~20,000	$18·5 \times 10^{-3}$

* The values of tensile strength of alloys may vary widely, depending on the heat treatment and cold working

where σ_{ult} denotes the tensile strength at an elevated temperature. The material with a high value of this parameter will generally have better thermal and strength characteristics.

Thermal properties and the thermal shock resistance parameter of some typical structural materials are given in Table 8.3.

8.15. CONCLUSIONS

Thermal stresses and associated thermal problems require careful consideration in the design of structures for elevated temperature applications. The thermoelastic theory has been developed to such an extent that the majority of thermal stress problems can be solved without much difficulty, particularly if the services of an electronic digital computer are available.

The fundamental theorems of thermoelasticity and the methods of solution described in this chapter can serve as a useful guide to the various methods available for the design and stress analysis of structures subjected to " temperature loading ", including the types of structures used in nuclear reactors.

REFERENCES

1. J. M. C. DUHAMEL, Mémoire sur le calcul des actions moléculaires développées par les changements de température dans les corps solides. *Mém. inst. France*, **5**, 440–98 (1838).
2. J. M. C. DUHAMEL, Seconde mémoire sur les phénomènes thermo-mécaniques, *J. école polytech (Paris)*, **15**, 1–57 (1837).
3. J. M. C. DUHAMEL, Mémoire sur le mouvement des différents points d'une barre cylindrique dont la température varie, *J. école polytech (Paris)*, **21**, 1–33 (1856).
4. B. E. GATEWOOD, *Thermal Stresses.* McGraw-Hill, First Edition, 1957.
5. S. TIMOSHENKO and J. N. GOODIER, *Theory of Elasticity*, Chapter 14. McGraw-Hill, Second Edition, 1951.
6. E. MELAN and H. PARKUS, *Wärmespannungen.* Springer Verlag, Wien, First Edition, 1953.
7. J. N. GOODIER, On the integration of the thermoelastic equations. *Phil. Mag.*, Series 7, **23**, 1017–32 (1937).
8. A. J. A. MORGAN, A proof of Duhamel's analogy for thermal stresses. *J. Aero/Space Sciences*, **25**, 466–7, July (1958).
9. J. S. PRZEMIENIECKI, Design of transparencies. *J. R. Ae. Soc.*, **63**, 620–36, November (1959).
10. N. I. MUSKHELISHVILI, Some basic problems of the mathematical theory of elasticity. Noordhoff, Groningen, Holland, 1953.
11. G. HORVAY, Thermal stresses in rectangular strips—I., *Proceedings of Second National Congress of Applied Mechanics.* ASME, 1954.
12. J. S. BORN and G. HORVAY, Thermal stresses in rectangular strips—II. *J. Appl. Mech.*, 401–6, September (1955).
13. R. R. HELDENFELS and W. M. ROBERTS, Experimental and theoretical determination of thermal stresses in flat plates. NACA TN.2769, August (1952).
14. J. SINGER, M. ANLIKER and S. LEDERMAN, *Thermal Stresses and Thermal Buckling.* Wright Air Development Center Technical Report 57–69, Polytechnic Institute of Brooklyn, April (1957).
15. G. HORVAY, The end problem of rectangular strips. *J. Appl. Mech.* **20**, 87–97, March (1953); and 576–82, December (1953).

16. G. HORVAY and J. S. BORN, Tables of self-equilibrating functions. *J. Math. Phys.* **33**, 360–73 (1955).
17. A. MENDELSON and M. HIRSCHBERG, *Analysis of Elastic Thermal Stress in Thin Plate with Spanwise and Chordwise Variation of Temperature and Thickness.* NACA TN.3778, November (1956).
18. J. S. PRZEMIENIECKI, Thermal stresses in rectangular plates. *Aero. Quart.* **10**, 65–78 (1959).
19. D. YOUNG and R. P. FELGAR, *Tables of Characteristic Functions Representing Normal Modes of Vibration of a Beam.* Publication No. 4913, University of Texas (1949).
20. J. S. PRZEMIENIECKI, Design charts for transient temperature and thermal stress distributions in thermally thick plates. *Aero. Quart.* **11**, 269–84 (1960).
21. A. NADAI, *Die Elastische Platten*, p. 264. Julius Springer Verlag, Berlin (1925).
22. A. E. H. LOVE, *Mathematical Theory of Elasticity*, Fourth Ed., p. 558. Cambridge University Press (1952).
23. M. L. WILLIAMS, Large deflexion analysis for a plate strip subjected to normal pressure and heating. pp. 458–64, *J. Appl. Mech.* (1955).
24. M. L. WILLIAMS, Further large deflexion analysis for a plate strip subjected to normal pressure and heating. *J. Appl. Mech.*, pp. 251–8 (1958).
25. E. W. PARKES, Panels under thermal stress. *Aircraft Engng.* **28**, 180–6 (1956).
26. J. L. MAULBETSCH, Thermal stresses in plates. *J. Appl. Mech.*, **2**, 141–6 (1935).
27. S. TIMOSHENKO, *Theory of Plates and Shells*, pp. 53–4, 176–80. McGraw-Hill (1940).
28. E. MEISSNER, Das Elastizitätsprobleme für dünne Schalen von Ringflächen—Kugel oder Kegelform. *Phys. Z.*, **14**, 343–9 (1913).
29. G. EICHELBERG, Temperaturverlauf und Wärmespannungen in Verbrennungsmotoren. *Forsch. Ing. Wesen, Berlin* No. 263 (1923).
30. H. PARKUS, Wärmespannungen in Rotationsschalen bei drehsymmetrischer Temperaturverteilung, *Öst. Akad. Wiss. (math.-natur. Kl.)* **160**, 1–13 (1951).
31. J. H. HUTH, Thermal stresses in conical shells. *J. Aero. Sci.* **20**, September (1953).
32. E. REISSNER, Asymptotic solutions in shell theory. *Proc. of Symposia in Applied Mathematics, Elasticity*, **3**, McGraw-Hill (1950).
33. J. S. PRZEMIENIECKI, *The General Theory of Axi-symmetrical Shells under Temperature Loading.* Bristol Aircraft Ltd., Technical Office Report No. 88, March (1956).
34. H. JEFFREYS and H. B. JEFFREYS, *Methods of Mathematical Physics*, p. 491. Cambridge University Press (1946).
35. S. A. AMBARTSUMYAN, On the calculation of shallow shells. *Prikl. Mat. i Mekh.*, **11**, 527–32 (1947). Translated as NACA TM 1425 December (1956).
36. W. FLÜGGE and D. A. CONRAD, A note on the calculation of shallow shells. *J. Appl. Mech.*, **26**, Series E, 683–5 (1959).
37. M. A. BIOT, Thermoelasticity and irreversible thermodynamics. *J. Appl. Phys.* **27**, 240–53 (1956).
38. J. H. ARGYRIS, Energy theorems and structural analysis: A generalised discourse with applications on energy principles of structural analysis including the effects of temperature and non-linear stress–strain relations. *Aircraft Engng.* **26**, October 1954 and November 1954; **27**, March (1955).
39. B. LANGEFORS, Structural analysis of swept-back wings by matrix transformation method. *Svenska Aeroplan Aktiebogelat* (S.A.A.B.), Technical Note No. 3, Linköping, Sweden (1951).
40. J. S. PRZEMIENIECKI, Matrix analysis of shell structures with flexible frames. *Aero. Quart.* **9**, 361–94 (1958).
41. S. S. MANSON, Thermal stresses, Part 9. Elastic stress solutions. *Machine Design*, 5th March (1959).
42. S. L. KOCHANSKI and J. H. ARGYRIS, Some effects of kinetic heating on the stiffness of thin wings. *Aircraft Engng.* **29**, 310–18, October (1957).
43. GOSSARD *et al.*, *Thermal Buckling of Plates.* NACA. TN. 2771, August (1952).
44. D. J. PAYNE, Thermal stresses in thin-walled circular cylinders. *Nuclear Reactor Containment Buildings and Pressure Vessels.* Butterworths (1960).

CHAPTER 9

THE PLASTICITY AND CREEP OF METALS

J. M. ALEXANDER*

9.1. INTRODUCTION

IN general it is true to say that a knowledge of the laws of plasticity is beneficial in giving a better understanding of engineering structures under load, leading to a more realistic and economical design. This is particularly true if creep effects occur in the structure, since these will often take place under a system of complex stress, and the metal will flow under conditions which can be predicted by the theory of plasticity. Even if creep does not occur, a knowledge of the laws of plastic flow is advantageous in that proper weight can be given to the stresses in any complex system of stress occuring in the structure, these stresses having been estimated from elasticity theory. In certain situations the methods of " limit analysis ", a recent development of plasticity theory, may be used to give more realistic estimates of the load-carrying capacity of a structure. These methods are often simpler to use than elastic methods of analysis, and may lead to more economic designs.

In what follows is given a broad discussion of the theory of plasticity and creep, treated entirely from the engineer's viewpoint, to give the reader some acquaintance with and introduction to the subject. Since thermal and irradiation creep buckling are important in relation to vertical reactor fuel elements, specific attention will be paid to this topic. In the main, attention will be restricted to the behaviour of a general three-dimensional continuum, since this suffices to illustrate the principles involved.

The problem of containment design involves plasticity, since certain basic studies in dynamic plasticity are of interest in connexion with accident hazards possible with some designs of nuclear reactors. The book by Hodge[34] may be consulted for certain theoretical studies of the dynamic plastic behaviour of structural elements such as bars, plates, and shells; the book by Rinehart and Pearson[35] for experimental studies of the plastic behaviour of metals under dynamic conditions; and the work of Baker[36, 37]

---

* Reader in Plasticity, Imperial College of Science and Technology.

for studies initiated directly in connexion with containment design problems. This is a very specialized subject, however, and will not be discussed further here.

Similarly, a specialized colloquium on creep in structures was held recently at Stanford University,[38] by the International Union of Theoretical and Applied Mechanics. At this colloquium a number of interesting papers were presented on particular creep problems, for example torsional creep buckling and creep problems for plates and shells. It is to be hoped that most of these papers will be published in the near future, representing as they do the most up-to-date advances in the subject.

The mathematical theory of plasticity is of necessity complicated, since it is concerned with the description of general three-dimensional stress and strain tensors, their interrelation, the establishment of constitutive (i.e. stress–strain) equations, and the use of partial differential equations. Such discussions are greatly simplified by the use of tensor notation, and for the formation of general theorems Cartesian tensors are sufficient. The books by Nadai,[1] Hill,[2] Prager and Hodge,[3] and Prager,[4] have come to be regarded as the standard works in this field, and use is made in them of such methods. (Prager[4a] has given a survey of progress in this field.) The present discussion will be made without the use of tensor notation, it being assumed that a knowledge of such techniques will be unfamiliar to many readers. The discussion suffers in many respects from this, but if the reader's interest is stimulated to enquire more deeply into this field, a study of the book on Cartesian tensors by Jeffreys[5] and an appendix in Hill's book[2] will provide the main techniques necessary to cope with the more general theorems.

9.2. GENERAL APPROACH

A suitable engineering approach to the theory of plasticity is by analogy with elasticity theory. Most engineers have to deal at some time or another with the three-dimensional theory of elasticity, so it is natural to proceed from this point to examine how the laws and equations of plasticity theory compare with those in elasticity. The main difference between the two fields of study lies, of course, in the magnitude of the strains which are possible as can be readily seen from a consideration of the behaviour of a metal when subjected to the normal tensile test. The magnitude of the strain for which the metal remains elastic is quite limited, being at most 0·4 per cent, whereas plastic strains of over 30 per cent are easily attained. If it were possible to subject a metal to an extension of 100 per cent, its length would have doubled, whilst if it could be subjected to a compression of 100 per cent the length would have been reduced to zero. Clearly these two strain systems are completely different, and a more realistic measure of straining must be adopted than the simple percentage extension or compression of the member. Such difficulties do not arise in elasticity theory, since the strains are small, but in plasticity theory, where large strains occur, it is necessary to introduce the concept of incremental strains and displacements, and of strain rates and velocities.

Any system of stress can be regarded as the sum of two stress systems, one being a system of hydrostatic stress (equal to the arithmetic mean of the normal stresses in a Cartesian reference frame), the other being the difference between the actual stress system and this hydrostatic stress system. This latter stress system is often termed the deviatoric stress system, since it is made up of stresses whose magnitudes are given by the deviation between the actual and the hydrostatic stress systems. Bridgman[6] and Crossland[7] have shown experimentally that little or no permanent deformation can be caused by the hydrostatic component, any plastic flow which occurs being due to the deviatoric stress system. Thus it is convenient to consider any given stress system as being split in this way, and part of the subsequent discussion will be based on this concept.

One of the main questions which the theory sets out to answer is as follows: " How can the behaviour of a metal subjected to a complex system of stress be correlated with its behaviour in simple tension or compression?" In this context it is convenient to introduce the concepts of an " equivalent " or " effective " stress, and its strain (or strain increment) counterpart, and this will also be done.

In solving any problem in elasticity, it is possible to write down a set of " laws "* which must be satisfied by the variables, as follows:

(a) The Laws of Elasticity

(1) Hooke's law (between stresses and strains).
(2) The equations of equilibrium (of stresses and forces).
(3) The equations of compatibility (of strains and displacements).
(4) The boundary conditions (usually for both stresses and strains).

An analogous set of rules for solving a problem in a region where plastic flow is occurring is as follows:

(b) The Laws of Plasticity

(1) Stress–strain relations.
(2) The equations of equilibrium.
(3) The equations of compatibility (between strain rates and velocities).
(4) The boundary conditions.
(5) The yield criterion (that function of the stresses necessary to cause *and maintain* plastic flow).

* A better term might be " ingredients ".

9.3. THE STRESS–STRAIN RELATIONS

The six equations describing Hooke's law for elastic behaviour are as follows, for an x, y, z Cartesian coordinate system,

$$\varepsilon_{xx} = \frac{1}{E}[\sigma_{xx} - v(\sigma_{yy} + \sigma_{zz})]$$

$$\varepsilon_{yy} = \frac{1}{E}[\sigma_{yy} - v(\sigma_{xx} + \sigma_{zz})] \tag{9.1}$$

$$\varepsilon_{zz} = \frac{1}{E}[\sigma_{zz} - v(\sigma_{xx} + \sigma_{yy})]$$

$$\gamma_{xy} = \frac{1}{G}\tau_{xy}, \quad \gamma_{yz} = \frac{1}{G}\tau_{yz}, \quad \gamma_{xz} = \frac{1}{G}\tau_{zx} \tag{9.2}$$

where $\qquad\qquad G = \dfrac{E}{2(1+v)}$ is the shear modulus,

E is Young's modulus,
v is Poisson's ratio,
σ is direct stress,
τ is shear stress,
ε is direct strain,
γ is shear strain (engineering definition).

The elastic volume change is found from summing the equations (9.1), to be

$$\varepsilon_{xx} + \varepsilon_{yy} + \varepsilon_{zz} = \frac{1-2v}{E}(\sigma_{xx} + \sigma_{yy} + \sigma_{zz}) \tag{9.3}$$

As has been pointed out, there is no permanent volume change possible, so that the quantity analogous to Poisson's ratio in the plasticity stress–strain relations must be $\frac{1}{2}$, from equation (9.3). Elastic changes of volume are still possible during plastic flow, however, so that the most general stress–strain relations will be made up of both elastic and plastic parts, the following being a typical equation for the x direction:

$$d\varepsilon_{xx} = \frac{1}{E}[d\sigma_{xx} - v(d\sigma_{yy} + d\sigma_{zz})] + d\lambda[\sigma_{xx} - \tfrac{1}{2}(\sigma_{yy} + \sigma_{zz})] \tag{9.4}$$

(These equations are known as the Prandtl–Reuss equations, see Hill[2].)

The use of incremental quantities is necessary for the reasons already mentioned, and underlines the fact that the complete solution of any problem involving plastic flow can be achieved only by integrating the equations along the strain path. It will be noticed that the increment of plastic strain is proportional to a function of the *total* stresses—this is again in accord with experimental observation. The quantity $d\lambda$ can be shown to be analogous to $1/E$ for the elastic strain increment—it is a proportionality factor which may change from point to point or time to time in the material, its main function being to interconnect the several components of the stress and strain tensors at a given point and instant.

In many problems the plastic strains are so large that the elastic strains can be neglected. This simplifies the equations considerably, and further simplifications can be achieved by neglecting work-hardening of the material and assuming that the yield stress remains constant during plastic flow. To simplify the discussion the six stress–strain relations may be reduced to three, if the x, y, z directions are chosen to coincide with the principal stress directions 1, 2, 3. Equations (9.1), for example, would then reduce to:

$$\left.\begin{array}{l} \varepsilon_1 = \dfrac{1}{E}[\sigma_1 - v(\sigma_2 + \sigma_3)] \\[2ex] \varepsilon_2 = \dfrac{1}{E}[\sigma_2 - v(\sigma_3 + \sigma_1)] \\[2ex] \varepsilon_3 = \dfrac{1}{E}[\sigma_3 - v(\sigma_1 + \sigma_2)] \end{array}\right\} \tag{9.5}$$

9.4. THE YIELD CRITERION

To simplify the problem it is necessary to postulate that the material is isotropic and homogeneous. In other words its properties do not vary with direction at any point and they do not vary from point to point in the material. For this idealized material the yield criterion must be a function of the " invariants " of the stress tensor. One way of displaying these invariants is to consider the " principal stress cubic ". This is the cubic equation whose roots are the principal stresses at a point, and is as follows:

$$\left.\begin{array}{l} p^3 - p^2(\sigma_{xx} + \sigma_{yy} + \sigma_{zz}) - p(\sigma_{xy}^2 + \sigma_{yz}^2 + \sigma_{zx}^2 - \sigma_{xx}\sigma_{yy} - \sigma_{yy}\sigma_{zz} - \sigma_{zz}\sigma_{xx}) \\[2ex] -(\sigma_{xx}\sigma_{yy}\sigma_{zz} + 2\sigma_{xy}\sigma_{yz}\sigma_{zx} - \sigma_{xx}\sigma_{yz}^2 - \sigma_{yy}\sigma_{zx}^2 - \sigma_{zz}\sigma_{xy}^2) = 0 \end{array}\right\} \tag{9.6}$$

Clearly it should not matter how the x, y, z, Cartesian axes are orientated in the material; for a given stress system at a given point any set of Cartesian axes should give the same values for the bracketed coefficients in equation (9.6), since the roots of the equation must always be the same. Thus the bracketed coefficients are " invariants " of the stress tensor, as follows:

$$\left.\begin{array}{l} J_1 = \sigma_{xx} + \sigma_{yy} + \sigma_{zz} = \sigma_1 + \sigma_2 + \sigma_3 \\[2ex] J_2 = \sigma_{xy}^2 + \sigma_{yz}^2 + \sigma_{zx}^2 - \sigma_{xx}\sigma_{yy} - \sigma_{yy}\sigma_{zz} - \sigma_{zz}\sigma_{xx} = -\sigma_1\sigma_2 - \sigma_2\sigma_3 - \sigma_3\sigma_1 \\[2ex] J_3 = \sigma_{xx}\sigma_{yy}\sigma_{zz} + 2\sigma_{xy}\sigma_{yz}\sigma_{zx} - \sigma_{xx}\sigma_{yz}^2 - \sigma_{yy}\sigma_{zx}^2 - \sigma_{zz}\sigma_{xy}^2 = \sigma_1\sigma_2\sigma_3 \end{array}\right\} \tag{9.7}$$

Thus the yield criterion may be expressed in the following way: For yield to occur some function of the invariants must attain a certain value. Furthermore for plastic flow to continue that function of the invariants must remain constant (if the material is non-work-hardening), or increase in a way determined by the work-hardening properties characteristic of the material.

It is from such ideas that the concept of the equivalent stress has arisen, since it is natural to arrange the function of the invariants so that it will attain the value of the tensile yield stress of the material in simple tension. Thus if $\bar{\sigma}$ denotes the effective stress, we may write for the yield criterion:

$$\bar{\sigma} = f(J_1, J_2, J_3) \tag{9.8}$$

Now the mean stress σ is given by

$$\sigma = \tfrac{1}{3}(\sigma_{xx} + \sigma_{yy} + \sigma_{zz}) \tag{9.9}$$

and is, from equation (9.7), equal to $J_1/3$. Since plastic flow is not influenced by the mean stress, we may simplify the yield criterion to

$$\bar{\sigma} = f(J_2', J_3') \tag{9.10}$$

where J_2' and J_3' are invariants of the reduced stress tensor with principal components

$$\left. \begin{array}{c} \sigma_1' = \sigma_1 - \sigma \\ \sigma_2' = \sigma_2 - \sigma \\ \sigma_3' = \sigma_3 - \sigma \end{array} \right\} \tag{9.11}$$

There are two particularly important yield criteria in common use, those of Maxwell[7a] (or von Mises) and Tresca. The Maxwell criterion, in its simplest form, is

$$\bar{\sigma} = \frac{1}{\sqrt{2}} \sqrt{[(\sigma_1 - \sigma_2)^2 + (\sigma_2 - \sigma_3)^2 + (\sigma_3 - \sigma_1)^2]} \tag{9.12}$$

A physical meaning can be ascribed to this quantity, which is proportional to the root-mean-square shear stress, the octahedral shear stress, or the square root of the shear strain energy. Mathematically, it is proportional to J_2', the factor $1/\sqrt{2}$ having been chosen so that for uniaxial stress $(\sigma_1, 0, 0)$, $\bar{\sigma} = \sigma_1$.

The Tresca criterion in its simplest form is

$$\bar{\sigma} = \sigma_{max} - \sigma_{min} \tag{9.13}$$

In this case $\bar{\sigma}$ is proportional to the greatest maximum shear stress in the system, and can be shown to be a function of J_2' and J_3'. It is inferior to the Maxwell criterion in that no " weight" is given to the intermediate stress. Mathematically it is often more convenient, however, and can be

made to approximate the Maxwell criterion in any given problem by multiplying the right-hand side of equation (9.13) by a factor between 1 and 0·866.

If the principal stresses are plotted as vectors in a Cartesian system, then
equation (9.12) represents a circular, whereas equation (9.13) represents a
hexagonal, prism whose axis passes through the origin, this axis having equal
direction cosines with the Cartesian axes. The hexagonal prism of the Tresca
criterion will be either inside or outside the circle depending upon which

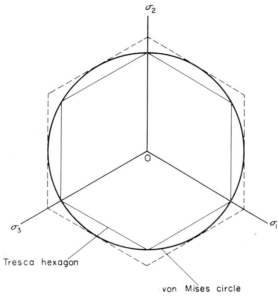

FIG. 9.1. Yield criteria.

of the factors 1 or 0·866 is used, as illustrated in Fig. 9.1. As long as the
total stress vector remains inside the prism, yielding will not occur and
conditions will remain elastic. During plastic flow the end of the total stress
vector will remain on the yield surface, which will change in size and possibly
shape if the material work-hardens.

In a similar way it is possible to define the equivalent or effective plastic
strain increment as

$$d\bar{\varepsilon}^p = \sqrt{\tfrac{2}{9}}\sqrt{[(d\varepsilon_1^p - d\varepsilon_2^p)^2 + (d\varepsilon_2^p - d\varepsilon_3^p)^2 + (d\varepsilon_3^p - d\varepsilon_1^p)^2]} \qquad (9.14)$$
$$\text{(Maxwell)}$$

or

$$d\bar{\varepsilon}^p = \tfrac{2}{3}(d\varepsilon_{max}^p - d\varepsilon_{min}^p) \qquad (9.15)$$
$$\text{(Tresca)}$$

Again the factors $\sqrt{\tfrac{2}{9}}$ and $\tfrac{2}{3}$ have been chosen so that for uniaxial tension,
in which

$$d\varepsilon_2^p = d\varepsilon_3^p = -\tfrac{1}{2}d\varepsilon_1^p, \quad d\bar{\varepsilon}^p = d\varepsilon_1^p.$$

Careful experimental work by Taylor and Quinney,[8] Morrison and

Shepherd,[9] Lianis and Ford[10] have shown that the Maxwell criterion is the more realistic for ductile metals.

The plastic strain increments are, from equation (9.4),

$$\left.\begin{array}{l} d\varepsilon_1^p = d\lambda[\sigma_1 - \tfrac{1}{2}(\sigma_2 + \sigma_3)] \\ d\varepsilon_2^p = d\lambda[\sigma_2 - \tfrac{1}{2}(\sigma_3 + \sigma_1)] \\ d\varepsilon_3^p = d\lambda[\sigma_3 - \tfrac{1}{2}(\sigma_1 + \sigma_2)] \end{array}\right\} \tag{9.16}$$

and substituting these into equation (9.14) which may be written more simply as

$$d\bar{\varepsilon}^p = \sqrt{\tfrac{2}{3}}\sqrt{[(d\varepsilon_1^p)^2 + (d\varepsilon_2^p)^2 + (d\varepsilon_3^p)^2]} \tag{9.14a}$$

it is found that

$$d\lambda = \frac{d\bar{\varepsilon}^p}{\bar{\sigma}} \tag{9.17}$$

and the analogy with elastic behaviour is complete, for the Maxwell criterion, in that E is replaced by $\bar{\sigma}/d\bar{\varepsilon}^p$. Similarly, for the Tresca criterion, if $d\varepsilon_1^p$ and $d\varepsilon_2^p$ are taken to be $d\varepsilon_{max}^p$ and $d\varepsilon_{min}^p$, for example, substitution of equation (9.16) into (9.15) gives the same result, namely equation (9.17).

If the material work-hardens, the effective stress and strain are interdependent, through the stress–strain curve of the material in simple tension, which may be written as

$$\bar{\sigma} = H(\smallint d\bar{\varepsilon}^p) \tag{9.18}$$

The slope of this curve will be $H' = d\bar{\sigma}/d\bar{\varepsilon}^p$, so that $d\bar{\varepsilon}^p$ in equation (9.17) may be replaced by $d\bar{\sigma}/H'$, giving

$$d\lambda = \frac{d\bar{\sigma}}{\bar{\sigma}H'} \tag{9.19}$$

To solve any given problem it is often necessary to adopt a step-by-step method of solution, in which case equation (9.19) may be more convenient to use. If the material does not work-harden, the first step in the solution is usually to eliminate the factor $d\lambda$ between two of the three principal stress–strain equations by division.

9.5. TRUE STRAIN

The equivalent plastic strain increment in the tension test is simply

$$d\varepsilon_1^p = d\varepsilon_1 - \frac{d\sigma_1}{E} \tag{9.20}$$

where $d\varepsilon_1$ is the total strain increment at any instant, namely dl/l, l being the current length, so that the total plastic strain may be defined as

$$\varepsilon_1^p = \int d\varepsilon_1^p = \int_{l_0}^{p_1} \frac{dl}{l} - \int_0^{\sigma_1} \frac{d\sigma_1}{E} = \ln\frac{l_1}{l_0} - \frac{\sigma_1}{E} \tag{9.21}$$

The elastic strain σ_1/E is usually negligible so that the total strain which is often referred to as the true strain, or logarithmic strain is given by $\varepsilon_1 = \ln(l/l_0)$. The reason for using this as a measure of the strain is clear if, for example, we consider two uniaxial tests, one in compression, one in tension. If we extend the material 100 per cent in tension, this is clearly an equal and opposite amount of strain to compressing the material by 50 per cent. Thus any realistic measure of strain must give equal and opposite strains for these two deformation modes. For tension, true strain $= \ln 2$, since $l_1/l_0 = 2$. For compression,

$$\text{true strain} = \int_{h_0}^{h_1} \frac{dh}{h}$$

h being the current height of the specimen, giving an answer $\ln \frac{1}{2}$, since $h_1/h_0 = \frac{1}{2}$. Thus the compressive strain is equal to $-\ln 2$, equal and opposite to the tensile strain, as required.

If e_1 is the unit strain in any direction, equal to $(l_1 - l_0)/l_0$ for the tension test, for example, then it is easily seen that the true strain $\varepsilon_1 = \ln(l_1/l_0) = \ln(1 + e_1)$. If true strains are used then the equation of constancy of volume for small strains, $d\varepsilon_1 + d\varepsilon_2 + d\varepsilon_3 = 0$, may be extended to large strains by integration to give

$$\varepsilon_1 + \varepsilon_2 + \varepsilon_3 = 0 \tag{9.22}$$

This can be seen to be true by substituting $\ln(1 + e_1)$ for ε_1, etc., in equation (9.22), giving the well-known result necessary for zero volume change:

$$(1 + e_1)(1 + e_2)(1 + e_3) = 1 \tag{9.23}$$

To summarize, the most general equations for plastic flow are those of Prandtl–Reuss, as follows:

$$
\left.
\begin{aligned}
d\varepsilon_1 &= \frac{d\bar{\varepsilon}^p}{\bar{\sigma}}[\sigma_1 - \tfrac{1}{2}(\sigma_2 + \sigma_3)] + \frac{1}{E}[d\sigma_1 - v(d\sigma_2 + d\sigma_3)] \\[2mm]
d\varepsilon_2 &= \frac{d\bar{\varepsilon}^p}{\bar{\sigma}}[\sigma_2 - \tfrac{1}{2}(\sigma_3 + \sigma_1)] + \frac{1}{E}[d\sigma_2 - v(d\sigma_3 + d\sigma_1)] \\[2mm]
d\varepsilon_3 &= \frac{d\bar{\varepsilon}^p}{\bar{\sigma}}[\sigma_3 - \tfrac{1}{2}(\sigma_1 + \sigma_2)] + \frac{1}{E}[d\sigma_3 - v(d\sigma_1 + d\sigma_2)]
\end{aligned}
\right\} \tag{9.24}
$$

In these equations $d\bar{\varepsilon}^p$ and $\bar{\sigma}$ are given by equations (9.14) and (9.12), respectively. In effect these equations simply state that the total strain increment in any direction is made up of a plastic plus an elastic increment of strain, the plastic strain increment being associated with the *total* stress tensor, the elastic strain increment with the *increment* of stress. To be even more general, an additional term αT could be added to each of the three equations (9.24), to allow for temperature stresses, α being the coefficient of thermal expansion, T the temperature of the point of the body being considered.

For large plastic deformations, it is reasonable to neglect the elastic terms in equation (9.24), and the equations reduce to a much simpler form, usually referred to as the Lévy–Mises relations. To eliminate incremental quantities it is quite usual to divide through by dt, the time increment, and write

$$
\left.
\begin{aligned}
\dot{\varepsilon}_1 &= \mu[\sigma_1 - \tfrac{1}{2}(\sigma_2 + \sigma_3)] \\
\dot{\varepsilon}_2 &= \mu[\sigma_2 - \tfrac{1}{2}(\sigma_3 + \sigma_1)] \\
\dot{\varepsilon}_3 &= \mu[\sigma_3 - \tfrac{1}{2}(\sigma_1 + \sigma_2)]
\end{aligned}
\right\}
\tag{9.25}
$$

where μ is a constant of proportionality, equal in fact to $(1/\bar{\sigma})(d\bar{\varepsilon}^p/dt)$, for a work-hardening material.

9.6. THE THEORY OF THE SLIP LINE FIELD

For many purposes slip line field theory gives a reasonably precise estimate of the behaviour of metal subjected to large plastic deformation. To produce a workable theory it is necessary to make some rather drastic assumptions, but in spite of this realistic results are obtained. In the first place, what is known as a "plastic-rigid" material is assumed. This is a hypothetical material having infinite Young's modulus and a constant yield stress, usually denoted by Y, so that the stress–strain curve is simply a horizontal line parallel to the abscissa. In such a material, although elastic zones are permissible, in which the stresses are below the yield limit, there will be no associated strains, the material remaining rigid. Plastic flow is possible in the plastic regions, of course, so that the material is either plastic (in the plastic zones) or rigid (in the zones in which the stresses are just at or below the yield criterion). In the plastic regions the material flows under a constant yield stress, work-hardening being neglected.

The further restriction is made that deformation occurs under "plane strain" conditions. That is to say, the strain in one direction is zero, this direction being a principal stress direction. Thus, in equations (9.25), if $\dot{\varepsilon}_2$ is zero, then

$$
\left.
\begin{aligned}
\sigma_2 &= \frac{\sigma_1 + \sigma_3}{2} \\[2mm]
\sigma &= \frac{\sigma_1 + \sigma_2 + \sigma_3}{3} = \frac{\sigma_1 + \sigma_3}{2} \\[2mm]
\dot{\varepsilon}_3 &= -\dot{\varepsilon}_1
\end{aligned}
\right\}
\tag{9.26}
$$

The Mohr's circle representation of stress and strain is well-known to engineers, and provides a ready tool for use in the discussion of slip-line

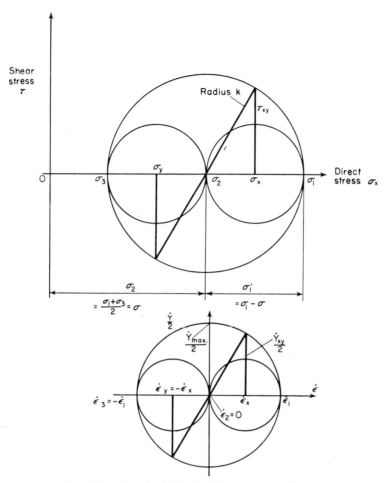

FIG. 9.2. Mohr's circles for plane strain conditions.

field theory. In Fig. 9.2 are shown the three Mohr's circles of stress for the state of plane strain, together with the three geometrically similar strain-rate circles. The mean stress is equal to σ_2, the principal stress in the direction of zero strain, and if we subtract this from each of the stresses we see that the deviatoric stresses (such as σ_1'), are proportional to the corresponding strain rates, as required by the Lévy–Mises relations [equations (9.25)].

   If the material is flowing plastically, then the yield criterion must be satisfied. Substituting the stresses given by equations (9.26) into the Maxwell criterion (equation (9.12)), we find that

$$\bar{\sigma} = \frac{\sqrt{3}}{2}(\sigma_1 \quad \sigma_3) = \sqrt{3}k,$$

where k is the maximum shear stress at the point under consideration. In Fig. 9.1, k is of course represented by the radius of the largest Mohr's circle. For the hypothetical plastic rigid material it is customary to denote $\bar{\sigma}$ by Y, so that yielding occurs, according to the Maxwell criterion, when $k = Y/\sqrt{3}$. For the Tresca criterion, substitution into equation (9.13) gives $k = Y/2$. To summarize, since the state of stress is simply a state of pure shear superimposed on a hydrostatic stress (which has no effect on yielding), both the Maxwell and Tresca criteria (and indeed any other appropriate yield criterion) take the same form, namely that the maximum shear stress attains a certain value ($Y/\sqrt{3}$ Maxwell, $Y/2$ Tresca). The yield criterion is often expressed in the following form, which can be easily derived from the largest Mohr's circle:

$$\tfrac{1}{4}(\sigma_x - \sigma_y)^2 + \tau_{xy}^2 = k^2 \tag{9.27}$$

It should be noted that the shear strain rates used in this discussion are in fact the *engineering* definition of shear strain rate, so that for example, $\dot{\gamma}_{max} = \dot{\varepsilon}_1 - \dot{\varepsilon}_3$ ($= 2\dot{\varepsilon}_1$ under plane strain conditions).

During plastic flow, the planes of maximum shear form an orthogonal curvilinear network, each element being subjected to the maximum shear stress k, and the normal mean stress σ on its faces, as illustrated in Fig. 9.3.

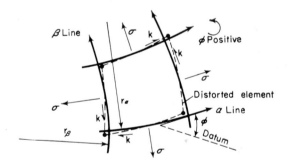

FIG. 9.3. Element of slip-line field.

Since there can be no volume change in the hypothetical plastic-rigid material, σ causes no change of dimensions, and the local deformation is a pure shear as shown. Since the planes of maximum shear are the characteristics* of the equations, which are hyperbolic* for the plastic-rigid material, it is convenient to regard them as the unknowns to be determined in any given problem, and refer the equations to them. The curvilinear system is customarily denoted by a set of α- and β-lines, of local elemental lengths $\delta\alpha$ and $\delta\beta$, and of local curvature $1/r_\alpha$ and $1/r_\beta$, as illustrated in Fig. 9.3. It is

* See Hill[2] for explanation of the terms " characteristics " and " hyperbolic ".

easily shown by considering the equilibrium of forces on a curvilinear element, that the equilibrium equations are:

$$\left.\begin{array}{l} \dfrac{\partial \sigma}{\partial \alpha} + \dfrac{\partial k}{\partial \beta} - \dfrac{2k}{r_\alpha} = 0, \quad \text{along an } \alpha\text{-line} \\[3mm] \dfrac{\partial \sigma}{\partial \beta} + \dfrac{\partial k}{\partial \alpha} + \dfrac{2k}{r_\beta} = 0, \quad \text{along a } \beta\text{-line} \end{array}\right\} \qquad (9.28)$$

If ϕ is the angular displacement of a characteristic from some datum line (measured positive anti-clockwise), then

$$\frac{1}{r_\alpha} = \frac{\partial \phi}{\partial \alpha} \quad \text{and} \quad \frac{1}{r_\beta} = \frac{\partial \phi}{\partial \beta}$$

By integration, equations (9.28) become

$$\left.\begin{array}{l} \sigma - 2k\phi + \displaystyle\int \dfrac{\partial k}{\partial \beta}\, d\alpha = \text{constant, along an } \alpha\text{-line} \\[4mm] \sigma + 2k\phi + \displaystyle\int \dfrac{\partial k}{\partial \alpha}\, d\beta = \text{constant, along a } \beta\text{-line} \end{array}\right\} \qquad (9.29)$$

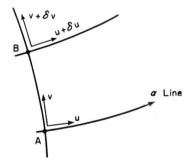

FIG. 9.4. Neighbouring points in slip-line field.

These equations include terms to allow for the possibility of work-hardening of the material, and were first introduced by Christopherson et al.,[11] to find a solution for the problem of machining. Without the integral terms, and with σ replaced by $-p$, they reduce to the well-known Hencky relations.

Analogous equations for the velocities were first derived by Geiringer (see Hill[2]), from the condition that there is zero extension along the characteristics (or slip lines), as can be seen from the Mohr's strain-rate circles. In Fig. 9.4 are shown neighbouring points A and B in a slip-line field, the angular change in moving from A to B along the β-line being $\delta\phi$. Resolution in the v direction at A, shows that for there to be no extension of the element AB,

$$(v+\delta v)\cos\delta\phi+(u+\delta u)\sin\delta\phi = v$$

and hence

$$\left.\begin{array}{l} \dfrac{\partial u}{\partial\phi} - v = 0, \text{ along an } \alpha\text{-line} \\[4mm] \dfrac{\partial v}{\partial\phi} + u = 0, \text{ along a } \beta\text{-line} \end{array}\right\} \qquad (9.30)$$

(i) Velocity Discontinuities

The equations for the plastic-rigid material show that velocity discontinuities are possible. In Fig. 9.5 such a discontinuity is shown and it is clear that, if A and B are neighbouring points on each side of the line, the velocity components normal to the line (v and v'), must be equal. If they

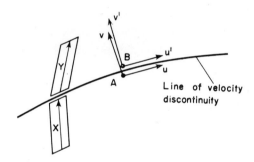

Fig. 9.5.   Conditions at a velocity discontinuity.

were not, it would imply that material was either " piling up " at the discontinuity, or leaving a void there. There is no such restriction on the tangential components of velocity u' and u, and these may be different. If they are different, this implies that there must be " block slipping " of the material along the velocity discontinuity, and by applying the relevant Geiringer equation (9.30) along each side of the discontinuity it is seen that the discontinuity in velocity $u'-u$ must, in fact, be constant along the line. It is possible to apply the Geiringer equations along the velocity discontinuity because it must coincide with a slip line. The reason for this is that the discontinuity in tangential velocity implies an infinite shear strain *rate* along the line and it must, therefore, be a slip line. Although the shear strain *rate* is infinite, the shear strain is finite, and an element such as X approaching the discontinuity in Fig. 9.5 might be sheared into the shape shown as Y on passing across the discontinuity. A velocity discontinuity could not exist in a work-hardening material, since the yield shear stress would be different on each side of the discontinuity due to the work-hardening caused by the shear strain and equilibrium conditions would be violated.

In a real material, in fact, velocity discontinuities do not exist, although bands of intense shear often occur, as for example in extrusion and machining. These bands may be replaced by velocity discontinuities in the idealized material to give a first estimate of the behaviour.

(ii) *Stress Discontinuities*

Stress discontinuities are also possible. In Fig. 9.6 two regions *A* and *B* are separated by a line of stress discontinuity, and two neighbouring elements are shown, one on each side of the discontinuity. Considering the equi-

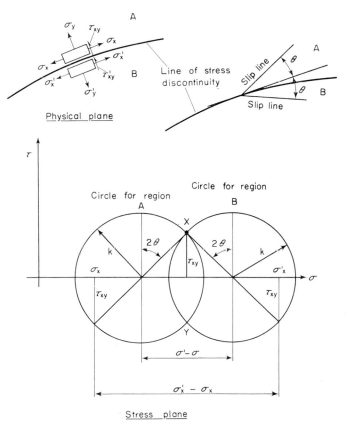

Fig. 9.6. Conditions at a stress discontinuity.

librium of the elements it is clear that the normal direct stress σ_y must be continuous, i.e. $\sigma'_y = \sigma_y$, as must also be the shear stress τ_{xy}. It is not necessary for the tangential component of stress σ_x to be continuous, so that σ'_x may not be equal to σ_x. The situation is most easily represented by the Mohr's circles as shown, and it will be seen from considering these that a stress discontinuity can never coincide with a slip line. If θ is the angle between the shear- or slip-line direction and the line of stress discontinuity, then it can be seen that the only way in which the slip lines could be made to coincide with the line of stress discontinuity would be for the two Mohr's circles to become coincident, thus eliminating the discontinuity. Since the radii of the Mohr's circles both have to be rotated through equal angles of 2θ in order to coincide with the maximum shear stress (the topmost point of each circle), it is clear that the slip lines are " reflected " at equal angles at the line of stress discontinuity, as shown in the small inset diagram. From the stress plane

$$\sigma' - \sigma = 2k \sin 2\theta \qquad (9.31)$$

(If the discontinuity is small, $\sigma' - \sigma \to \delta\sigma$, and $2\theta \to \delta\phi$ and Hencky's equation $\delta\sigma - 2k\,\delta\phi = 0$ is recovered.)

Stress discontinuities are " reflected " at 90° from an axis of symmetry or frictionless boundary, as can be seen by considering the slip lines shown in Fig. 9.7. The slip lines must cross the axis of symmetry at 45°, since the

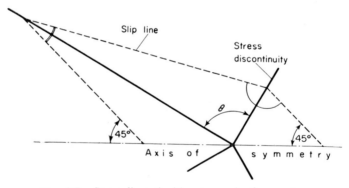

FIG. 9.7.   Stress discontinuities at an axis of symmetry.

axis of symmetry is a principal plane. Using this fact, and the fact that they are reflected at equal angles at a stress discontinuity it is easily shown that the angle θ in Fig. 9.7 must be a right angle. Thus there will always be four lines of stress discontinuity meeting at an axis of symmetry.

The stress discontinuity may be regarded as representing the last vestige of an elastic layer, in the real material. For, in Fig. 9.6, if the stress in region A is represented by the left-hand Mohr's circle, the stress in region B by the right-hand circle, in passing from region A to region B across a narrow layer the stress states in the fibres of the layer will be represented by Mohr's circles which must all pass through points X and Y in the figure, to satisfy equilibrium conditions. Such circles must all therefore be of radii less than k, implying that the stress state in the layer would be elastic.

(iii) *Prager's Geometrical Method*

Any discussion of slip-line field theory intended for engineers would be incomplete without a description of Prager's geometrical method. This consists in representing the solution to any given problem by three diagrams, the physical plane, stress plane, and hodograph. The physical plane is a drawing of the slip-line or shear-line field itself, the stress plane is a representation of the Mohr's circles of stress for the whole slip-line field, and the hodograph is a velocity diagram, from which it is possible to find the velocity of any point in the slip-line field. A detailed description of the underlying principles is given by Prager,[12] but the method will be outlined briefly here, as follows.

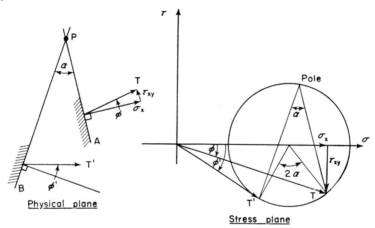

FIG. 9.8. The " pole " of Mohr's circle.

The "pole" of the Mohr's circle was defined by Mohr as follows: "A line drawn from the pole of the Mohr's circle parallel to any plane passing through a point being considered in the physical plane cuts the Mohr's circle at the point representing the state of stress on the plane." Thus, in Fig. 9.8, if P is the considered point in the physical plane, the stress on the plane PA through P is represented, say, by the traction T in the stress plane, and the pole is found by drawing a line from T to cut the Mohr's circle at the point marked *pole*. The stress on any other plane through P (PB for example) is given immediately by drawing a parallel line through the pole of the Mohr's circle until it cuts the circle again to give T', the traction on PB. The construction rests on the geometrical fact that the central angle subtended by a sector of a circle is twice the angle subtended at a point on the circumference, as illustrated by the angles α and 2α in the diagram, and was apparently first made use of by Terzaghi.[12a] Prager introduced the convention that the angle ϕ through which the positive σ axis must be rotated in order to coincide with the traction T in the stress plane is equal and opposite to the angle through which the normal to the considered plane has to be rotated to coincide with the traction in the physical plane.

In moving along a slip line, it is readily shown from Hencky's relations ($\delta p = \pm 2k\,\delta\phi$) that the pole of the Mohr's circle of constant radius k traces out a cycloid in rolling without slipping along either top or bottom tangent, as shown in the example in Fig. 9.9, of lubricated sheet extrusion, 3:1 ratio. Corresponding elements of the cycloid and the slip-line field are at right angles. The Mohr's circle for the state of stress along 01 is first drawn, the boundary condition being that there must be no horizontal force on the material issuing from the die. This fixes the position of the origin of the stress plane (actually two solutions are possible, one with tensile, the other with compressive stresses—the compressive one is chosen for this problem), and the pole of the Mohr's circle. The cycloid can immediately be drawn corresponding to the slip-line field shown in the upper half of the symmetrical physical plane by rolling the Mohr's circle along the top tangent. More than one solution to any problem is possible; the one shown is the most realistic for this particular problem.

Having drawn the slip-line field and an acceptable stress plane, it is necessary to check that the velocity boundary conditions can be satisfied. In terms of Prager's geometrical method, this involves drawing an acceptable hodograph. The condition of zero extension along slip-lines means that corresponding elements of the hodograph and slip-line field must be at right angles. An acceptable solution for the extrusion problem under discussion is shown in Fig. 9.8, the starting point being the corner (point 4 in the physical plane). The inset diagram shows that it is necessary to introduce a velocity discontinuity along the slip line 1234, the suffixes L, R, A, B in the hodograph being used to mean " left ", " right ", " above ", and " below ", respectively. Thus the velocity of the material just to the left of point 4 is represented by the vector 04_L and just below point 4 by the vector 04_B, for example. The hodograph shows that the material emerges from the die with velocity $U = 3u$ as required by consideration of zero volume change. The vector 4_B4_L represents the velocity discontinuity which is constant throughout the whole field, along slip line 01 and 1234, equal to 2_L2_R, 1_L1_A, and 1_A1_R.

The example just discussed is a particularly simple one, and the real power of Prager's method is found in the step-by-step construction of more complicated fields, by a small-arc process. A particular example is that of hot rolling, a possible solution having been found by Alexander[13] using

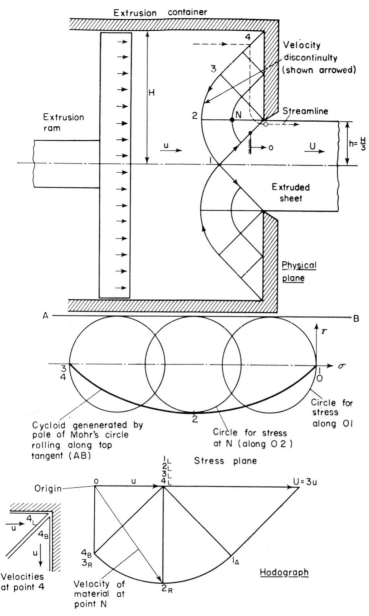

FIG. 9.9. Plane strain extrusion with zero friction (3:1 ratio).

Prager's method. An example is shown in Fig. 9.10, in which a centred fan of slip lines is to be extended to the left, the axis of symmetry forming one boundary which the slip lines must cross at 45°. To find the point 2′

in the physical plane, the slip-line 02 is extended to A and the length $2A$ made equal to the length $A2'$. This is equivalent to replacing a small arc of the slip-line field by a circular arc. Similarly for the point $3'$ in the physical plane the distances $3B$ and $2'C$ are made equal to $B3'$ and $C3'$, respectively. The angular disposition of the slip lines at the point $3'$ is found from the intersection of the two cycloids in the stress plane.

Having obtained a solution it is necessary to check that the stresses and distortions are compatible. This can be done by inspection of the physical

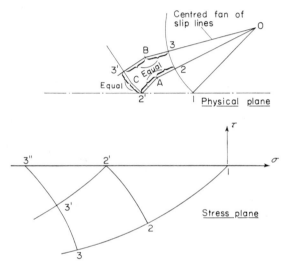

Fig. 9.10.   Small-arc process for constructing slip-line fields.

plane and hodograph, it being necessary to check that the direction of the velocities and shear stresses are compatible, to give the sort of distortion illustrated in Fig. 3, for example.   Also it is necessary to check that assumed rigid zones will not in fact yield under the distribution of stresses postulated as existing on their boundaries.   Hill[14] and Bishop[15] describe suitable techniques for this.   Hill considers the yielding of wedge-shaped vertices of material, and Bishop extends the slip-line field into the rigid regions, to show whether an equilibrium stress field can be found for the whole solution. More detailed discussion of Prager's method is given by Alexander.[16]

9.7.   LIMIT ANALYSIS

This is an extension of plasticity theory, and provides a powerful tool for bounding, both from above and from below, the collapse load of a structure or continuum.   The theorems have been formulated in slightly different ways by Hill, and by Greenberg, Drucker, and Prager.   Drucker[17] gives a useful summary. To put it in the simplest possible terms, the theorems rest on two concepts:

(1) The statically admissible stress field.
(2) The kinematically admissible velocity field.

A statically admissible stress field is any field of stress for a given problem which is in statical equilibrium within itself and with the externally applied forces. A kinematically admissible velocity field is a velocity field which is compatible within itself and with the allowable velocities at the boundaries. If a statically admissible stress field can be found such that the yield criterion

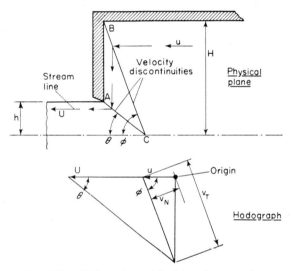

FIG. 9.11. " Upper bound " picture for extrusion.

is nowhere exceeded, then the solution will give a lower bound to the collapse or yield-point load. If a kinematically admissible velocity field can be found then the loads required to enforce it will constitute an upper bound to the collapse load.

All slip-line field solutions are upper bound solutions, since the stresses in the rigid regions are not usually examined, and therefore it cannot be said that they constitute safe statically admissible stress fields. Bishop[15] describes techniques for extending partial slip-line field solutions into the rigid regions to show whether a safe statically admissible stress field can be associated with the partial solution. If it can, the solution is both a lower and an upper bound solution, thus giving the solution to the problem. The field of Fig. 9.9 is such a field and can be extended in this way.

Johnson[19] has used velocity discontinuities to give upper bound solutions to many problems of metal working, an example being shown in Fig. 9.11.

AC and BC are two velocity discontinuities and the path of an element through the field is shown. The shear strain in crossing discontinuity BC, for example, is v_T/v_N where v_T and v_N are the tangential and normal velocities across the discontinuity. It is readily shown that the shear strain is $1/\sin\phi\cos\phi$ across BC and $1/\sin\theta\cos\theta$ across AC. Also $H\cot\phi = h\cot\theta$, and $\cot\phi = 1/n\cot\theta$, where $n = H/h$. Since the mean extrusion pressure equals the work done in the process ($= \Sigma k$. shear strain), it is given by

$$\bar{p}_u = \frac{k(1+n)(1+n\tan^2\theta)}{n\tan\theta} \tag{9.32}$$

This is a minimum at a value of $\theta = \tan^{-1}(1/\sqrt{n})$, giving the best (lowest) upper bound as

$$\frac{\bar{p}_u}{2k} = \frac{1+n}{\sqrt{n}} \tag{9.33}$$

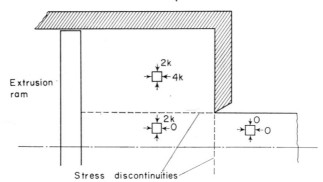

Fig. 9.12. " Lower bound " picture for extrusion.

A lower bound solution to this problem can be obtained (as for many others) by using stress discontinuities. A very simple safe statically admissible stress field, comprising regions of constant stress separated by stress discontinuities is shown in Fig. 9.12, and a more complicated field in Fig. 9.13. In these figures the stresses acting on the principal planes in each region have been shown on the inset squares. The solutions are discussed in more detail by Alexander.[18]

These techniques have stemmed from the extensive studies carried on in the U.S.A. (particularly by Professor W. Prager's School at Brown University) during the last few years into the limit analysis of structures, plates, and shells. A simple example of the application of these principles to structures is shown in Fig. 9.14, for an encastré beam. The bending moment diagram labelled " lower bound picture " is a statically admissible stress field and leads to the value for P of

$$P_L = 2M_0\left(\frac{1}{a} + \frac{1}{b}\right) \tag{9.34}$$

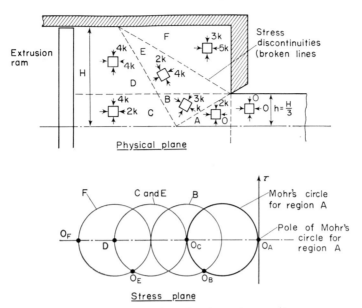

Physical plane

Stress plane

FIG. 9.13. " Lower bound " picture for extrusion.

where M_0 is the " hinge " moment for the beam, developed when the beam has attained full plasticity at its most heavily stressed points. The upper bound picture gives the same value for P_u, by equating the work done by the external load to the work done by each plastic hinge in a small rotation, as shown. This gives the true collapse load for the structure since in this simple case the correct pictures have been chosen for both upper and lower bounds. In more complicated situations many different collapse

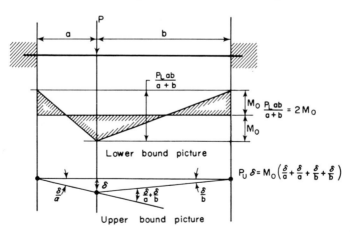

Lower bound picture

Upper bound picture

FIG. 9.14. Limit analysis of an encastré beam.

pictures may be possible and the loads must be minimized by controlled methods. Much depends, of course, on the relative sizes of the applied loads and the relative stiffnesses of individual members of the frame. It is difficult to allow for distributed loads and for column buckling, but the methods are realistic and allow optimization of design, in particular the possibility of designing structures of minimum weight. (See, for example, Heyman.[20])

9.8. CREEP

The characteristic form of creep curve is that shown at A in Fig. 9.15; B and C are typical variants of it. Such curves are usually obtained at constant load and temperature, although the results are often quoted as

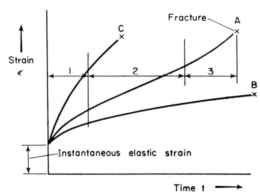

FIG. 9.15.   Typical creep curves for different metals.

having been obtained at constant stress. Most metals creep at all temperatures, although engineering metals such as steel, aluminium, and copper exhibit very little creep at room temperature. High temperatures lead to rapid creep, however, often accompanied by metallurgical changes. Cottrell, Sully, Stanford, and Rotherham[21-24] have discussed metallic creep in great detail, and give references to the pioneer work of other investigators, notably Andrade and Odquist.

It is intended here to give only a general background of the important features, although detailed consideration will be given to the problem of creep buckling.

There are four main features of creep extension:

(a) The initial instantaneous strain which is predominantly elastic, but may be partly plastic also.
(b) A period of decreasing creep rate (primary phase).
(c) A period of constant (minimum) rate of flow (secondary phase).
(d) A period of accelerating strain, ending in fracture (tertiary phase).

In thinking about creep it is curve *A* (Fig. 9.15) which must readily come to mind, as this is the basic curve describing creep behaviour. Roughly speaking, a physical explanation of the three stages of creep is as follows:

1. *Primary Stage*

This is the period of decelerating creep during which the material work-hardens more rapidly than it is softened by the high temperature. The flow appears to be similar to plastic flow, in that dislocations move in the crystals, giving rise to slip bands which may be observed at the surface of specimens.

2. *Secondary Stage*

During this phase a balance is struck between work-hardening and thermal softening, so that the material creeps at a steady rate. Deformation is mainly by severe distortion of the intercrystalline material at crystal boundaries, and therefore differs from that in the primary stage.

3. *Tertiary Creep*

This is the accelerating creep phase during which cracks slowly open up in the material, mainly due to the stress concentrations existing on the slipping grain boundaries. A basic problem to be studied both experimentally and theoretically is the process of fracture during creep. It certainly differs considerably from fracture at higher rates of stressing; in particular the elongation at fracture in creep is often much less.

The engineer is not so much interested in the basic deformation behaviour of metals, in terms of the movement of dislocations, slip along grain boundaries and so forth, as in trying to determine an allowable stress to which he may subject his material. Thus he needs to have as much data as possible on creep behaviour, and to describe these data in a concise manner by finding empirical laws, in the absence of a physical theory. This has led to the " phenomenological " study of creep, as distinct from the basic physical approach.

As long ago as 1910, Andrade proposed a creep law of the form

$$\varepsilon = \alpha t^{1/3} + \beta t \tag{9.35}$$

where t is time, α and β are constants for a particular stress and temperature, which describes the primary and secondary phases of the creep curve fairly well for common metals.

It is clear that if either temperature or stress is increased the creep strain will be increased, so that families of creep curves exist, as illustrated in Fig. 9.16. Thus α and β in Andrade's equation must be functions of both stress and temperature. Phenomenological studies have been directed towards determining these functions, it being generally accepted that Andrade's original equation gives a fair representation of the strain–time relation.

More recently, Graham and Walles[25] have proposed the introduction of a t^3 term to allow for the tertiary stage, so that Andrade's equation may be modified to:

$$\varepsilon = \alpha t^{1/3} + \beta t + \gamma t^3 \tag{9.36}$$

where γ is a function of both stress and temperature.

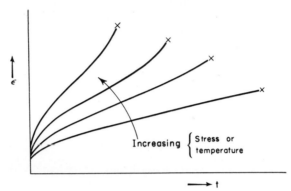

FIG. 9.16.   Typical creep curves for a metal.

In the past, attention has been concentrated mainly on the steady-state phase, although it must be remembered that in any creep process there will nearly always be a period of primary creep during which a non-linear effect occurs. Thus the problem is to determine the function β, the $\alpha t^{1/3}$ and γt^3 terms being neglected in equation (9.36).

Typical of the physical approaches to this problem is the discussion given by Larsen and Miller.[26] Their analysis is based, as have been many others, on a rate-process theory leading to an equation of the form

$$r = A \exp\left(-\frac{Q}{RT}\right) \tag{9.37}$$

where r is the rate at which the process takes place,

A is a constant,

Q is the activation energy for the particular material and process (e.g. movement of dislocations, diffusion of vacancies, slip between crystals, etc.),

R is Boltzmann's constant,

T is the absolute temperature.

[Equation (9.37) is one familiar to students of statistical mechanics—it is derived from considering the probability that a number of elements of the material possess sufficient energy to initiate the particular process concerned.]

For the creep process equation (9.37) may be written in the form

$$\left(\frac{Q}{R}\right)_\sigma = T(B + \log t) \tag{9.38}$$

where t is the time to rupture, or to a specified strain, B is a constant (for a given strain), and $(Q/R)_\sigma$ indicates that the activation energy depends on the stress level.

This temperature–time parameter $T(B + \log t)$, designated the " Larsen–Miller " parameter, correlates data over a wide range of times and temperatures for many steels, high-temperature alloys, and aluminium alloys.

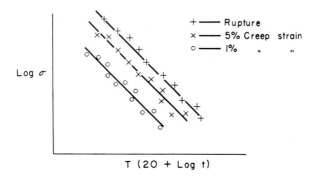

FIG. 9.17.   Typical " master " creep curves.

In particular, if stress σ, or log σ, is plotted against this parameter the experimental results will often lie about the same straight line, with some inevitable scatter. The scatter can be reduced by altering the value of B, which may lie between about 17 and 23 (20 being typical).

The particular line obtained depends on the particular strain chosen, of course, and for any given value of B, a set of lines will be obtained as shown in Fig. 9.17. Such curves are often referred to as " master creep curves ".

In spite of this apparently orderly behaviour in creep it is most unwise to extrapolate results obtained from short-term tests to long-term ones, and some long-term tests should be carried out whenever possible. The only alternative is to accelerate creep testing by raising the temperature, which gives fairly reliable prediction by extrapolation, providing severe metallurgical changes do not invalidate the results.

Graham and Walles have proposed a more sophisticated approach although it needs considerable data to allow evaluation of the many constants involved in the equations. Its chief advantage is that it can include all three phases of creep. They propose that the creep strain be represented as the sum of a number of terms of the form:

$$\varepsilon = \sum_{i=1}^{i=n} C_i \sigma^{\beta_i} t^{\kappa_i} |T_i' - T|^{\pm 20\kappa_i} \tag{9.39}$$

The C_i, β_i, κ_i, T_i' are independent constants (which may differ from term to term). Following Andrade, the κ_i's take the values $\frac{1}{3}$, 1, and 3, whilst a study of experimental results reveals that the ratios κ/β take values from a standard series 1, $\frac{1}{2}$, $\frac{1}{4}$, $\frac{1}{8}$, $\frac{1}{16}$—and can be determined from cross-plotting $\log \sigma$ and $\log t$. To analyse creep data the basic $\varepsilon - t$ curves are split into their $t^{1/3}$, t^1 and t^3 components and each component considered separately, by a systematic graphical procedure.

Returning to the Larsen–Miller equation it is easily shown that, at a constant temperature, the relationship between stress and strain rate for the secondary phase is

$$\sigma = C\dot{\varepsilon}^n \tag{9.40}$$

where C and n are constants which can be determined from the data. This is a useful equation for many practical purposes.

9.9. CREEP BUCKLING

A typical example of the application of creep data to an engineering problem is to be found in nuclear reactor fuel elements. If they are vertical, as in the Calder Hall type of reactor, they are prone to creep buckling under their own weight. The creep may be due either to the usual metallurgical changes taking place at high temperature, or to irradiation effects, or to both these causes acting together. An approximate theory for this problem is given by Alexander,[27] and the salient features of this solution will now be discussed.

It is assumed that the temperature is constant over the fuel element. In practice the temperature varies both radially and axially in the fuel elements, but such effects could not be included in any simple theory. The geometry of the type of fuel element under discussion is such that only a small amount of buckling, or bowing, is possible before the element rests against the wall of the fuel channel. Thus it is reasonable to assume that the element takes up a simple sinusoidal shape, having a maximum deflexion at the centre of its length. It can also reasonably be assumed that plane sections remain plane, so that the distribution of strain and strain rate across the section is linear. Under these circumstances the distribution of stress across the section is given by equation (9.40), as illustrated in Fig. 9.18 for a circular rod. The mean stress on the buckling rod is denoted by $\bar{\sigma} = P/A$, P being the end load, A the cross-sectional area of the rod.

Considering elastic buckling, the Euler buckling load is derived from the differential equation

$$EI\frac{d^2Z}{dy^2} = -PZ \tag{9.41}$$

where E is Young's modulus,

    I is the second moment of area of the cross-section,

    y is distance from one end of the strut,

    Z is deflexion at any section.

Equation (9.41) has the solution

$$Z = A\cos\sqrt{\frac{P}{EI}}\,y + B\sin\sqrt{\frac{P}{EI}}\,y \tag{9.42}$$

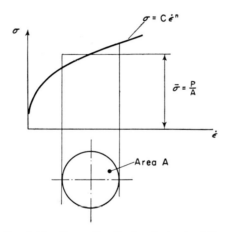

FIG. 9.18. Stress distribution during buckling.

where A and B are constants of integration, giving the Euler buckling load

$$P_{cR} = \frac{\pi^2 EI}{L^2} \tag{9.43}$$

where L is the length of the strut.

If it is assumed that the strut has an initial sinusoidal bow given by the equation

$$Z_0 = Z_{0_c}\sin\frac{\pi}{L}y \tag{9.44}$$

where Z_{0_c} is the initial central deflexion, then the differential equation governing further buckling becomes

$$EI\frac{d^2}{dy^2}(Z - Z_0) = -PZ \tag{9.45}$$

which has the particular integral

$$\frac{Z}{Z_{0_c}} = \frac{1}{1 - P/P_{cR}} \sin\frac{\pi}{L} y \qquad (9.46)$$

In particular, the central deflexion, Z_c, is given by

$$\frac{Z_c}{Z_{0_c}} = \frac{1}{1 - \alpha} \qquad (9.47)$$

where $\alpha = P/P_{cR}$. This is a useful formula for buckling problems, in particular for the design of vertical control rods in nuclear reactors which is governed by their behaviour on accidental dropping.

(i) The " Creep Rate Modulus "

In the equation $\sigma = C\dot{\varepsilon}^n$, if n is unity (it lies between $\frac{1}{16}$ and unity for most metals), then $C = \sigma/\dot{\varepsilon}$ is analogous to Young's modulus for elastic behaviour, but relating creep strain with the applied stress, and introducing the time element. Investigators in the U.K.A.E.A. have often referred to this quantity as $\dot{E}$, in view of the analogy. At any given stress level, considering the secondary phase only, $\dot{\varepsilon} = \varepsilon/t$, where ε is the creep strain suffered in time t. Thus $\dot{E} = (\sigma/\varepsilon)t = E't$, where E' is an equivalent Young's modulus, relating creep strain with stress. This concept allows use to be made of available elastic analyses to predict creep behaviour. It will be appreciated that this is only an approximate way of treating problems of creep, since it has been assumed that n is unity, and primary creep has been neglected.

(ii) The Sagging Bar Test

As an example, consider a simply supported prismatic bar, length L, sagging under its own weight W. The familiar result derived from elasticity theory for the central deflexion δ is

$$\delta = \frac{5WL^3}{384EI} \qquad (9.48)$$

For the creep problem $E' = \dot{E}/t$ may be substituted for E, giving the central deflexion in time t as

$$\delta = \frac{5WL^3}{384\dot{E}I} t \qquad (9.49)$$

The value of $\dot{E}$ for uranium has been conveniently measured in this way, by observing the central deflexion of a heated uranium bar sagging under its own weight inside a sealed container.

(iii) *Thermal Creep Buckling of a Uranium Rod*

From equation (9.47) it is easily shown that the incremental elastic central deflexion on applying a load P to an initially bowed rod is

$$\delta Z_c = \alpha Z_c = \frac{PL^2}{\pi^2 EI} Z_c \quad \text{(elastic)} \qquad (9.50)$$

For the analogous creep problem the incremental central deflexion is

$$\delta Z_c = \dot{\alpha} Z_c \, \delta t = \frac{PL^2 Z_c}{\pi^2 \dot{E} I} \delta t \quad \text{(creep)} \qquad (9.51)$$

Integrating this equation, the time for the central deflexion to increase from Z_{0_c} to Z_c is found to be

$$t = \frac{1}{\dot{\alpha}} \ln \frac{Z_c}{Z_{0_c}} \qquad (9.52)$$

where

$$\dot{\alpha} = \frac{PL^2}{\pi^2 \dot{E} I}$$

Thus the bow-doubling time is $0.693/\dot{\alpha}$, and the " e-folding " time $1/\dot{\alpha}$. The following values serve to give an illustrative example:

$$\dot{E} = 10^8 \, \frac{\text{lb}}{\text{in}^2} \cdot \text{hr} \quad \text{for natural uranium at } 500^\circ \text{C.}$$

$$I = \frac{\pi \times 1 \cdot 1^4}{64} = 0 \cdot 0718 \, \text{in}^4, \; L = 40 \, \text{in.,}$$

$P = 3 \cdot 65 \times 26 = 95 \, \text{lb.}$ (three fuel elements on top of one fuel element, 0.65 of the weight of the lowest fuel element being customarily taken).

Hence $\dot{\alpha} = \dfrac{2 \cdot 15}{10^3} \, \text{hr}^{-1}$, and the bow-doubling time is $322 \, \text{hr.}$

If, for example, $Z_{0_c} = 0 \cdot 02 \, \text{in.}$, $Z_c = 0 \cdot 2 \, \text{in.}$ (to touch the channel wall) the time to reach the channel wall will be

$$t = \frac{10^3}{2 \cdot 15} \ln 10 = 1070 \, \text{hr}, \quad \text{or about forty-five days.}$$

(iv) *Irradiation Creep Buckling*

This effect was predicted, discovered, and investigated by Cottrell.[28] Due to irradiation the grains of the material expand so that large intergranular stresses are introduced, finally bringing them into the plastic state.

In this condition a small externally applied additional stress is sufficient to cause plastic flow. Cottrell gives the following estimate of the time of irradiation necessary to bring the grains into a plastic state:

$$t_m = \frac{\sigma_Y}{E\dot{\varepsilon}_g} \tag{9.53}$$

where σ_Y is the yield strength of the uranium, approximately $50,000 \text{lb/in}^2$,

E is Young's modulus, approximately $25 \times 10^6 \text{lb/in}^2$,
$\dot{\varepsilon}_g$ is the growth rate, approximately $4 \times 10^{-9} \text{sec}^{-1}$ for natural uranium in a thermal neutron flux of intensity 10^{12} neutrons/cm^2 per sec.

For these values, equation (9.53) gives a value of about one week. The material is then spontaneously plastic, behaving virtually as a Newtonian fluid. Such a material will flow at a rate

$$\dot{\varepsilon} = \frac{\text{overall elastic strain}}{\text{relaxation time}} = \frac{\sigma/E}{t_m}$$

For natural uranium in a slow neutron flux of 10^{12} neutron/cm^2 per sec, therefore, the uranium will flow at a rate of one elastic deflexion (σ/E) per week. For example, under an applied stress of only 100lb/in^2 (i.e. $0 \cdot 2$ per cent of the yield stress) a steady creep rate of $0 \cdot 36$ per cent in $100,000 \text{hr}$ would occur.

Theoretical and experimental work under Cottrell's supervision at Harwell has shown that the irradiation creep is approximately one elastic deflexion per megawatt-day per tonne at $200 °C$. The variation with temperature does not appear to have been determined with any certainty, although the irradiation creep is generally assumed to be zero at about $0 °C$ and $450 °C$, with a maximum at about $200 °C$.

Considering the problem of irradiation creep buckling, if α is small in relation to Z_c, and m is the number of elastic deflexions required to achieve a given bow, then

$$\delta Z_c = \alpha Z_c \, \delta m$$

and

$$m = \frac{1}{\alpha} \ln \frac{Z_c}{Z_{0_c}} \tag{9.54}$$

where

$$\alpha = \frac{PL^2}{\pi^2 EI}$$

Further information about this problem is given in the paper by Hardy and Lawton.[29]

(v) *Thermal and Irradiation Creep Buckling of both Uranium and Magnox Can*

Considering the uranium rod only, there will be an incremental deflexion $dZ_t = \dot{\alpha} Z_c \, dt$ due to thermal creep, plus $dZ_i = \alpha . F\delta/24 . Z_c \, dt$ due to irradiation creep, where F is the irradiation power in MW/tonne, δ is the irradiation creep rate in elastic deflexion/MW-day per tonne. Hence the total incremental central deflexion will be

$$dZ_c = \left(\dot{\alpha} + \frac{F\delta}{24} \alpha \right) Z_c \, dt$$

and the buckling time, including both thermal and irradiation creep for the uranium rod, will be

$$t = \frac{\pi^2 \dot{E}_{U_{eq}} I_U}{P_U L^2} \ln \frac{Z_c}{Z_{0_c}} \tag{9.55}$$

where the suffixes U refer to the uranium rod, and

$$\frac{1}{\dot{E}_{U_{eq}}} = \frac{1}{\dot{E}_U} + \frac{F\delta}{24 E_U}$$

To include the effect of the magnesium alloy can, for which it is assumed $\sigma = C\varepsilon^n$ ($n \neq 1$), the mean strain rates for both can and rod, denoted by $\dot{\varepsilon}_M$ and $\dot{\varepsilon}_U$, respectively, are equal, since they must shorten together.

Now
$$\dot{\varepsilon}_U = \frac{\bar{\sigma}_U}{\dot{E}_{U_{eq}}} = \frac{P_U}{A_U \dot{E}_{U_{eq}}}$$

and
$$\dot{\varepsilon}_M = \left(\frac{\bar{\sigma}_M}{C} \right)^{1/n} = \left(\frac{P_M}{A_M C} \right)^{1/n} \tag{9.56}$$

(where suffixes M refer to the magnesium alloy can).

Also
$$P = P_U + P_M \tag{9.57}$$

Hence, from equating equations (9.56) and using (9.57),

$$\frac{A_U \dot{E}_{U_{eq}}}{(A_M C)^{1/n}} P_M^{1/n} + P_M - P = 0 \tag{9.58}$$

from which the load taken by the can, P_m, can be determined.

The rod and can also buckle together, so a transverse load must be introduced, of intensity assumed to be

$$w = w_c \sin \frac{\pi}{L} y \tag{9.59}$$

20

With the addition of this transverse load, the bending moment at any section of the uranium rod is found to be

$$M_U = -P_U Z_c \sin\frac{\pi}{L} y + \frac{w_c L^2}{\pi} \sin\frac{\pi}{L} y \qquad (9.60)$$

and, after some algebra, the final buckling time is given by the equation

$$t = \frac{\pi^2 \, \Sigma(\dot{E}I)}{PL^2} \ln\frac{Z_c}{Z_{0_c}} \qquad (9.61)$$

where

$$\Sigma(\dot{E}I) = (\dot{E}_{eq} I)_U + (\dot{E}I)_M$$

For the can material, n is not assumed to be unity, so that the value of $\dot{E}_M$ is taken as the tangent modulus of the σ versus $\dot{\varepsilon}$ curve at the mean stress. Thus

$$\dot{E}_M = \left(\frac{d\sigma}{d\dot{\varepsilon}}\right)_{\bar{\sigma}} = nC^{1/n}\bar{\sigma}^{1-1/n} = nC^{1/n}\left(\frac{P_M}{A_M}\right)^{1-1/n} \qquad (9.62)$$

There are sound reasons for making this assumption, which have been discussed elsewhere.[27]

The main deficiency of these theories appears to be the neglect of primary creep, and a current investigation by Alexander and Webster at Imperial College is directed towards remedying this. Briefly, if the creep strain is represented by the equation:

$$\varepsilon = \alpha t^{1/3} + \beta t$$

then

$$\dot{\varepsilon} = \tfrac{1}{3}\alpha t^{-2/3} + \beta \qquad (9.63)$$

and

$$\left(\frac{\partial\dot{\varepsilon}}{\partial\sigma}\right)_{\bar{\sigma}} = \frac{1}{\dot{E}} = \frac{1}{3t^{2/3}}\left(\frac{\partial\alpha}{\partial\sigma}\right)_{\bar{\sigma}} + \left(\frac{\partial\beta}{\partial\sigma}\right)_{\bar{\sigma}} = \frac{\phi}{3t^{2/3}} + \chi, \text{ say.}$$

therefore

$$\frac{dZ_c}{Z_c} = \frac{PL^2}{\pi^2 I}\left(\frac{\phi}{3t^{2/3}} + \chi\right)dt$$

and integrating

$$\phi t^{1/3} + \chi t = \frac{\pi^2 I}{PL^2} \ln\frac{Z_c}{Z_{0_c}} \qquad (9.64)$$

Hence t can be determined. A convenient method of determining the functions ϕ and χ is to use the Graham and Walles analysis of available creep data.

The problem when there are two members buckling together with different values of C and n is very complex, although an attempt has been made to determine an approximate theoretical solution, as discussed by Alexander and Webster.[30]

9.10. CONCLUDING REMARKS

An attempt has been made in this paper to set out the basic principles underlying the plastic flow and creep of metals, as seen from an engineering viewpoint. There are many situations in practice in which a knowledge of these principles is invaluable, and the design of atomic reactor components is no exception. For one reason or another, plastic flow in such components must be accepted and estimated. Typical examples are fuel element cans, in which large distortions of the fuel rod may have to be accommodated, and distortions during manufacture estimated. A particular case of the latter occurs in the pressurization of the can into the anti-rachetting grooves of the rod, when it is desired to know how the material of the can will flow and whether the heat transfer surface will distort excessively. Of course, the final test is by experiment, but a knowledge of the theory of plasticity will assist in designing the best shape of groove and its relative dimensions.

Another example occurs in the design of shock absorbers. These are necessary in a vertical arrangement to guard against the accidental dropping of components such as fuel elements or control rods. There are many possible systems which can be used, but those most favoured involve plastic flow of a replaceable component. In Calder Hall, a type of broach was used, so that the plasticity process involved was that of machining. The collapse of a thin cylindrical shell compressed along its axis can be used as a shock absorber. This is a process involving plastic flow, and has been discussed by Pugsley[31] and Alexander.[32]

Creep under complex systems of stress has not been discussed *per se* in this article—suffice it to say that plasticity theory gives a good indication of such behaviour, although for more precise estimation it is necessary to include the effects of anisotropy. An excellent review of this topic is given by Johnson.[33] A typical example of the sort of problem raised in this connexion is to be found in the creep of a reactor pressure vessel. For simplicity, a spherical vessel will be considered. The first question which arises is: if σ_v is the stress in the vessel, at what stress σ_T should a uniaxial tensile creep test be conducted in order to predict the creep behaviour of the vessel? An answer to this question is immediately found by using the concept of equivalent stress $\bar{\sigma}$ (equation (9.12)). For the vessel, $\sigma_1 = \sigma_2 = \sigma_v$, $\sigma_3 = 0$, hence $\bar{\sigma} = \sigma_v$. For the tension test $\sigma_2 = \sigma_3 = 0$, and $\bar{\sigma} = \sigma_T$. Accordingly the tensile creep test must be conducted at the same stress as exists in the vessel.

Equation (9.14a) shows that the equivalent strain rate will be given by the equation

$$\dot{\varepsilon} = \sqrt{[\tfrac{2}{3}(\dot{\varepsilon}_1^2 + \dot{\varepsilon}_2^2 + \dot{\varepsilon}_3^2)]}$$

For the tensile test

$$\dot{\varepsilon}_2 = \dot{\varepsilon}_3 = -\tfrac{1}{2}\dot{\varepsilon}_1$$

For the spherical vessel

$$\dot{\varepsilon}_1 = \dot{\varepsilon}_2, \text{ and } \dot{\varepsilon}_3 = -2\dot{\varepsilon}_1$$

so that $\bar{\dot{\varepsilon}} = 2\dot{\varepsilon}_1$

Since the equivalent strain rate will be the same in both the test and the vessel, and denoting the axial strain rate in the tensile test piece by $\dot{\varepsilon}_T$ and the strain rate in any plane of the spherical vessel by $\dot{\varepsilon}_v$, then $2\dot{\varepsilon}_v = \dot{\varepsilon}_T$. Therefore the creep strain rate in the vessel will be only half that given by the tensile specimen.

An alternative way of approaching this problem is by considering the rate of plastic working in the specimen and the vessel. According to the theory of plasticity these should be equal. The rate of working $\dot{W} = \sigma_1\dot{\varepsilon}_1 + \sigma_2\dot{\varepsilon}_2 + \sigma_3\dot{\varepsilon}_3$. For the tensile test both σ_2 and σ_3 are zero, whilst for the vessel σ_2 only is zero. Since the stresses are all equal, the strain rates $\dot{\varepsilon}_1$ and $\dot{\varepsilon}_2$ in the vessel need to be equal to only half of $\dot{\varepsilon}_1$ in the tensile test to give the same work rate.

It is worth remarking here that consideration has only been given to creep under circumstances in which stress is the controlling factor, the creep rate being dependent on the stress. There are many cases in which strain is the controlling factor, and creep leads to a relaxation of stress. A bolted joint in a high-temperature pipeline or boiler is a typical example, in which the initial extension or strain of the bolt is determined by the tightening spanner. At high temperature this strain, which was wholly elastic initially, becomes partly elastic and partly creep strain, so that the elastic strain and therefore the stress in the bolt reduces. As far as the atomic reactor is concerned, a similar problem exists in the graphite restraint garters used to embrace the graphite structure and hold it together against the bursting forces imposed from within through various causes. An equation of the type given by equation (9.40) can be used to solve such problems, although the behaviour of the graphite restraint garter is complicated by the fact that the graphite itself changes shape due to neutron irradiation.

REFERENCES

1. A. NADAI, *Plasticity*. McGraw-Hill (1931).
2. R. HILL, *The Mathematical Theory of Plasticity*. Clarendon Press, Oxford (1950).
3. W. PRAGER and P. G. HODGE, *The Theory of Perfectly Plastic Solids*. Wiley (1951).
4. W. PRAGER, *Introduction to Plasticity*. Addison-Wesley (1959).
4a. W. PRAGER, Theory of plasticity: A survey of recent achievements. *Proc. Inst. Mech. Engrs.* **169**, 41 (1955).
5. H. JEFFREYS, Cartesian tensors. Cambridge University Press (1931).
6. P. W. BRIDGMAN, *Studies in Large Plastic Flow and Fracture*. McGraw-Hill (1952).
7. B. CROSSLAND, *Proc. Inst. Mech. Engrs.* **168**, 935 (1954).
7a. D. G. SOPWITH and J. L. M. MORRISON, Letter to *The Engineer*, 7th Dec. 1956, p. 810.
8. G. I. TAYLOR and H. QUINNEY, *Phil. Trans. Roy. Soc.* A **230**, 323 (1931).

9. J. L. M. MORRISON and W. M. SHEPHERD, *Proc. Inst. Mech. Engrs.* **163**, 1 (1950).
10. G. LIANIS and H. FORD, *J. Mech. Phys. Solids* **5**, 215 (1957).
11. D. G. CHRISTOPHERSON, P. L. B. OXLEY and W. B. PALMER, *Engineering* **186**, 113 (1958).
12. W. PRAGER, *Trans. Roy. Inst. Tech.* Stockholm, no. 65 (1953).
12a H. TERZAGHI, *Theoretical Soil Mechanics*, p. 18. Chapman & Hall (1942).
13. J. M. ALEXANDER, *Proc. Inst. Mech. Engrs.* **169**, 1021 (1955).
14. R. HILL, *J. Mech. Phys. Solids* **2**, 278 (1954).
15. J. F. W. BISHOP, *J. Mech. Phys. Solids* **2**, 43 (1953).
16. J. M. ALEXANDER, *Conference on Technology of Engineering Manufacture, 1958. Proc. Inst. Mech. Engrs.*, Paper No. 42.
17. D. C. DRUCKER, *Appl. Mech. Rev.* **169**, 421 (1954).
18. J. M. ALEXANDER, On complete solutions for frictionless extrusion in plane strain. *Quart. App. Math.* **19**, 31 (1961).
19. W. JOHNSON, *Proc. Inst. Mech. Engrs.* **173**, 61 (1959).
20. J. HEYMAN, *Int. J. Mech. Sci.* **1**, 121 (1960).
21. A. H. SULLY, *Metallic Creep and Creep Resistant Alloys.* Butterworths (1949).
22. A. H. COTTRELL, *Dislocations and Plastic Flow in Crystals.* Clarendon Press, Oxford (1953).
23. E. G. STANFORD, *The Creep of Metals and Alloys.* Temple Press (1949).
24. L. ROTHERHAM, *Creep of Metals.* Institute of Physics (1951).
25. A. GRAHAM, Phenomenological theories of creep. *Engineer* **5**, 18, 198–201, 234–6 (1952).
26. F. R. LARSEN and J. MILLER, A time-temperature relationship for rupture and creep stresses. *Trans. Amer. Soc. Mech. Engrs.* **74** (5) 765–75 (1952).
27. J. M. ALEXANDER, An approximate theory for the thermal and irradiation creep buckling of a uranium fuel rod and its magnesium can. *J. Mech. Engng. Sci.* **1**, 211 (1959).
28. A. H. COTTRELL, Effect of nuclear radiation on engineering materials. *Chart. Mech. Eng.* 105–19 (1960).
29. H. K. HARDY and H. LAWTON, *Proceedings of the Second U.N. International Conference on the Peaceful Uses of Atomic Energy, Geneva, 1958.* Paper 15, p. 1306.
30. J. M. ALEXANDER and G. A. WEBSTER, The creep buckling of composite members. *J. Mech. Engng. Sci.* **2**, 342 (1960).
31. A. PUGSLEY and M. MACAULEY, The large-scale crumpling of thin cylindrical columns. *Quart. J. Mech. Appl. Math.* **13**, 1 (1960).
32. J. M. ALEXANDER, An approximate analysis of the collapse of thin cylindrical shells under axial loading. *Quart. J. Mech. Appl. Math.* **13**, 10 (1960).
33. A. E. JOHNSON, Complex stress creep. *Met. Rev.* **5**, 447 (1960).
34. P. G. HODGE, JR., *Plastic Analysis of Structures.* McGraw-Hill (1959).
35. J. S. RINEHART and J. PEARSON, *Behaviour of Metals under Impulsive Loads.* American Society for Metals, Cleveland, Ohio (1954).
36. W. E. BAKER, The elastic-plastic response of thin spherical shells to internal blast loading. *J. Appl. Mech. (Trans. Amer. Soc. Mech. Engrs.)* E, **27**, 139 (1960).
37. W. E. BAKER, Modeling of large transient elastic and plastic deformations of structures subjected to blast loading. *J. Appl. Mech. (Trans. Amer. Soc. Mech. Engrs.)* E, **27**, 521 (1960).
38. *Colloquium on Creep in Structures.* International Union of Theoretical and Applied Mechanics, Stanford University, 11th–15th July (1960).

CHAPTER 10

THE DIRECT DESIGN OF GRILLAGES

N. W. Murray

NOTATION

D_x, D_y = rigidity moduli of plate in the x and y directions.
E = Young's elastic modulus.
F = residual or error in solution.
I = second moment of area of grillage members.
K = depth of semi-elliptical beam.
P = general load applied to a beam.
R = radius of grillage.
W = load applied at a regular nodal point.
X = load carried by beam running in the X direction.
Y = load carried by beam running in the Y direction.
a, b = spacing of grillage members in y and x directions.
k = dimensionless quantity describing point at which deflexion is required.
n = dimensionless quantity describing position of load on a beam.
q = lateral load per unit area.
r = radius from centre of grillage.
x, y = cartesian co-ordinates.
α = dimensionless quantity describing half length of beam.
δ = lateral deflexion.
γ = dimensionless quantity defined by equation (10.9).
θ = polar co-ordinate of angle.

10.1. INTRODUCTION

IN a gas-cooled graphite-moderated reactor a core of graphite is contained within a pressure circuit and its self weight is carried by means of a core support. The core support is also called a grillage, grid and sometimes diagrid. Its purpose is to carry the weight of the core, gas seal, guide pans and of the fuel elements themselves and to span the distance between the supports so as to allow free access of the cooler gas to the bottom of the core. A typical layout of the pressure vessel and core is shown in Fig. 10.1

where the dimensions are merely meant to be representative of a 250 MW reactor. In this case the vessel is spherical and supported on a lower skirt which is carried on up through the shell of the vessel so that the grillage can rest on top of this inner skirt. The diameter of the skirts, grillage and core are all approximately equal in the diagram but it is quite easy to imagine a system in which the skirts are of smaller diameter than the grillage and core.

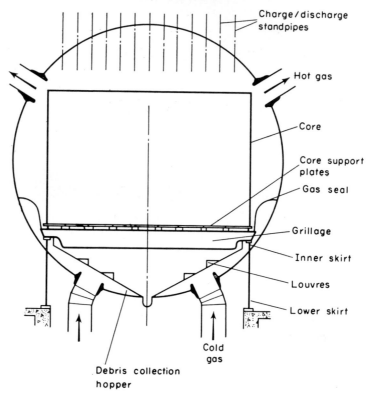

FIG. 10.1. Reactor layout with large diameter skirt.

(Core height = 27 ft., Lower skirt diameter = 40 ft.)

In that case the bending moments in the grillage are smaller than when the three diameters are approximately equal. This is obviously very desirable but the layout of the duct system may be affected by this apparently minor change. The reason for this statement is that the perforations in the pressure-containing shell must not unduly weaken the vessel by introducing high stresses. With ducts of the order of 5½ ft. diameter care must be exercised at the layout stage to ensure that two or more of these large perforations do not come too close to one another. By reducing the skirt diameter the ducts are of necessity located outside of the skirt periphery to avoid this problem.

A typical layout of this type is shown in Fig. 10.2. This arrangement tends to increase the diameter of the vessel to a small extent because clearance between the periphery of the grillage and the vessel must be provided to accommodate the amount of gas-flow without increased friction losses.

One layout which leads to some economies in the use of space within the reactor is shown on Fig. 10.3. Here a conical skirt is used and leads to

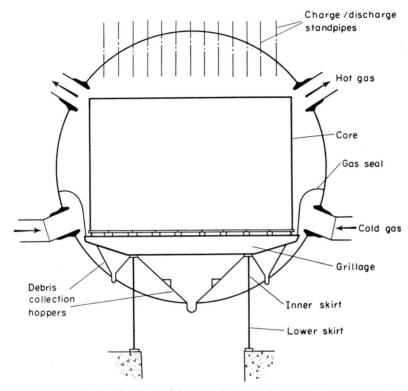

Fig. 10.2.   Reactor layout with small diameter skirt.

smaller bending moments in the grillage and hence to a shallower grillage. Another point is that the lobsterback bend in the cold duct is avoided so the ducts can be moved farther from the reactor axis.

Problems of this nature are typical of those which the designers of a nuclear power station must weigh in their minds to achieve the greatest possible economy. It is not possible to dogmatize about plant layout because there are so many variables that a design team is finally forced to make a decision based upon two or more design studies which were selected in the first place because they appeared to be the most favourable.

In addition to the changes of skirt diameter it is also possible to omit the inner skirt and support the grillage in rollers. This allows free expansion of the grillage and core relative to the vessel. Usually the inner skirt is made sufficiently long for the bending stresses developed at the top of the inner skirt to attenuate to small values at the skirt to shell junction. The length of the inner skirt can be increased by using a smaller diameter skirt but this may affect the duct layout as stated previously. The use of rollers allows greater flexibility with the layout of the vessel and its contents because the minimum

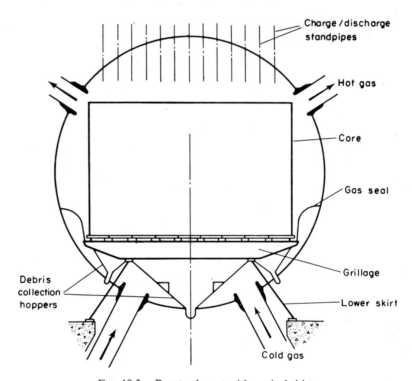

FIG. 10.3.   Reactor layout with conical skirt.

length of the inner skirt is no longer a governing factor. In Figs 10.1, 10.2 and 10.3 a spherical pressure vessel is illustrated but even this may be changed to, say, a cylinder with torispherical or ellipsoidal ends. This change should not affect the layout of the grillage.

In the early nuclear power stations built and under construction in Britain the graphite core is pierced by holes which are located on a square grid. It is therefore logical that the grillages which support these cores should follow the geometry of the fuel channels and also be located on a square system. This is particularly true if the charging is carried out from beneath the reactor. Apart from the core and the charge–discharge nozzles, which of necessity follow the square layout, many of the other components of the reactor have axially symmetric geometry. For example, the overall shape of the core approximates to a cylinder, the skirts are cylindrical and the vessel is either cylindrical or spherical. A grillage which follows this type of geometry would consist of a number of arms radiating from the central axis of the reactor to the support near the edge. This system automatically gives a uniform reaction on to the inner skirt because of the symmetry and allows the pressure vessel–skirts combination to be treated as an axially symmetrical problem. This leads to a great simplification of the analysis of the stresses in the pressure vessel and skirts. The designer is confronted with having to decide whether the geometrical layout of the grillage should follow the geometry of the fuel channels, say square, or the geometry of the vessel, skirts, etc., i.e. axisymmetric.

This decision rests upon the designer's attitude to debris removal. During the normal operation of a reactor a small amount of debris accumulates in the primary pressure circuit. It is mainly graphite dust but there may also be small amounts of rust and if a fuel can bursts any of its components may fall down the channel into the bottom of the pressure vessel. It is desirable to remove this material from the reactor for reasons of health, safety and the physical effects upon reactor operation and efficiency. For these reasons debris collection hoppers are located beneath the grillage. If the layout of the grillage is such that there is an unimpaired path for the debris between the fuel channels and the debris collection hoppers no debris should lodge on top of the grillage. This is the case when the beams follow the geometrical layout of the core. In the case of the radial type grillage some fuel channels will lay directly above part of a beam. This does not affect gas flow because the support plates on which the cores rest are raised to allow free access of the gas to the bottom of the channel. However, it does mean that debris can lodge on top of the members. Arrangements are, therefore, made that this material can be removed by the charge–discharge machine.

Returning to the question of the diameter of the skirts in relation to that of the core. Reference to Figs. 10.1, 10.2 and 10.3 show that the problem of debris removal is very much simpler when the skirt supports the core at its periphery. All debris is collected in a single hopper and removal can be effected either by a chute or the charge–discharge machine.

To summarize the problem about skirt diameter, a large diameter skirt simplifies the debris-removal problem and possibly allows a slightly smaller diameter vessel to be used but will lead to the use of a short inner skirt. A smaller diameter skirt may lead to a more compact grillage, allows the use of a longer inner skirt but complicates the problem of debris removal. In this paper it is assumed that the inner skirt supports the grillage near its periphery and that the core subjects the support plates to a uniformly distributed load.

A study of possible grillage/support plate arrangements showed that it is difficult to make use of a radial type grillage if the fuel channels are set out on a square network because the arrangement of support plates is not orderly. If some headroom is sacrificed it is possible to use two grillages, a light square one resting upon a stronger radial one. This arrangement allows regular support plates to be used and has effectively an axisymmetrical boundary reaction.

Recently the possibility of using a hexagonal pitch for the fuel channels has been explored and this opens up the possibility of a more convenient layout of support plates and radial type grillage in view of the larger number of axes of symmetry. In this paper only those grillages which follow a square or rectangular layout are dealt with.

Having considered the overall layout of the grillage, core and vessel it is necessary to pass on to the detail design of the grillage structure.

In the next section the results of an investigation into the possible use of four types of grillage are presented. The outcome of this examination is that the grillage which consists of two sets of evenly spaced beams intersecting at right angles is the most satisfactory and can be designed to give a uniform boundary reaction. Two methods of design are described in Sections 10.3 and 10.4. Both lead directly to the second moment of areas of the members of the grillage and are therefore direct design methods. This is in contrast to some previous design procedures in which the sizes of the beams are guessed at and an analysis of this grillage carried out. Several guesses may be required before a satisfactory design is obtained.

10.2. SOME TYPES OF GRILLAGE INVESTIGATED

In the early reactors in Britain the " egg-box " type of grillage [Fig. 10.4(a)] was used. It consisted of two sets of beams intersecting at right angles to one another to form a square network. In practice the beams are made up of welded plate girders which are stress relieved in the reactor. If all of the beams have the same second moment of area then the boundary reaction is not uniformly distributed. This is because the short beams near the boundary are much more rigid than the long beams. For instance, in the quadrant of a grillage shown in Fig. 10.5 the beam BB' is very rigid and the transverse beam AA' looks upon C as the boundary instead of A'. Thus the reaction is relieved at A' and transferred to B'. This uneven distribution of boundary load does not induce high stresses but it may set off the support skirt into a buckling mode associated with this load distribution. Also if the grillage is supported on equi-spaced rollers then it is desirable that all rollers should be equally loaded. To overcome this disadvantage it is possible to reduce the stiffness of the short beams. This can be done in two ways:

(a) by decreasing their depth;

(b) by reducing their second moment of area but keeping their depth constant.

Livesley[1] treated the grillage as an anistropic plate. The basic differential equation of this type of plate was first discovered by Boussinesq[4] in 1879.

$$D_x\frac{\partial^4\delta}{\partial x^4}+2H\frac{\partial^4\delta}{\partial x^2\partial y^2}+D_y\frac{\partial^4\delta}{\partial y^4}=q \qquad (10.1)$$

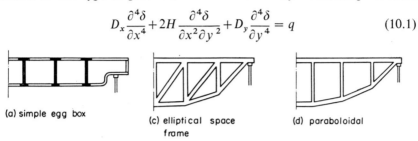

(a) simple egg box

(c) elliptical space frame

(d) paraboloidal

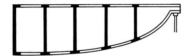

(b) elliptical egg box   Fig. 10.4.   Types of grillage.

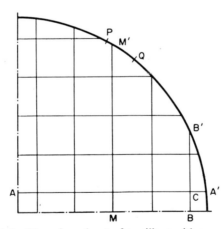

Fig. 10.5.   Plan of quadrant of a grillage with a square net.

Because reactor grillages consist of a number of deep narrow beams with very little torsional rigidity the term H is very small and can be neglected. The equation which remains is really just the familiar bending equation of a beam. Livesley[1] shows that if the beams are spaced apart at intervals in both directions then a uniform boundary reaction will result if the load, W, at each intersection divides equally between the x- and y-beams. In Appendix III this statement is proved in the general case when the spacings in the x- and y-directions are different. If the spacings are equal then the load per unit run carried by each beam is $W/2a$. Simple beam theory gives the following equation for the x-beam.

$$\frac{\partial^2}{\partial x^2}\left(I_x \frac{\partial^2 \delta}{\partial x^2}\right) = \frac{W}{2aE} \qquad (10.2)$$

By integrating twice and substituting the conditions that the shear is zero at the centre $(x = 0)$ and the bending moment is zero at the boundary

$$\frac{\partial^2 \delta}{\partial x^2} = \frac{W}{4aE} \frac{r^2 - R^2}{I_x(x, y)} \qquad (10.3)$$

A similar expression may be written for the y-direction beam.

$$\frac{\partial^2 \delta}{\partial y^2} = \frac{W}{4aE} \frac{r^2 - R^2}{I_y(x, y)} \qquad (10.4)$$

From the point of view of fabrication of the grillage it is most expedient to make the beams of the same depth where they intersect. If the inertias are made equal and related to the inertia at $r = 0$

$$\frac{I_x(x, y)}{R^2 - r^2} = \frac{I_y(x, y)}{R^2 - r^2} = \frac{I_0}{R^2} = \text{constant} \qquad (10.5)$$

then from (10.3) and (10.4) the deflected shape of the grillage is a paraboloid of revolution. By considering only the flange of the beams as contributing all of the second moment of area of the beams Livesley shows that the shape of the beams must be semi-elliptical. Thus if the area of the flanges is A and the depth of the beam K then the second moment of area of the beam is $2a\,AK^2$. Substituting in (10.5)

$$I = 2a\,AK^2 = I_0\left(1 - \frac{r^2}{R^2}\right) = 2a\,AK_0^2\left(1 - \frac{r^2}{R^2}\right)$$

whence
$$\frac{K^2}{K_0^2} + \frac{r^2}{R^2} = 1 \qquad (10.6)$$

i.e. the beams are semi-elliptical in shape.

In practical grillages which match the core layout the flanges are deliberately made quite small to allow the debris free access to the collection hoppers. This means that most of the strength of the beams is contributed by their webs. If all webs have thickness, t, then

$$I = \frac{tK^3}{12} = I_0\left(1 - \frac{r^2}{R^2}\right) = \frac{tK_0^3}{12}\left(1 - \frac{r^2}{R^2}\right)$$

whence
$$\frac{K^3}{K_0^3} + \frac{r^2}{R^2} = 1 \qquad\qquad (10.7)$$

In practice there is only a small difference between equations (10.6) and (10.7). For example at $r/R = 0.5$ equation (10.6) gives $K/k_0 = 0.8660$ and equation (10.7) gives 0.9086, a difference of only $4\frac{1}{2}$ per cent. A grillage design using the principles just explained is illustrated in Fig. 10.4(b). The cost of fabricating this type of grillage is probably quite high because of the large amount of welding, accurate cutting and fitting required.

One method of overcoming this problem to some extent is by building the grillage up into the form of a space frame with the bottom members located on an ellipse. Such a grillage is shown in Fig. 10.4(c).

In this type of grillage the members carry most of the forces in the axial directions in much the same way as a plane framework. This results in small changes in the lengths of the members so that the members are forced to bend and twist to accommodate the small geometrical changes. Each joint has in fact three degrees of freedom of displacement and three of rotation. The accurate analysis of such a framework is possible only with a high-speed electronic digital computer. Even with the use of a Ferranti " Mercury " computer this limits the number of joints in the space-frame to about sixteen unless some method of packing the members is employed, i.e. only the non-zero members are stored in the machine. A programme was written by the author for solving a space-frame with up to thirty-two joints by neglecting the effects of secondary stresses, i.e. the rotations of the joints were neglected which halved the number of degrees of freedom at each joint. By incorporating into the programme a system which took into account the effects of symmetry it was possible to use this programme to analyse the behaviour of space frame grillages which had their beams equally spaced in both directions.

At the time that this programme was prepared the effects of Wigner shrinkage in neutron irradiated graphite were discovered and a system of hexagonal graphite blocks with keys and keyways was used for the core. This naturally placed the fuel channels on a hexagonal network. A space-frame on a rectangular grid which followed the geometry of the fuel channels had the spacing of the frames running in the x-direction different from that in the y-direction. This meant that some of the symmetry of the grillage was lost and in its analysis it was necessary to consider a quadrant instead of an octant. The number of joints increased to about fifty and it was decided to go back to the simple " egg-box " type of grillage with beams of varying inertia.

At this point it is worth mentioning one interesting grillage which was investigated, viz. the paraboloidal type, Fig. 10.4(d). It was thought that

this grillage would carry the load from the support plates in pure tension
in the bottom chord. When, however, the changes in axial lengths of the
members were considered it was found that the deformations of the frames
which intersect can be made to match only if some bending occurs. These
bending stresses were found to be quite large in the bottom chord.

The analysis of a given " egg-box " type grillage can be carried out using
the deflexion at each intersection point as the unknown. The resulting set
of simultaneous equations can be solved either by hand or electronic computer. The equations are, however, not easy to solve because the terms on
the leading diagonal are not appreciably greater than the others. In other
words the equations are " ill-conditioned ". A more satisfactory method
is to call the unknowns the load carried by the beams running in the x-
direction at each intersection point. Obviously this method of analysis can
be applied to the design of grillages by using trial designs as a starting point.

This sort of approach has been used by Stanek[2] whose paper shows a
method for systematizing the computation. Edwards et al.[3] use a method
which is almost identical and show that the central deflexions and stresses
in typical square grillages can be closely estimated by assuming that their
behaviour is similar to that of a flat circular plate. The bending properties
of a unit width of plate are made the same as those of an average unit width
of the grillage. In both of these papers all beams are made identical in
cross-section. No account is taken of the consequences of the variations in
boundary reaction. These effects could be reduced in the trial designs but
this would involve making several guesses.

In an effort to overcome the limitations of these analyses two design
methods have been evolved. Both methods lead directly to a satisfactory
grillage design. In Section 10.3 the first method of design is described. It
was subsequently found that a much simpler method of direct design was
possible and this is described in Section 10.4.

10.3. FIRST METHOD OF DESIGN OF AN "EGG-BOX" GRILLAGE WITH UNIFORM BOUNDARY REACTION

Consider the half of a symmetrically loaded beam shown in Fig. 10.6. It
is required to derive a general expression for the deflexion at any point
distance kd ($k = 0.5$, 1.5, 2.5, etc.) from the centre line when the load P is
applied at points nd ($n = 0.5$, 1.5, 2.5, etc.) from the centre line. The overall
length of the half beam is αd. By using Macauley's theorem and notation
the following expression for the bending moment can be written:

$$EI\frac{d^2\delta}{dx^2} = P[nd - kd] - P[\alpha d - kd]$$

where the expressions in the square brackets must be considered as zero if their numerical values are negative. By integrating and using the boundary conditions that the deflexion is zero at the support and the slope is zero at the centre line the deflexion can be expressed in the following manner.

$$\frac{6EI\,\delta}{d^3} = P\{[n-k]^3 - [\alpha-k]^3 + 3(\alpha^2 - n^2)(\alpha-k)\} \tag{10.8}$$

Let
$$\gamma = [n-k]^3 - [\alpha-k]^3 + 3(\alpha^2 - n^2)(\alpha-k) \tag{10.9}$$

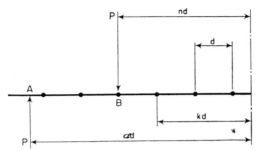

FIG. 10.6. Symmetrically loaded beam from the grillage.

The expressions for γ will depend upon α, n and k and since its computation is merely a repetitive process it has been found most expedient to write a programme for a digital computer. Values of γ for a particular grillage whose dimensions are given in Fig. 10.7 are contained in Table 10.1. Because of symmetry the loads at point 5, 9 and 11 will split equally into the x- and y-beams and all of load 1 goes on to the skirt. There are therefore seven unknowns associated with seven joints. It is possible to make either the joint deflexions or load distributions the unknowns. The equations are easier to solve if the latter is the case. The unknowns are thus the amount of load carried by the beam which runs in the x-direction. X_n is this load at joint n, W_n is the applied load and, therefore, $(W_n - X_n)$ is the load taken by the y-beam at this joint. The values of W_n can be determined from the plan of the grillage, the total load being distributed according to the area of load surrounding each joint. [The value of W is taken as unity at a regular point (Table 10.2).]

It is now possible to write the deflexion equations at each of the seven joints (2, 3, 4, 6, 7, 8, 10). For example at joint 3

$$\frac{6E\,\delta_3}{a^3} = \frac{1}{I_A}(41X_2 + 76X_3 + 100X_4 + 56W_5)$$

and

$$\frac{6E\,\delta_3}{a^3} = \frac{1}{I_C}[11 \cdot 5297X_{10} + 25 \cdot 7399W_{11} + 83 \cdot 7797(W_8 - X_8) + 102 \cdot 4297(W_3 - X_3)]$$

N.R.E.

TABLE 10.1.   VALUES OF X

Beam	k	n				
		4·5	3·5	2·5	1·5	0·5
A $\alpha = 4·5$ length $= 21·65$ ft.	4·5	0	0	0	0	0
	3·5	0	23	41	53	59
	2·5	0	41	76	100	112
	1·5	0	53	100	135	153
	0·5	0	59	112	153	176
B $\alpha = 4·2721$ length $= 20·25$ ft.	4·5	1·3548	−4·1028	−8·2050	−10·9398	−12·3072
	3·5	−4·1028	13·4394	27·3372	36·6024	41·2350
	2·5	−8·2050	27·3372	58·2351	79·5003	90·1329
	1·5	−10·9398	36·6024	79·5003	111·7655	128·3981
	0·5	−12·3072	41·2350	90·1329	128·3981	150·0307
C $\alpha = 3·7750$ length $= 18·6388$ ft.	3·5		1·6297	6·5797	9·8797	11·5297
	2·5		6·5797	28·5297	43·8297	51·4797
	1·5		9·8797	43·8297	70·1297	83·7797
	0·5		11·5297	51·4797	83·7797	102·4297
D $\alpha = 2·8724$ length $= 15·0302$ ft.	2·5			2·1836	6·6524	8·8868
	1·5			6·6524	22·1211	30·3555
	0·5			8·8868	30·3555	43·5900
E $\alpha = 0·5$ length $= 7·9942$ ft.	1·5				5	0
	0·5				0	0

By equating these expressions a single equation can be obtained at each joint. The number of equations is equal to the number of unknown X_n values. However, it is desirable that the boundary reaction per unit length should be constant and this can be achieved by selecting the inertia ratios.

TABLE 10.2.   VALUES OF W

Point	W	Point	W
1	0·764	7	1·0
2	1·0	8	1·0
3	1·0	9	1·0
4	1·0	10	1·230
5	1·0	11	1·0
6	0·554		

This is done by making the inertia ratios into four more unknowns. ($I_A/I_B =$ X_{12}, $I_A/I_C = X_{13}$, $I_A/I_D = X_{14}$, $I_A/I_E = X_{15}$.) In an ordinary grillage it is possible to write down a number of equations equal to the number of beams. Each equation would state that the condition that the boundary reaction of the beams is uniform. For example (Fig. 10.5) the reaction of beam MM' at M' is proportional to the length of skirt PQ associated with that beam. One of these equations is superfluous because the fact that the sum of the applied loads W is equal to the sum of the boundary reactions is implicit in the deflexion equations. In the grillage being considered (Fig. 10.7) another equation is eliminated because the points of support of beams

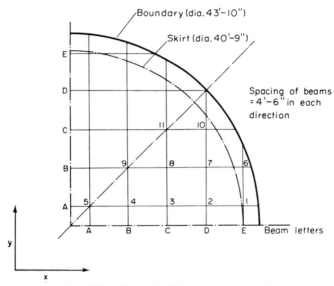

Fig. 10.7. Plan of grillage used in example.

A and E coincide at point 1. It is therefore only possible to lump their boundary reactions together and write one equation which states how much load is taken by the skirt in the vicinity of point 1. This means that now there is one too many unknowns for the number of equations available. To reduce the number of unknowns it is possible to choose one of them and since it is best to standardize on as many beams as possible then beams A and B are made identical, i.e. $I_A/I_B = X_{12} = 1\cdot0$. Another way of reducing the unknowns would be to omit beam E.

To summarize, if there are n joints in the grillage at which the load distributions are unknown then there are n equations which equate the deflexions of the intersecting beams. If there are m beams, then, in general, there are $(m-1)$ additional unknowns which are inertia ratios but an equal number of equations can be written to distribute the boundary reaction in a uniform manner. However, if two beams intersect at the reactive point then the unknowns and equations must be reduced for each of these points. The complete set of equations for the grillage shown in Fig. 10.7 is contained in Appendix I. Equations (10.12)–(10.18) are the deflexion equations and (10.19)–(10.21) are the boundary equations.

The solution of this set of equations is almost impossible by hand computation but they are readily solved by use of an electronic digital computer. The equations can be written in the general form

$$F_n = k_n C + a_n X_1 + b_n X_2 + \ldots + m_n X_1 X_2 + n_n X_1 X_3 + \ldots$$
$$= H_n + G_n \tag{10.10}$$

where H_n includes all terms of the type, constant multiplied by unknown, and G_n includes all terms which involve the product of two unknowns. C is a constant which will be made either unity or zero in the programme and F_n is called a " residual ". F_n ought to be made zero but we may not be able to make it quite equal to zero in the step-by-step method adopted. Suppose we have a set of X-values which we think are reasonably close to the true solution then by substituting into equations of type (10.10), the values of F_n can be established. The next step in the computation is to change the X-values in such a way that the F_n-values will be reduced to zero, i.e. we want to change the F_n-values by $-F_n$. The way in which the changes in X-values are chosen is explained as follows. Consider the set of equations (10.10). The change in F_n, dF_n, due to changing the X_1-, X_2-, X_3-, etc., values by dX_1, dX_2, dX_3, etc., respectively, is,

$$dF_n = \frac{\partial F_n}{\partial X_1} dX_1 + \frac{\partial F_n}{\partial X_2} dX_2 + \frac{\partial F_n}{\partial X_3} dX_3 + \ldots \tag{10.11}$$

But

$$\frac{\partial F_n}{\partial X_1} = a_n + m_n X_2 + n_n X_3 + \ldots$$

$$= (H)_{\substack{C=0 \\ X_r=0 \\ X_1=1}} + (G)_{\substack{X_r=Y_r \\ X_1=1}} - (G)_{\substack{X_r=Y_r \\ X_1=0}}$$

where Y_r is the estimated solution for the X-values but because it is estimated it is not quite correct. Similarly

$$\frac{\partial F_n}{\partial X_2} = b_n + m_n X_1 + \ldots$$

$$= (H)_{\substack{C=0 \\ X_r=0 \\ X_1=1}} + (G)_{\substack{X_r=Y_r \\ X_1=1}} - (G)_{\substack{X_r=Y_r \\ X_1=0}}$$

and so on. This part of the computer programme is illustrated as a flow

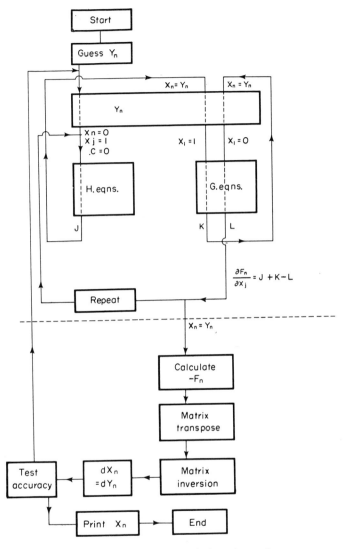

FIG. 10.8. Flow chart for solution of equations

$$F_n = k_n c + a_n X_1 + b_n X_2 + \ldots + m_n X_1 X_2 + n_n X_1 X_3 \ldots = H + G.$$

chart in Fig. 10.8 above the interrupted line. Having calculated the derivatives on the right-hand side of equation (10.11) the changes in the residuals dF_n on the left-hand side are made equal to $-F_n$. After transposing and inverting the matrix the unknowns in equation (10.4), i.e. the values of dX_n ($n = 1, 2, 3$, etc.) can be obtained. The changes in the unknowns can be added to the previous values Y_n until these changes are sufficiently small. For the example considered the following X-values were obtained:

$$X_2 = 0\cdot6398 \qquad X_{13} = I_A/I_C = \;\; 0\cdot9928$$

$$X_3 = 0\cdot3197 \qquad X_{14} = I_A/I_D = \;\; 2\cdot3173$$

$$X_4 = 0\cdot4366 \qquad X_{15} = I_A/I_E = 44\cdot9853$$

$$X_6 = 0\cdot6308$$

$$X_7 = 0\cdot6768 \qquad (X_{12} = I_A/I_B = 1\cdot0 \text{ assumed})$$

$$X_8 = 0\cdot3599$$

$$X_{10} = 0\cdot1935$$

It now remains to decide on the design of beam A for stresses and deflexion and then select the sizes of the remaining beams to suit the above inertia ratios. Since the value of X_{13} is so close to unity it is apparent that beams A, B and C should be made identical and since X_{15} is so large beam E can be omitted.

In the above analysis shear has been neglected. To see whether this effect was important the analysis was repeated with the effects of shear added. The same depth of web was used (49 in. overall) and beam E was omitted from this analysis. The following results were obtained.

$$X_2 = 0\cdot4944 \qquad X_{12} = I_A/I_B = 0\cdot8792$$

$$X_3 = 0\cdot4541 \qquad X_{13} = I_A/I_C = 1\cdot1808$$

$$X_4 = 0\cdot3709 \qquad X_{14} = I_A/I_D = 1\cdot6789$$

$$X_7 = 0\cdot4840$$

$$X_8 = 0\cdot5639 \qquad \left(X_{15} = \frac{I_A}{I_E} \to \infty \text{ assumed} \right)$$

$$X_{10} = 0\cdot5317$$

There is no great difference between these results and the previous ones which did not include shear effects. By deliberately making beams A, B and C identical and selecting X_{14} from the second solution the following values of X were obtained (shear is included).

$$X_2 = 0\cdot4760 \qquad X_7 = 0\cdot5680$$

$$X_3 = 0\cdot3742 \qquad X_8 = 0\cdot4927$$

$$X_4 = 0\cdot4444 \qquad X_{10} = 0\cdot4113$$

Again it is apparent from these results that the effect on the load distribution of changing the inertia ratios by small amounts is not important. In the last case examined the maximum variation from the mean boundary load is 13 per cent.

It has been found that this method worked quite satisfactorily for the example given. There were ten unknowns and convergence took place in four iterations. When the core design was changed from square to hexagonal pitch it was found necessary to change the spacing of the beams so that those in the x-direction were spaced differently from those in the y-direction. This meant that the number of unknowns increased to twenty-two. The method just described proved unsatisfactory because the solution diverged. It was necessary to find some other method and the one presented in the next section was used. The method is applied to the same grillage layout as before but, for reasons described later, it should be appreciated that this example is not a particularly good one. This method is extremely powerful because it leads directly to a grillage design without having to solve simultaneous equations.

10.4. SECOND METHOD OF DESIGN OF AN "EGG-BOX" GRILLAGE WITH UNIFORM BOUNDARY REACTION

In Appendix III it is shown that if the load applied to the grillage is uniformly distributed and is taken half by the x-beams and half by the y-beams then the boundary reaction is uniformly distributed. The proof offered is merely an extension of an earlier one by Livesley[1] to the more general case of the beams with different spacings in the x- and y-directions.

The theory is not strictly applicable to a grillage with such an overhang but it will be applied to the previous grillage to illustrate the method.

Suppose the beams of the grillage are completely separated from one another and placed on separate supports of the correct length for each beam. If half the applied load at each point is now placed on an x-beam and half on a y-beam each of the beams will deflect by an amount which is inversely proportional to its inertia. By choosing the inertia ratios it is possible to match the deflexion of a point in an x-beam with that of the corresponding point in a y-beam. One then has a list of inertia ratios which may or may not cross-check with one another. In three cases examined by the author they have checked with great accuracy except at points near the boundary when the grillage has an overhang. This means that the inertia ratios which give a uniform boundary reaction and match the deflexions at corresponding points on the x- and y-beams automatically match the deflexions at the other points in the grillage.

To illustrate the method, consider the grillage treated previously with the difference that beam E is omitted. This means that X_6 will be equal to W_6

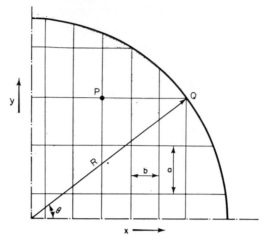

FIG. 10.9. Quadrant of grillage with rectangular net.

(Table 10.2). Now make X_n equal to $0.5W_n$ in equations (10.12)–(10.18) (Appendix I) but ignore equation (10.15). This results in the following set of inertia ratios.

TABLE 10.3. INERTIA RATIOS FROM DEFLEXION EQUATIONS

Point	2	$I_A/I_D = 1.4492$	Point	7	$I_D/I_B = 0.5318$
	3	$I_A/I_C = 1.30622$		8	$I_C/I_B = 0.8503$
	4	$I_A/I_B = 1.1132$		10	$I_D/I_C = 0.6076$

From these figures it is possible to establish the ratio of inertias in a number of different ways. For instance the ratio I_A/I_B is given directly at point 4. However, it is also possible to obtain I_A/I_B by multiplying the ratios from points 3 and 8, i.e. $I_A/I_B = 1.1107$. All values computed in this way are given in Table 10.4.

TABLE 10.4. INERTIA RATIOS COMPUTED FROM TABLE 10.3

I_A/I_B		I_A/I_C		I_A/I_D	
Points	Ratios	Points	Ratios	Ratios	Ratios
2 and 7	0.7707	2 and 10	0.8805	4 and 7	2.0933
3 and 8	1.1107	4 and 8	1.3092	3 and 10	2.1497
4	1.1132	3	1.3062	2	1.4492

It must be remembered that the deflexions of the beams will automatically match at points on the axis of symmetry, i.e. (Fig. 10.7) points 5, 9 and 11, and deflexions match at the boundary because they are zero. Table 10.4 indicates that it is easy to equate deflexions in intersecting beams at points 3, 4 and 8. Disagreement between inertia ratios and therefore deflexions occurs at those points which lie near the boundary. It is thought that this is partly due to the presence of the overhang which makes the theory suspect in this region. By neglecting the values in Table 10.4 which are suspect, a set of ratios is obtained which agree remarkably well with the first set quoted in Section 10.2.

This method was used to redesign the grillage when the core layout was altered. In this case the number of unknowns was twenty-two (fifteen joints and seven inertia ratios) and it was found that the computer programme described in Section 10.2 slowly diverged because it was not possible to guess the initial values close enough to the exact solution. The second method proved to be quite satisfactory because much better agreement was found in the inertia ratios.

In Appendix II the method is examined in a general way and it is shown that although some inaccuracy occurs at certain points near the boundary the inertias will match over a very large part of the grillage. The greatest inaccuracy is about 11 per cent, which is sufficiently small for design purposes.

10.5. CONCLUSIONS

One of the features of an ideal grillage for a nuclear reactor is that it should have a uniform boundary reaction so that the skirt is not overstressed locally and so that the pressure vessel can be analysed as an axi-symmetric problem. In practice this is fictional because the " egg-box " type of grillage consists of a number of beams which must place concentrated loads onto the skirt. This effect can, however, be minimized by making each section of the skirt carry as near to the average load as possible.

Two methods of direct design are presented in this paper. The first treats the load distributions and inertia ratios as the unknowns. This results in a number of non-linear simultaneous equations which can be solved by using an iterative process and an electronic digital computer. Although this method is quite satisfactory when the number of unknowns is small it is difficult to guess starting values sufficiently close to the true solution to ensure convergence. In the second method it is shown that if the loads are distributed equally between the x- and y-beams then the boundary reaction will be uniformly distributed. The loads are distributed in this way and the deflexions matched at each intersection point by varying the inertia ratios. It is found that the ratios can be cross-checked in several ways and agreement is obtained. A small overhang upsets this agreement at points near the boundary, but apart from these it is possible to establish inertia ratios for a grillage design. This method is extremely powerful because there are no simultaneous equations to be solved.

REFERENCES

1. R. K. LIVESLEY, Circular grillages, their design and analysis. *Nucl. Engng.*, 116–19, March (1960).
2. F. J. STANEK, *Stress Analysis of Beam Grillages*. Oak Ridge Nat. Laboratory Central Files No. 59–9–4. Sept. (1959).
3. J. C. M. EDWARDS, S. S. GILL and J. PERKINS, A method of calculating the deflexion of the graphite support grid for a gas-cooled reactor. *Civil Eng. and Pub. Wks. Rev.* **53**, No. 630, 1400–2 (1958).
4. S. TIMOSHENKO, *Theory of Plates and Shells*, pp. 188–94. McGraw-Hill (1940).

APPENDIX I

Deflexion and Boundary Equations

Point 2

$$23X_2 + 41X_3 + 53X_4 + 29\cdot5W_5 = X_{14}\{8\cdot8868(W_{10} - X_{10}) + $$
$$+ 30\cdot3555(W_7 - X_7) + 43\cdot5900(W_2 - X_2)\} \qquad (10.12)$$

Point 3

$$41X_2 + 76X_3 + 100X_4 + 56W_5 = X_{13}\{11.5297X_{10} + 25\cdot7399W_{11} + $$
$$+ 83\cdot7797(W_8 - X_8) + 102\cdot4297(W_3 - X_3)\} \qquad (10.13)$$

Point 4

$$53X_2 + 100X_3 + 135X_4 + 76\cdot5W_5 = X_{12}\{-12\cdot3072X_6 + $$
$$+ 41.2350X_7 + 90.1329X_8 + 64\cdot1991W_9 + 150\cdot0307(W_4 - X_4)\} \qquad (10.14)$$

Point 6

$$X_{12}\{1\cdot3548X_6 - 4\cdot1028X_7 - 8\cdot2050X_8 - 5\cdot4699W_9 - $$
$$- 12\cdot3072(W_4 - X_4)\} = X_{15}(5W_6 - 5X_6) \qquad (10.15)$$

Point 7

$$X_{12}\{-4\cdot1028X_6 + 13\cdot4394X_7 + 27\cdot3372X_8 + 18\cdot3012W_9 + $$
$$41.2350(W_4 - X_4)\} = X_{14}\{6\cdot6523(W_{10} - X_{10}) + $$
$$+ 22\cdot1211(W_7 - X_7) + 30\cdot3555(W_2 - X_2)\} \qquad (10.16)$$

Point 8

$$X_{12}\{-8\cdot2050X_6 + 27\cdot3372X_7 + 58\cdot2351X_8 + 39\cdot7502W_9 + $$
$$90\cdot132(W_4 - X_4)\} = X_{13}\{9\cdot8797X_{10} + 21\cdot9149W_{11} + $$
$$+ 70\cdot1297(W_8 - X_8) + 83\cdot7797(W_3 - X_3)\} \qquad (10.17)$$

Point 10

$$X_{13}\{1\cdot6297X_{10}+3\cdot2899W_{11}+9\cdot8797(W_8-X_8)+$$
$$+11\cdot5297(W_3-X_3)\} = X_{14}\{2\cdot1836(W_{10}-X_{10})+$$
$$+6\cdot6524(W_7-X_7)+8\cdot8868(W_2-X_2)\} \quad (10.18)$$

Beams A and E

$$X_2+X_3+X_4-X_6 = 0\cdot7653 \quad (10.19)$$

Beam B

$$X_6+X_7+X_8-X_4 = 1\cdot2310 \quad (10.20)$$

Beam C

$$X_3+X_8-X_{10} = 0\cdot4862 \quad (10.21)$$

APPENDIX II

Justification of Second Design Method

Consider the half beam of length L shown in Fig. 10.10. The deflexion curve of the beam can be shown to be

$$EI\,\delta = \frac{5}{24}wL^4 - \frac{wL^2x^2}{4} + \frac{wx^4}{24} \quad (10.22)$$

Now consider the grillage shown in Fig. 10.11 where the beams running parallel to the x-direction are spaced at distance b and those in the y-direction are spaced at distance a. It was shown in Section 10.3 that if the

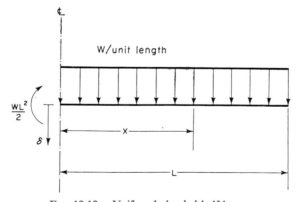

Fig. 10.10. Uniformly loaded half beam.

grillage is uniformly loaded with q per unit area then a uniform boundary reaction is obtained if half the load is taken by each of the x- and y-beams.

Thus the loads on the x- and y-beams are $qb/2$ and $qa/2$ per unit length respectively, and their half lengths L are $\sqrt{(R^2-y^2)}$ and $\sqrt{(R^2-x^2)}$. At P the deflexion in the x-beam is obtained by using equation (10.22).

$$_x\delta_p = \frac{qb}{48EI_x}[5(R^2-y^2)^2-6(R^2-y^2)x^2+x^4]$$

$$= \frac{qbR^4}{48EI_x}[5(1-\bar{y}^2)^2-6(1-\bar{y}^2)x^2+\bar{x}^4]$$

where $\bar{x} = x/R$ and $\bar{y} = y/R$.

Similarly the deflexion at P in the y-beam is

$$_y\delta_p = \frac{qaR^4}{48EI_y}[5(1-\bar{x}^2)^2-6(1-\bar{x}^2)\bar{y}^2+\bar{y}^4]$$

By equating the deflexions the following ratio is obtained

$$\frac{I_x}{I_y} = \frac{b}{a}\frac{5(1-\bar{y}^2)^2-6(1-\bar{y}^2)\bar{x}^2+\bar{x}^4}{5(1-\bar{x}^2)^2-6(1-\bar{x}^2)\bar{y}^2+\bar{y}^4}$$

$$= \frac{b}{a}\left[\frac{1-\bar{y}^2-0\cdot2\bar{x}^2}{1-\bar{x}^2-0\cdot2\bar{y}^2}\right] \qquad (10.23)$$

This equation defines the ratio of inertias at any point inside of the grillage. To demonstrate that this is very close to a unique solution consider the four beams indicated in Fig. 10.11.

At the centre O ($\bar{x} = 0$, $\bar{y} = 0$)

$$\frac{I_2}{I_1} = \frac{b}{a}$$

at B ($\bar{x} = 0$, $\bar{y} \neq 0$)

$$\frac{I_3}{I_1} = \frac{b}{a}\left[\frac{1-\bar{y}^2}{1-0\cdot2\bar{y}^2}\right]$$

at A ($\bar{x} \neq 0$, $\bar{y} = 0$)

$$\frac{I_2}{I_4} = \frac{b}{a}\left[\frac{1-0\cdot2\bar{x}^2}{1-\bar{x}^2}\right]$$

at P ($\bar{x} \neq 0$, $\bar{y} \neq 0$)

$$\frac{I_3}{I_4} = \frac{b}{a}\left[\frac{1-\bar{y}^2-0\cdot2\bar{x}^2}{1-\bar{x}^2-0\cdot2\bar{y}^2}\right]$$

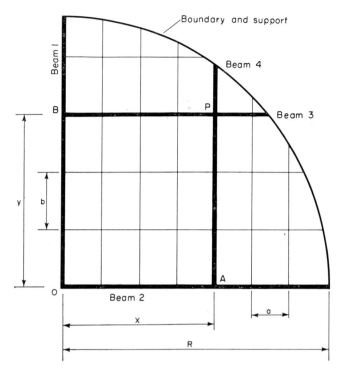

FIG. 10.11.   Plan of quadrant of " egg-box " grillage.

The inertia ratio I_4/I_1 can now be determined in two ways:
from O and A

$$\frac{I_4}{I_1} = \frac{1-\bar{x}^2}{1-0\cdot 2\bar{x}^2}$$

and from B and P

$$\frac{I_4}{I_1} = \left[\frac{1-\bar{x}^2-0\cdot 2\bar{y}^2}{1-\bar{y}^2-0\cdot 2\bar{x}^2}\right]\left[\frac{1-\bar{y}^2}{1-0\cdot 2\bar{y}^2}\right]$$

If these ratios were identical for all $\bar{x}$ and $\bar{y}$ then the solution would be unique, i.e. the beams would have a constant inertia ratio which was independent of $\bar{x}$ and $\bar{y}$.

The ratios are not equal for all $\bar{x}$ and $\bar{y}$ but the equality does exist at $\bar{x} = \bar{y}$ and at $\bar{x} = 0$ and again at $\bar{y} = 0$. The ratios are very nearly equal when $\bar{x}$ and $\bar{y}$ are small. Greatest inequality will occur near the boundary at about 22° from the axes of symmetry, e.g. at $\bar{x} = 0\cdot 8$; $\bar{y} = 0\cdot 2$ the first ratio is 0·328 while the second is 0·4094. The mean of these ratios would be sufficiently close for the inertia of beam 4 to be established.

APPENDIX III

Conditions for " Uniform " Boundary Reaction

Consider a grid which has spacing a of the beams in the x-direction and b of the beams in the y-direction. A quarter of the grillage is shown in Fig. 10.9.

If the load on any beam at any mesh point is $W/2$ we may treat the beams as having a uniformly distributed load equal to the total load on the beam. Consider the beam which passes through P and runs in the x-direction. The reaction at Q is $(WR\cos\theta)/2b$. Similarly the beam which runs in the y-direction and meets the boundary at Q has a reactive force of $(WR\sin\theta)/2a$. The beam running in the x-direction has its reaction spread over a distance around the boundary of $a/\cos\theta$ while the other beam has its reaction spread over a distance of $b/\sin\theta$. Thus the boundary reaction per unit length is the sum of the boundary reactions per unit length from the x-beams and the y-beams, i.e. the boundary reaction per unit length is:

$$\frac{WR\cos\theta}{2b}\frac{\cos\theta}{a} + \frac{WR\sin\theta}{2a}\frac{\sin\theta}{b} = \frac{WR}{2ab}$$

This is independent of θ and therefore if the load at each mesh point is carried equally by the x and y beams the boundary reaction will be uniformly distributed. One point which is important is that this theory is applicable to a grillage which has no overhang beyond the support skirt.

CHAPTER 11

ЭACTOR PRESSURE VESSEL ANALYSIS

R. W. Bailey

NOTATION

R_v = radius of spherical vessel.
R_s = radius of cylindrical skirts.
t_v = thickness of vessel shell.
t_s = thickness of skirt.
D, λ = constants for skirts as defined.
β = constants for vessel as defined.
2ϕ = angle subtended by skirt and centre of sphere ($\sin \phi = R_S/R_v$).
L = length of outside skirt.
x = distance down outside skirt.
γ = coefficient of thermal expansion.
E = Young's modulus.
v = Poisson's ratio.
P = internal pressure in vessel.
W = axial load on inner skirt.
W_{VT} = external load on top portion of vessel.
W_{VB} = external load on bottom portion of vessel.
ρ = density of vessel shell.
T = temperature in outer skirt.
T_0 = temperature at top of skirt.
T_L = temperature at base of skirt.
M = moment per unit length.
Q = shear force, per unit length, in horizontal plane.
$N\theta$ = hoop force.
$N\phi$ = meridional membrane force.
ω = radial displacement of vessel shell.
v = tangential displacement of vessel shell.
δ = horizontal displacement.
θ = angle of rotation.

Suffices

VT = vessel top.	ST = skirt top.
VB = vessel base.	SB = skirt base.

11.1. INTRODUCTION

THE design of a reactor pressure vessel is basically determined by the codes of practice. The British code of practice for pressure vessels, British Standard 1500, calls for an examination of the stresses due to local loadings but does not define an acceptable level for stress concentrations resulting from local effects.

Reactor vessels are of larger size than those usually associated with conventional plant and the requirements of high pressure and temperature together with the internal loading condition of the vessel are unique. For these reasons particular attention must be paid to those locations on the

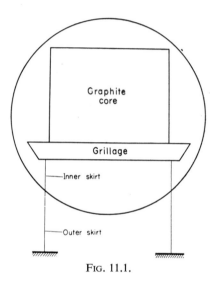

Graphite
core

Grillage

Inner skirt

Outer skirt

FIG. 11.1.

reactor vessel where concentrations of stress may occur, and this introduces a number of major problems. These include the avoidance of restraint in support regions, the effect of patterns of perforations and the accommodation of large openings.

Because of a material thickness limitation the larger pressure vessels will usually be spherical, the theoretically ideal shape for containment of gas under pressure. These vessels, excluding the contents may weigh over one thousand tons and the spherical shape introduces the problem of support. This location will normally be the most highly stressed area of the pressure vessel and attention is confined, in this section, to the analysis, under various loading conditions of this region.

Various methods of supporting these shells have been proposed. This support must be flexible to allow thermal expansions to occur and at the same time not to impose high localized loading on the vessel. The form of support will depend on the design conditions, but the most satisfactory design is probably the use of internal and external skirts as shown in Fig. 11.1. With this type of construction the weight of the core is transferred directly to the foundations and the local reactions on the pressure vessel are uniformly distributed around the circumference so that local stress effects are minimized.

The following discussion deals with this form of construction with particular reference to the effects of:

(a) internal pressure;
(b) axial load on skirts;
(c) self weight of vessel;
(d) external load on vessel;
(e) temperature effects.

11.2. THE CALCULATION OF STRESSES AT THE SUPPORT REGION

The constraining effect of a cylindrical skirt has been investigated, and a solution derived by Hicks.[1] In the present analysis the mathematics are only taken to a stage suitable for use with a digital computer.

Heytényi,[2] showed that a spherical vessel can be replaced by an equivalent conical section because the meridional length of the region of high stresses is small compared with the diameter of the vessel. He showed that when R_v/t_v is large the approximate analysis is in close agreement with the exact theory. A further simplification is that due to Geckeler[3] where the spherical vessel is replaced by an equivalent cylinder and this approximation can be shown to be valid in regions near the equator of the vessel. Although, for simplicity, Geckeler's solution is used in the following, only a minor modification is necessary for the use of Heytényi's relations.

For the behaviour of cylindrical shells under axial symmetric loading, Heytényi[4] has shown that the induced bending stresses are confined to a region close to the load application so that, practically, the length of the skirt has no effect on the magnitude of the induced stresses. He also showed that for practical shells the membrane stresses have a negligible effect on the induced bending stresses. The procedure adopted in the following is therefore to calculate the displacements and rotations due to membrane forces and then determine the corresponding bending and shear stresses necessary to maintain compatibility.

(i) *Compatibility at Skirt to Vessel Junction*

As shown in Fig. 11.2 a positive convention of signs is given to outwards deflexions and shears and anti-clockwise moments and rotations

22

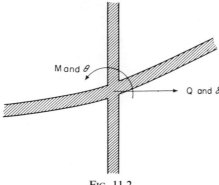

M and θ

Q and δ

FIG. 11.2.

The horizontal displacements and tangential rotations of a spherical cap under edge forces are given by Roark.[5] When the ratio of vessel radius to wall thickness is large and the angle of the junction (ϕ) has practical values, these relations may be written, with the above convention of signs as

$$M_{VT} = (R_s \theta - \beta\delta)\frac{Et_v R_v}{2\beta^3 R_s}$$

$$Q_{VT} = (2\beta\delta - R_s \theta)\frac{Et_v R_v}{2\beta^2 R_s^2}$$

$$M_{VB} = (R_s \theta + \beta\delta)\frac{Et_v R_v}{2\beta^3 R_s} \qquad (11.1)$$

$$Q_{VB} = (2\beta\delta + R_s \theta)\frac{Et_v R_v}{2\beta^2 R_s^2}$$

where

$$\beta^4 = 3(1-v^2)\frac{R_v^2}{t_v^2}$$

The horizontal displacements and tangential rotations of a cylindrical skirt are given by Roark,[5] with the above convention of signs, as

$$M_{ST} = 2D_{ST}\lambda_{ST}(\theta - \lambda_{ST}\delta)$$

$$Q_{ST} = 2D_{ST}\lambda_{ST}^2(2\lambda_{ST}\delta - \theta)$$

$$M_{SB} = 2D_{SB}\lambda_{SB}(\theta + \lambda_{SB}\delta) \qquad (11.2)$$

$$Q_{SB} = 2D_{SB}\lambda_{SB}^2(\theta + 2\lambda_{SB}\delta)$$

where

$$D = Et_s^3/12(1-v^2)$$

$$\lambda^4 = 3(1-v^2)/R_s^2 t_s^2$$

If a moment (M) and shear force (Q) are applied to the junction then since each member at the junction must have the same rotation and deflexion, summing the moments and shears in equations (11.1) and (11.2)

$$\left.\begin{array}{l} \theta\left[\dfrac{Et_v R_v}{\beta^3}+2D_{ST}\,\lambda_{ST}+2D_{SB}\,\lambda_{SB}\right]+\delta\left[2D_{SB}\,\lambda_{SB}^2-2D_{ST}\,\lambda_{ST}^2\right]=M \\[4mm] \theta\left[2D_{SB}\,\lambda_{SB}^2-2D_{ST}\,\lambda_{ST}^2\right]+\delta\left[\dfrac{2Et_v R_v}{\beta R_s^2}+4D_{ST}\,\lambda_{ST}^3+4D_{SB}\,\lambda_{SB}^3\right]=Q \end{array}\right\} \quad (11.3)$$

The solution of these two equations yields the deflexion and rotation of the junctions. The moments and shears acting on each member at the junction may then be obtained from equations (11.1) and (11.2).

(ii) *Particular Loading Conditions*

(a) *Internal pressure.* If the vessel were free to expand, the horizontal deflexion at the junction would be

$$\delta_{VT}=\delta_{VB}=\frac{p(1-v)R_s R_v}{2Et_v}$$

If this deflexion was completely constrained, then from equation (11.1), moments and shears would have to be applied to

$$\left.\begin{array}{l} M_{VT}=-M_{VB}=\dfrac{p(1-v)R_v^2}{4\beta^2} \\[4mm] Q_{VT}=Q_{VB}=\dfrac{-p(1-v)R_v^2}{2\beta R_s} \end{array}\right\} \quad (11.4)$$

The condition results in an unbalanced shear $=Q=+p(1-v)R_v{}^2/\beta R_s$. Substitution of this shear into equation (11.3) gives together with equations (11.4) the moments and shears acting on each member of the junction.

(b) *Axial load on skirts.* If the skirts were free to expand, under this axial load, the horizontal displacement would be

$$\delta_{ST}=\frac{vw}{2\pi Et_{ST}} \quad \text{and} \quad \delta_{SB}=\frac{vw}{2\pi Et_{SB}}$$

The forces to be applied to cancel these deflexions are, from equation (11.2),

$$\left.\begin{array}{ll} Q_{ST}=\dfrac{-vw}{2\pi R_s^2\,\lambda_{ST}}, & Q_{SB}=\dfrac{-vw}{2\pi R_s^2\,\lambda_{SB}} \\[4mm] M_{ST}=\dfrac{-Q_{ST}}{2\lambda_{ST}} & M_{SB}=\dfrac{Q_{SB}}{2\lambda_{SB}} \end{array}\right\} \quad (11.5)$$

These forces result in an unbalanced moment and shear force and the forces on each member of the junction which must be added to equations (11.5) can be obtained from equation (11.3).

(c) *Self weight of spherical pressure vessel.* For a spherical vessel supported by a tangential reaction at the junction the deflexions of the surface are given by Timoshenko[6] p. 371 as

$$
\left.
\begin{aligned}
\frac{dv}{d\phi} - v\cot\phi &= \frac{R_v(1+v)}{Et_v}(N_\phi - N_\theta) \\[6pt]
\omega &= v\cot\phi - \frac{R_v}{Et_v}(N_\theta - vN_\phi) \\[6pt]
0 &= \frac{v}{R_v} + \frac{1}{R_v}\frac{\partial\omega}{\partial\phi} \\[6pt]
\delta &= v\cos\phi - \omega\sin\phi
\end{aligned}
\right\}
\tag{11.6}
$$

and the membrane forces ($N\theta$ and $N\phi$) on p. 359 of the same reference as

$$
N_\phi = -\frac{R_v t_v \rho}{1+\cos\phi}
$$

$$
N_\theta = R_v t_v \rho \left\{ \frac{1}{1+\cos\phi} - \cos\phi \right\}
$$

Substitution of these equations into equation (11.6) gives the deflexion and rotation at the junction of

$$
\theta_{VB} = -\frac{R_v \rho}{E}(2+v)\sin\phi
$$

$$
\delta_{VB} = \frac{-R_v^2 \rho(1+v)}{E} \left\{ \frac{1}{1+\cos\phi} - \frac{\cos\phi}{1+v} \right\}\sin\phi
$$

Similarly for the top portion of the vessel

$$
\theta_{VT} = -\frac{R_v \rho(2+v)}{E}\sin\phi
$$

$$
\delta_{VT} = \frac{R_v^2 \rho(1+v)}{E} \left\{ \frac{1}{1-\cos\phi} + \frac{\cos\phi}{1+v} \right\}\sin\phi
$$

The above deflexions have been calculated assuming the support to consist of a tangential reaction (i.e. membrane theory). The load consists of the vertical dead weight, so that for equilibrium a shear force of value

$$Q = -\frac{4\pi\rho R_v^2 t_v}{2\pi R_s}\cot\phi \tag{11.7}$$

must be added.

If the lower skirt were free to expand under the vertical load, the horizontal displacement would be

$$\delta_{SB} = \frac{2\rho v t_v R_v^2}{Et_{SB}}$$

The forces that must be applied to the members of the junction, to cancel the above rotations and deflexions are obtained from equations (11.1) and (11.2) as

$$\left.\begin{aligned}
M_{VT} &= \frac{\rho R_v^2 t_v}{2\beta^2}\left\{\frac{1+v}{1-\cos\phi} + \cos\phi + \frac{(2+v)}{\beta}\sin\phi\right\} \\[2mm]
Q_{VT} &= \frac{-\rho R_v^2 t_v}{2\beta R_s}\left\{\frac{(1+v)2}{1-\cos\phi} + 2\cos\phi + \frac{(2+v)}{\beta}\sin\phi\right\} \\[2mm]
M_{VB} &= \frac{\rho R_v^2 t_v}{2\beta^2}\left\{\frac{(1+v)}{1+\cos\phi} - \cos\phi + \frac{(2+v)}{\beta}\sin\phi\right\} \\[2mm]
Q_{VB} &= \frac{\rho R_v^2 t_v}{2\beta R_s}\left\{\frac{2(1+v)}{1+\cos\phi} - 2\cos\phi + \frac{(2+v)}{\beta}\sin\phi\right\} \\[2mm]
M_{SB} &= \frac{-vR_v^2 t_v\rho}{R_s^2\lambda_{SB}^2}, \quad Q_{SB} = \frac{-2vR_v^2 t_v\rho}{R_s^2\lambda_s\beta}
\end{aligned}\right\} \tag{11.8}$$

The summation of these forces together with equation (11.7) results in an unbalanced moment and shear at the junction. The distribution of these forces between the members at the junction may be obtained from equations (11.3) and added to equations (11.8) to give the true forces acting on each member of the junction.

(d) *External load on sphere.* For the load system shown in Fig. 11.3, the membrane forces are given by Timoshenko[6] p. 359 as,

$$N_{\phi,VT} = \frac{W_{VT}}{2\pi R_v\sin^2\phi}$$

$$N_{\theta,VT} = \frac{W_{VT}}{2\pi R_v\sin^2\phi}$$

$$N_{\phi,VB} = \frac{W_{VB}}{2\pi R_v\sin^2\phi}$$

$$N_{\theta,VT} = \frac{-W_{VB}}{2\pi R_v\sin^2\phi}$$

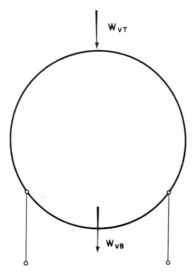

FIG. 11.3.

Substituting these values in equations (11.6) it can be shown that

$$\delta_{VT} = \frac{(1+v)W_{VT}}{2\pi Et_v \sin \phi}$$

$$\delta_{VB} = \frac{-(1+v)W_{VB}}{2\pi Et_v \sin \phi}$$

$$\theta_{VT} = \theta_{VB} = 0$$

and the expansion of the bottom skirt will be

$$\delta_{SB} = \frac{v(W_{VT} + W_{VB})}{2\pi Et_{SB}}$$

As in the previous case the above deflexions have been obtained on the assumption of a tangential reaction at the junction. For equilibrium a shear must be applied of value

$$Q = -\frac{(W_{VT} + W_{VB})}{2\pi R_s} \cdot \cot \phi \tag{11.9}$$

The forces that must be applied to the members of the junction, to cancel the above rotations and deflexions are obtained from equations (11.1) and (11.2) as

$$M_{VT} = \frac{(1-v)W_{VT}}{4\pi\beta^2}\frac{R_v^2}{R_s^2}, \qquad Q_{VT} = -\frac{(1+v)W_{VT}R_v^2}{2\pi\beta R_s^3}$$

$$M_{VB} = \frac{(1+v)W_{VB}}{4\pi\beta^2}\frac{R_v^2}{R_s^2}, \qquad Q_{VB} = \frac{(1+v)W_{VB}R_v^2}{2\pi\beta R_s^3} \left.\right\} \quad (11.10)$$

$$M_{SB} = -\frac{v(W_{VT}+W_{VB})}{4\pi R_s^2 \lambda_{SB}^2}, \qquad Q_{SB} = -\frac{v(W_{VT}+W_{VB})}{2\pi R_s^2 \lambda_{SB}}$$

The summation of these forces together with equation (11.9) results in an unbalanced moment and shear at the junction. The distribution of these forces at the junction can be obtained from equation (11.3) and added to equation (11.10) to give the true forces acting on each member of the junction.

An example of the results of these calculations, using a digital computer, together with the necessary data is shown below.

$$R_v = 375\,\text{in.}$$
$$R_s = 244 \cdot 56\,\text{in.}$$
$$t_v = 3 \cdot 25\,\text{in.}$$
$$t_{ST} = 2 \cdot 5\,\text{in.}$$
$$t_{SB} = 2 \cdot 5\,\text{in.}$$
$$p = 0 \cdot 10089\,\text{tons/in}^2 = \text{internal pressure.}$$
$$W = 2528\,\text{tons} = \text{weight of core.}$$
$$W_{VT} = 468\,\text{tons} = \text{weight of upper standpipes.}$$
$$W_{VB} = 0 = \text{weight of lower standpipes.}$$
$$W_\rho = 976\,\text{tons} = \text{weight of shell and insulation.}$$

	M_{VT}	M_{VB}	Q_{VT}	Q_{VB}	M_{ST}	M_{SB}	Q_{ST}	Q_{SB}
Internal pressure	4·593	−4·593	−0·519	−0·519	−4·988	4·988	0·519	0·519
Wt. of core	−0·223	0·233	0·025	0·025	0·242	−0·242	−0·025	−0·025
Wt. of standpipe	1·237	−0·962	−0·149	−0·100	0·371	−0·646	−0·044	−0·062
Wt. of shell	2·590	−1·998	−0·311	−0·207	0·763	−1·355	−0·091	−0·129

11.3. THE CALCULATION OF THERMAL STRESSES IN THE OUTER SKIRT

For a cylinder subjected to an axially symmetric temperature distribution the deflexion of the shell wall must satisfy Heytényi's[4] equation.

$$\frac{\mathrm{d}^4\delta}{\mathrm{d}x^4} + 4\lambda^4(\delta - \gamma RT) = 0 \qquad (11.11)$$

and the appropriate boundary conditions. The above differential equation can be satisfied by expressing δ in the Fourier series

$$\delta = \gamma R \left\{ T_0 - (T_0 - T_L)\frac{x}{L} + \sum_{n=1}^{\infty} a_n \sin\frac{n\pi x}{L} \right\} \tag{11.12}$$

and the boundary conditions satisfied by applying radial moments and shears to the cylinder ends. Substituting δ for in equation (11.11)

$$\sum_{n=1}^{\infty} a_n \left\{ 1 + \frac{n^4\pi^4}{4\lambda^4 L^4} \right\} \sin\frac{n\pi x}{L} = T - \left\{ T_0 - (T_0 - T_L)\frac{x}{L} \right\}$$

and the coefficients a_n may now be obtained by simple Fourier analysis as

$$a_n = \frac{2}{L} \frac{\displaystyle\int_0^L \left\{ T - T_0 - \frac{(T_0 - T_L)x}{L} \right\} \sin\frac{n\pi x}{L}\,dx}{\left\{ 1 + \frac{n^4\pi^4}{4\lambda^4 L^4} \right\}} \tag{11.13}$$

The temperature distribution down the skirt length will depend on the form of insulation used. This is arranged to minimize the stresses at the skirt to vessel junction and will normally consist of a " radiation pocket " plus a lagged length of skirt. With this form of insulation the temperature curve will be represented by a series of exponential terms and equation (11.13) can then be integrated exactly. Where the temperature distribution is not known exactly, as, for example, in the case of experimentally measured temperatures down the skirt, numerical methods give reasonable accuracy.

These values of the constants a_n, substituted into equation (11.12) give the deflexion of the skirt supposing these were pinned connections at both ends.

The slope of the skirt is given by the differential of equation (11.12) as

$$\frac{d\delta}{dx} = \gamma R \left\{ -\frac{(T_0 - T_L)}{L} + \frac{\pi}{L} \sum_{n=1}^{\infty} a_n \cos\frac{n\pi x}{L} \right\}$$

and at the top of the skirt ($x = 0$)

$$\theta_0 = \gamma R \left\{ \frac{T_0 - T_L}{L} - \frac{\pi}{L} \sum_{n=1}^{\infty} n a_n \right\}$$

At the base of skirt ($x = L$)

$$\theta_L = \gamma R \left\{ \frac{T_0 - T_L}{L} - \frac{\pi}{L} \sum_{1}^{\alpha} (-1)^n a_n \right\}$$

In practice, at the base of the skirt, the temperature will be ambient, and the boundary conditions will approach the case of full fixity. The above solution can be made to satisfy this condition by applying forces to the base of the skirt of value [equation (11.2)].

$$M = 2D\lambda\theta_L, \quad V = -2D\lambda^2\theta_L$$

The deflexion and rotation at the top of the skirt will depend on the stiffness of the members forming the junction. If there were no rotation or deflexion at the top of the skirt then a moment must be applied of value

$$M = 2D\lambda\theta_0$$

and a shear force of value

$$Q = -D\left(\frac{d^3\delta}{dx^3}\right) + 2D\lambda^2\theta_0$$

$$= -D\gamma R \sum_1^\alpha \frac{n^3\pi^3}{L^3} a_n + 2D\lambda^2\theta_0$$

The true forces acting on the members forming the junction are obtained by substitution of M and Q into equations (11.3).

The bending stresses down the length of the skirt are given by

$$M_x = D\frac{d^2\delta}{dx^2} + (\text{end corrections})$$

$$= \frac{D\gamma R\pi^2}{L^2} \sum_1^\alpha n^2 a_n \sin\frac{n\pi x}{L} + M_{ST} e^{-\lambda x}(\cos \lambda x + \sin \lambda x)$$

$$- Q_{ST}\frac{1}{\lambda} e^{-\lambda x} \sin \lambda x - 2D\lambda\theta_L e^{-\lambda(L-x)} \cos \lambda(L-x)$$

and the hoop stress by

$$\frac{N_\theta}{t} = \gamma ET - \frac{E\delta}{R} + (\text{end corrections})$$

$$= \gamma E\left\{ T - \left[T_0 - \left(\frac{T_0 - T_L}{L}\right)x \right] - \sum_1^\alpha a_n \sin\frac{n\pi x}{L} \right\}$$

$$-\frac{2\lambda^2 R}{t} M_{ST} e^{-\lambda x}(\cos \lambda x - \sin \lambda x) + \frac{2\lambda R Q_{ST}}{t} e^{-\lambda x} \cos \lambda x +$$

$$+\frac{4D\lambda^3}{t} R\theta_L c^{-\lambda(L-x)} \sin \lambda(L-x)$$

An example of this calculation together with the necessary data for the stress calculations is shown below:

$$R_v = 375\,\text{in.}$$
$$R_s = 244\cdot56\,\text{in.}$$
$$t_v = 3\cdot25\,\text{in.}$$
$$t_{ST} = 2\cdot50\,\text{in.}$$
$$t_{SB} = 2\cdot50\,\text{in.}$$

The actual temperature distribution depends on the form of insulation and heat transfer properties of the materials. A particular case, together with the calculated stresses is shown in Fig. 11.4.

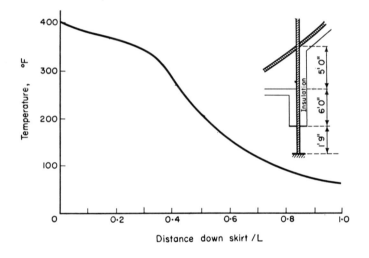

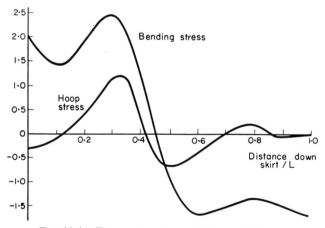

Fig. 11.4. Temperature stresses in lower skirt.

REFERENCES

1. R. HICKS, *Theoretical Analysis of the Stresses Induced in a Spherical Pressure Vessel due to the Constraining Effect of a Cylindrical Skirt*, vol. **172**. Inst. Mech. Engrs. (1958).
2. M. HEYTÉNYI, *Spherical Shells Subjected to Axial Symmetrical Bending*. Inst. Ass. Br. Struct. Engrs. (1938).
3. J. W. GECKELER, *Forsch. Arb.* No. 276, Berlin (1926).
4. M. HEYTÉNYI, *Beams on Elastic Foundations*. University of Michigan Studies, Science Series 16 (1946).
5. R. ROARK, *Formulas for Stress and Strain*. McGraw-Hill (1954).
6. S. TIMOSHENKO, *Theory of Plates and Shells*. McGraw-Hill (1940).

CHAPTER 12

GAS DUCT FLEXIBILITY ANALYSIS

J. F. Poynor

NOTATION

$\mathbf{A}$ = matrix of influence coefficients.

$\mathbf{B}, \mathbf{B_0}, \mathbf{B_1},$
$\mathbf{D}, \mathbf{G}, \mathbf{c}, \mathbf{k}$ = matrices as defined in text.

C = constant in creep equation.

D = creep coefficient as defined in text.

E = Young's modulus.

$\mathbf{{}_BF}, \mathbf{{}_0F}, \mathbf{{}_pF}, \mathbf{\alpha_i}$ = force matrices as defined in text.

$\mathbf{F_C}$ = matrix of reactions at origin after time t.

f_{11}, f_{12}, etc. = influence coefficients.

I = second moment of area of duct cross-section.

I_c = second moment of area of duct cross-section under creep conditions as defined in text.

K, k_1, k_2, k_3 = flexibility factors for duct bends.

$\mathbf{L}$ = matrix of direction cosines.

L_{11}, L_{12}, etc. = coefficients as defined in text.

$\mathbf{{}_BM}, \mathbf{{}_0M}, \mathbf{{}_pM}, \mathbf{M}, \mathbf{\beta_i}$ = moment matrices as defined in text.

${}_pM$ = bending moment at point p after time t under creep conditions.

Mx, My, Mz = moments about axes at p.

N = number of cycles for fatigue criteria.

n = creep index.

OX, OY, OZ = co-ordinate axes, origin O.

px, py, pz = co-ordinate axes, origin p.

R = radius of curvature of bend axis.

r = mean radius of duct cross-section.

t = thickness of duct bend, also any time after elastic conditions apply.

U = strain energy of bending.

X, Y, Z = co-ordinates of any point p on duct, distance l from built in end A.

X_B, Y_B, Z_B = co-ordinates of free end B of duct.

Γ = gamma function.

Δ_C = matrix of creep displacements at origin after time t.

$_B\Delta, _B\phi$ = displacement and rotation matrices at B.

$_O\Delta, _O\phi$ = displacement and rotation matrices at O.

α, β, γ = rotation of hinge joints.

δ_{ij} = Krönecker deltas.

$\dot\varepsilon$ = creep strain rate under stress σ.

$\dot\varepsilon_0$ = reference creep strain rate.

κ = curvature of element of duct.

λ = dimensionless duct factor.

σ = membrane pressure stress in unpierced shell, also creep stress.

σ_a = alternating stress during a cycle.

σ_e = maximum equivalent stress on the von Mises criterion.

σ_l = maximum longitudinal stress in a bend.

σ_m = mean stress during a cycle.

σ_0 = reference creep stress.

σ_s = maximum permissible value of σ_m.

σ_{tr} = maximum transverse stress in a bend.

σ_u = ultimate tensile stress.

σ_v = allowable alternating stress.

σ_y = yield stress or proof stress in simple tension.

σ_θ = normal stress acting on a meridional section of a shell.

σ_ϕ = tangential stress acting on a meridional section of a shell.

ϕ = angle describing position of a point around the duct bore, $\phi = 0$ at extrados.

$d\phi$ = creep rotation of element dl in time dt.

12.1. INTRODUCTION

GAS duct flexibility analysis involves the evaluation of forces and moments set up in the main large diameter ducts which run between the reactor pressure vessel and the steam-raising units. The main structural problem centres around the absorption of the thermal expansions of these two components and the main ducts themselves, which convey the cooling medium from the core of the reactor to the steam-raising units. Four or more identical gas circuits are used with each reactor. From the viewpoints of duct flexibility, there are two possible basic systems, both of which are shown in Fig. 12.1.

(1) The reactor gas inlet duct illustrates the hinged-joint system and incorporates hinged bellows units to absorb the thermal expansion. The

units only rotate about their hinge pin axes, the ducting between the units remaining essentially undeflected.

(2) The reactor gas-outlet duct illustrates the inherently flexible system. Here no hinged joints are used, and all expansions are absorbed by deflexion of the duct work in bending.

All the present Central Electricity Generating Board's nuclear power stations incorporate the hinged-joint system. At the time of the design of .Calder Hall, hinged joints for the design conditions had not previously been

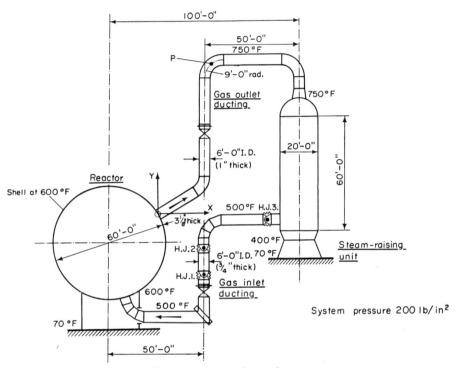

Fig. 12.1. Diagrammatic gas duct system.

manufactured, but it was fairly certain that a satisfactory design could be made. If this were done it would result in the least possible loading being transferred to the reactor by the ducting. In the event, this scheme was satisfactorily carried out, and the civil power stations subsequent to Calder Hall have been designed with the same object in mind. However, many designers feel that an equally satisfactory design, at a slightly lower overall cost, could be obtained if the upper ducting were to be inherently flexible, although this would result in higher loading being transferred to the reactor. It is for this reason that the structural problems arising from both systems will be considered.

Whatever design is used certain basic data must be obtained. The essential parameters are pressure, temperature, expansion of connected equipment and the number of pressure and temperature cycles expected in a twenty-year station life. Such data may be considered the starting point for any flexibility calculations.

12.2. DESIGN CODES

The design should satisfy an applicable code, together with client's and insurer's requirements. No code is yet available in this country which has been specifically written for the design of nuclear power stations. Under these circumstances, use is made of the existing British Standard 1500[1] for designing the ducting for pressure considerations only. No comparable British Standard is yet available for the analysis of duct thermal expansions. The American Code for Pressure Piping[2] could form a basis, but it is not considered to be completely adequate for nuclear applications. Hence, use must be made of published literature, together with a modified design philosophy based on the American code. It should not be felt that this lack of specific codes has in any way held up the progress of nuclear plant design, but specific codes would obviate the differences of opinion that must arise when use is made of the published literature.

12.3. STRUCTURAL ANALYSIS OF THE INHERENTLY FLEXIBLE DUCT SYSTEM

Design Considerations

The inherently flexible system requires the consideration of the following aspects:

(1) The calculation of forces and moments exerted on the duct by the reactor due to restrained thermal expansions.

(2) The evaluation of stresses at all significant points in the ducting system.

(3) The evaluation of the additional stresses set up in the reactor due to the duct reactions.

(4) The derivation of allowable limits to the above stresses if no directly applicable code is available.

Before items (1) and (2) can be evaluated numerically, by considering the duct as a tubular structure, stress–strain relationships must be established for the duct bends.

Development of Stress–Strain Theory for Duct Bends

Mitred or smooth bends as shown in Fig. 12.2, when subjected to a bending moment, give stresses and strains which are not predicted by normal bending theory.

This phenomenon is principally due to the ovalization of the duct cross-

section which results in considerably modified stresses and strains. Von
Kármán investigated this problem theoretically in 1911, and since then an
extensive bibliography has been built up together with a considerable number
of experimental investigations. The earlier workers in this field were mainly
concerned with long radius bends where R/r was not smaller than about 10.
In recent years, however, the use of short radius bends with R/r equal to
about 3 has required a more exact analysis, since some of the approximations
and assumptions of the earlier theories are no longer valid.

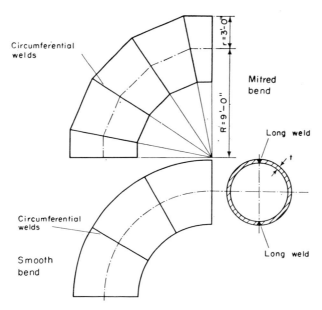

FIG. 12.2.   Mitred and smooth bends.

The following two approximations are the most important ones when
considering the extension of von Kármán's analysis to short radius bends:
(1) Where the Rayleigh Ritz method is used, giving a trigonometrical
series for displacement, insufficient terms have been taken to give the
required accuracy.
(2) Neglect of the transverse direct stress, i.e. transverse stresses are
assumed to be due to bending only.
Beskin[3] developed a theory similar to that of von Kármán, but took
sufficient terms to make his analysis applicable to short radius bends, thus
eliminating approximation (1) but retaining approximation (2).
Gross[4] eliminated approximations (1) and (2) by extending von Kármán's
analysis to three terms, and by introducing the transverse direct stress.
Turner and Ford[5] carried out a detailed theoretical investigation of the

effect of all the approximations made in the various theories and concluded that von Kármán's analysis, modified to allow for the transverse direct stress and taken to an adequate number of terms, is sufficiently accurate for short radius bends. Thus the work of Gross[4] may be used in the analysis of stresses and strains occurring in the short radius nuclear gas duct bends.

Many experimental investigations have been carried out, those by Gross[4] and Gross and Ford[6] being most extensive. They concluded that due to differences between manufactured and nominal dimensions, theory and experimental results can vary by 15 per cent. However, this accuracy should be considerably increased when analysing duct bends fabricated from plate using the best manufacturing techniques.

All the above work relates to a bend subjected to in-plane bending. Vigness[7] has dealt with the case of out-of-plane bending, but the literature on this type of loading is still very limited.

The effect of internal pressure on the stresses and strains in a bend due to an applied bending moment has been investigated by Rodabaugh and George,[8] but more work on this aspect of bend stress analysis is to be desired.

It is important to note that no satisfactory theoretical analysis has been derived for mitre bends, but it is known that they behave in a similar manner to an equivalent smooth bend.

Flexibility and Stress Factors for Smooth Duct Bends

To enable the stress–strain theories to be readily used by the designer, all authors have expressed their conclusions in the form of flexibility and stress factors. The deflexion properties of bends may be expressed in terms of the flexibility factor which is defined as:

$$K = \frac{\text{rotation per unit length of the bend produced by a moment}}{\text{rotation per unit length obtained by normal theory for the same moment}}$$

Fig. 12.3 indicates the variation of K with the dimensionless duct factor λ, and shows the range of K applicable to nuclear duct systems.

The stress distributions in bends are expressed in terms of a stress factor which may be defined as

$$\text{stress factor} = \frac{\text{actual stress}}{\text{nominal maximum stress predicted by simple theory}}$$

The flattening of the cross-section reduces the longitudinal stresses at $\phi = 0°$ and $180°$, but increases them at other points in the cross-section (Fig. 12.4). Transverse bending and direct compressive stresses are also set up in the cross-section and reach maximum values on the inner surface at $\phi = 90°$. These transverse stresses are the maximum that occur in the cross-

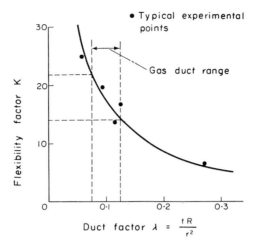

FIG. 12.3.   Flexibility factor, *K*.

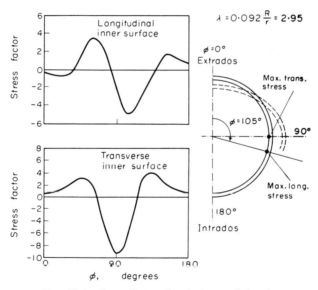

FIG. 12.4.   Stress factors for duct smooth bends.

section, and it is therefore evident that both longitudinal and transverse stress factors must be considered. Expressions for the stress factors in terms of λ and ϕ are somewhat cumbersome, and reference should be made to Gross[4] for formulae which are sufficiently accurate for use by the designer. Stress factors for pressure alone in a duct bend are well established and are given by Timoshenko.[9]

Analysis of the Duct as a Tubular Structure

With suitable inclusions of the flexibility and stress factors, items (1) and (2) of the Design Considerations may now be analysed.

(a) *Methods of analysis.* An inherently flexible duct with ends built in at the reactor and steam-raising unit, when subjected to thermal expansions, forms a highly redundant structure. Over many years various methods have been proposed to analyse the resulting end reactions and moments acting on the duct. Some of these methods are wholly analytical being based on strain energy methods, while moment–area and other methods have also been developed.

All these methods are equally exact, in that no assumptions need to be made other than those usually necessary in structural analysis problems. The selection of a particular method by a designer can therefore be governed by his preference for the specific structural approach used. Kellogg[10] gives an extensive bibliography of the literature available on this topic, but the critical nature of reactor design precludes the use of the many approximate methods that have been proposed for use with piping systems.

The use of electronic computers has increased the attention given to the strain energy approach which will be considered in outline here. The recent work of Morice[11] on modern structural analysis gives a basis for this purely analytical solution to the inherently flexible duct system.

(b) *Strain energy analysis.* Consider the three plane duct AB (Fig. 12.5), built in at A and with free end B. Let forces and moments

$$_B\mathbf{F} = \begin{bmatrix} _BF_X \\ _BF_Y \\ _BF_Z \end{bmatrix} \quad \text{and} \quad _B\mathbf{M} = \begin{bmatrix} _BM_X \\ _BM_Y \\ _BM_Z \end{bmatrix}$$

act on the duct at B.

Then the forces and moments at any point p on the duct are given by:

$$_p\mathbf{F} = {}_B\mathbf{F} \qquad _p\mathbf{M} = \mathbf{B}\,_B\mathbf{F} + {}_B\mathbf{M}$$

where

$$\mathbf{B} = \begin{bmatrix} 0 & (Z-Z_B) & -(Y-Y_B) \\ -(Z-Z_B) & 0 & (X-X_B) \\ (Y-Y_B) & -(X-X_B) & 0 \end{bmatrix}$$

Now choose axes x, y, z at p so that x is directed along the tangent to the duct at p and z is directed towards the centre of curvature of the duct at p. Let p' be any point with coordinates X', Y', Z' with respect to the origin O, and coordinates x', y', z' with respect to origin p. Then

$$\begin{bmatrix} X' \\ Y' \\ Z' \end{bmatrix} = \begin{bmatrix} X \\ Y \\ Z \end{bmatrix} + \mathbf{L} \begin{bmatrix} x' \\ y' \\ z' \end{bmatrix}$$

where **L** is the matrix of direction cosines,

$$\mathbf{L} = \begin{bmatrix} l_1 & l_2 & l_3 \\ m_1 & m_2 & m_3 \\ n_1 & n_2 & n_3 \end{bmatrix}$$

So the moment matrix referred to the axes at p is **M**, where

$$\mathbf{M} = \begin{bmatrix} M_x \\ M_y \\ M_z \end{bmatrix} = \mathbf{L'}_p \mathbf{M}$$

Now the strain energy of bending of the duct is:

$$U = \frac{1}{2EI} \int_A^B (\bar{\mathbf{c}}\mathbf{M})'(\mathbf{c}\mathbf{M}) \, dl$$

where

$$\mathbf{c} = \begin{bmatrix} c_1 & 0 & 0 \\ 0 & c_2 & 0 \\ 0 & 0 & c_3 \end{bmatrix}$$

I = second moment of area of duct cross-section
E = Young's modulus.
c is a matrix which makes allowance for the difference between the strain energy of torsion, in-plane bending and out-of-plane bending of the duct.
Now let

$$_B\mathbf{F}' = [\alpha_1 \; \alpha_2 \; \alpha_3] \qquad _B\mathbf{M}' = [\beta_1 \; \beta_2 \; \beta_3]$$
$$= [\alpha_i] \qquad\qquad = [\beta_i]$$

where i = 1, 2, 3 refer to the X, Y, Z directions respectively. Since $[\alpha_i]$ and $[\beta_i]$ are constants and **c** is independent of $[\alpha_i]$ and $[\beta_i]$, we have:

$$EI\frac{\partial U}{\partial \alpha_i} = \tfrac{1}{2} \int_A^B (\mathbf{D}_i + \mathbf{D}_i') \, dl \quad \text{and} \quad EI\frac{\partial U}{\partial \beta_i} = \tfrac{1}{2} \int_A^B (\mathbf{G}_i + \mathbf{G}_i') \, dl$$

where

$$\mathbf{D_i} = \left(\mathbf{c}\frac{\partial\mathbf{M}}{\partial\alpha_i}\right)'(\mathbf{cM}) \qquad \mathbf{G_i} = \left(\mathbf{c}\frac{\partial\mathbf{M}}{\partial\beta_i}\right)'(\mathbf{cM})$$

Now $\mathbf{D}$ and $\mathbf{G}$ are 1×1 matrices, therefore $\mathbf{D}' = \mathbf{D}$, $\mathbf{G}' = \mathbf{G}$.
Let $_\mathbf{B}\Delta_i$, $_\mathbf{B}\phi_i$ be the displacements and rotations at B.
Then

$$EI\,_\mathbf{B}\Delta_i = EI\frac{\partial U}{\partial\alpha_i} = \int_A^B \mathbf{D_i}\,dl$$

$$EI\,_\mathbf{B}\phi_i = EI\frac{\partial U}{\partial\beta_i} = \int_A^B \mathbf{G_i}\,dl$$

Now

$$\frac{\partial\mathbf{M}}{\partial\alpha_i} = \mathbf{L}'\frac{\partial_\mathbf{P}\mathbf{M}}{\partial\alpha_i} = \mathbf{L}'\mathbf{B}\begin{bmatrix}\delta_{i1}\\\delta_{i2}\\\delta_{i3}\end{bmatrix}$$

$$\frac{\partial\mathbf{M}}{\partial\beta_i} = \mathbf{L}'\frac{\partial_\mathbf{P}\mathbf{M}}{\partial\beta_i} = \mathbf{L}'\begin{bmatrix}\delta_{i1}\\\delta_{i2}\\\delta_{i3}\end{bmatrix}$$

where δ_{ij} are the Krönecker deltas, $\delta_{ij} = 1$ if $i = j$, $\delta_{ij} = 0$ if $i \neq j$.
  Therefore

$$\mathbf{D_i} = [\delta_{i1}\,\delta_{i2}\,\delta_{i3}]\,\mathbf{B}'\mathbf{LkL}'[\mathbf{B_B F}+{}_\mathbf{B}\mathbf{M}]$$

$$\mathbf{G_i} = [\delta_{i1}\,\delta_{i2}\,\delta_{i3}]\,\mathbf{LkL}'[\mathbf{B_B F}+{}_\mathbf{B}\mathbf{M}]$$

where

$$\mathbf{k} = \begin{bmatrix} k_1 & 0 & 0 \\ 0 & k_2 & 0 \\ 0 & 0 & k_3 \end{bmatrix} = \mathbf{c}^2 = \begin{bmatrix} c_1^2 & 0 & 0 \\ 0 & c_2^2 & 0 \\ 0 & 0 & c_3^2 \end{bmatrix}$$

So

$$EI\begin{bmatrix} _B\Delta_X \\ _B\Delta_Y \\ _B\Delta_Z \\ _B\phi_X \\ _B\phi_Y \\ _B\phi_Z \end{bmatrix} = \begin{bmatrix} \int[1\ 0\ 0]\,\mathbf{B}'\mathbf{LkL}'[\mathbf{B_B F}+{}_\mathbf{B}\mathbf{M}]\,dl \\ \int[0\ 1\ 0]\,\mathbf{B}'\mathbf{LkL}'[\mathbf{B_B F}+{}_\mathbf{B}\mathbf{M}]\,dl \\ \int[0\ 0\ 1]\,\mathbf{B}'\mathbf{LkL}'[\mathbf{B_B F}+{}_\mathbf{B}\mathbf{M}]\,dl \\ \int[1\ 0\ 0]\quad\mathbf{LkL}'[\mathbf{B_B F}+{}_\mathbf{B}\mathbf{M}]\,dl \\ \int[0\ 1\ 0]\quad\mathbf{LkL}'[\mathbf{B_B F}+{}_\mathbf{B}\mathbf{M}]\,dl \\ \int[0\ 0\ 1]\quad\mathbf{LkL}'[\mathbf{B_B F}+{}_\mathbf{B}\mathbf{M}]\,dl \end{bmatrix}$$

therefore

$$EI \begin{bmatrix} {}_B\Delta \\ {}_B\phi \end{bmatrix} = \begin{bmatrix} \int\mathbf{B'LkL'B}\,dl, & \int\mathbf{B'LkL'}\,dl \\ \int\mathbf{LkL'B}\,dl, & \int\mathbf{LkL'}\,dl \end{bmatrix} \begin{bmatrix} {}_B\mathbf{F} \\ {}_B\mathbf{M} \end{bmatrix}$$

Note that as $\mathbf{k'} = \mathbf{k}$

$$(\mathbf{LkL'})' = \mathbf{LkL'}$$

$$(\mathbf{LkL'B})' = \mathbf{B'LkL'}$$

$$(\mathbf{B'LkL'B})' = \mathbf{B'LkL'B}$$

So the matrix of influence coefficients of the forces and moments is symmetrical about its principal diagonal, as is required by Maxwell's reciprocal theroem.

It will be seen that the influence coefficients include the matrix $\mathbf{B}$, and hence the co-ordinates of the free end of the duct. For the purposes of tabulation, it is convenient to have the coefficients independent of these co-ordinates so we proceed as follows.

If there is a rigid connection between O and B and ${}_0\Delta$, ${}_0\phi$, are the displacement and rotation matrices at O then:

$$\begin{aligned}
{}_0\Delta &= {}_B\Delta - \mathbf{B_0'}\,{}_B\phi \quad \text{where } \mathbf{B_0} = \begin{bmatrix} 0 & -Z_B & Y_B \\ Z_B & 0 & -X_B \\ -Y_B & X_B & 0 \end{bmatrix} \\
{}_0\phi &= {}_B\phi
\end{aligned}$$

therefore

$$\begin{bmatrix} {}_B\Delta \\ {}_B\phi \end{bmatrix} = \begin{bmatrix} {}_0\Delta + \mathbf{B_0'}\,{}_0\phi \\ {}_0\phi \end{bmatrix} = \begin{bmatrix} \mathbf{I} & \mathbf{B_0'} \\ \mathbf{O} & \mathbf{I} \end{bmatrix} \begin{bmatrix} {}_0\Delta \\ {}_0\phi \end{bmatrix}$$

where $\mathbf{I} = $ unit matrix and $\mathbf{O} = $ the null matrix.

Now

$$\begin{bmatrix} \mathbf{I} & \mathbf{B_0'} \\ \mathbf{O} & \mathbf{I} \end{bmatrix}^{-1} = \begin{bmatrix} \mathbf{I} & -\mathbf{B_0'} \\ \mathbf{O} & \mathbf{I} \end{bmatrix}$$

therefore

$$EI \begin{bmatrix} {}_0\Delta \\ {}_0\phi \end{bmatrix} = \begin{bmatrix} \mathbf{I} & -\mathbf{B_0'} \\ \mathbf{O} & \mathbf{I} \end{bmatrix} \begin{bmatrix} \int\mathbf{B'LkL'B}\,dl, & \int\mathbf{B'LkL'}\,dl \\ \int\mathbf{LkL'B}\,dl, & \int\mathbf{LkL'}\,dl \end{bmatrix} \begin{bmatrix} {}_B\mathbf{F} \\ {}_B\mathbf{M} \end{bmatrix}$$

Now let $\mathbf{B} = \mathbf{B_0} + \mathbf{B_1}$, therefore

$$\mathbf{B} = \begin{bmatrix} 0 & Z & -Y \\ -Z & 0 & X \\ Y & -X & 0 \end{bmatrix}$$

therefore

$$EI \begin{bmatrix} {}_0\Delta \\ {}_0\phi \end{bmatrix} = \begin{bmatrix} \int(\mathbf{B}_1' \, \mathbf{L}k\mathbf{L}'\mathbf{B_O} + \mathbf{B}_1' \, \mathbf{L}k\mathbf{L}'\mathbf{B}_1)\,\mathrm{d}l, & \int\mathbf{B}_1' \, \mathbf{L}k\mathbf{L}'\,\mathrm{d}l \\ \int(\mathbf{L}k\mathbf{L}'\mathbf{B_O} + \mathbf{L}k\mathbf{L}'\mathbf{B}_1)\,\mathrm{d}l, & \int\mathbf{L}k\mathbf{L}'\,\mathrm{d}l \end{bmatrix} \begin{bmatrix} {}_\mathbf{B}\mathbf{F} \\ {}_\mathbf{B}\mathbf{M} \end{bmatrix}$$

$$= \begin{bmatrix} \int\mathbf{B}_1' \, \mathbf{L}k\mathbf{L}'\mathbf{B}_1 \, \mathrm{d}l, & \int\mathbf{B}_1' \, \mathbf{L}k\mathbf{L}'\,\mathrm{d}l \\ \int\mathbf{L}k\mathbf{L}'\mathbf{B}_1 \, \mathrm{d}l, & \int\mathbf{L}k\mathbf{L}'\,\mathrm{d}l \end{bmatrix} \begin{bmatrix} \mathbf{I} & \mathbf{O} \\ \mathbf{B_O} & \mathbf{I} \end{bmatrix} \begin{bmatrix} {}_\mathbf{B}\mathbf{F} \\ {}_\mathbf{B}\mathbf{M} \end{bmatrix}$$

therefore

$$EI \begin{bmatrix} {}_0\Delta \\ {}_0\phi \end{bmatrix} = \begin{bmatrix} \int\mathbf{B}_1' \, \mathbf{L}k\mathbf{L}'\mathbf{B}_1 \, \mathrm{d}l, & \int\mathbf{B}_1' \, \mathbf{L}k\mathbf{L}'\,\mathrm{d}l \\ \int\mathbf{L}k\mathbf{L}'\mathbf{B}_1 \, \mathrm{d}l, & \int\mathbf{L}k\mathbf{L}'\,\mathrm{d}l \end{bmatrix} \begin{bmatrix} {}_0\mathbf{F} \\ {}_0\mathbf{M} \end{bmatrix}$$

and the influence coefficients are independent of the coordinates of the free end of the duct. Positive directions of ${}_0\Delta$, ${}_0\phi$, ${}_0\mathbf{F}$, ${}_0\mathbf{M}$, are shown in Fig. 12.5. Expanding the matrices of influence coefficients we obtain:

$$EI \begin{bmatrix} {}_0\Delta_X \\ {}_0\Delta_Y \\ {}_0\Delta_Z \\ {}_0\phi_X \\ {}_0\phi_Y \\ {}_0\phi_Z \end{bmatrix} = \begin{bmatrix} f_{11} & f_{12} & \cdots & f_{16} \\ f_{21} & & \cdots & \\ & \cdots & & \\ & \cdots & & \\ & \cdots & & \\ f_{61} & \cdots & & f_{66} \end{bmatrix} \begin{bmatrix} {}_0F_X \\ {}_0F_Y \\ {}_0F_Z \\ {}_0M_X \\ {}_0M_Y \\ {}_0M_Z \end{bmatrix} \qquad (12.1)$$

where:

$$f_{11} = \int(L_{22}\,Z^2 - 2L_{23}\,YZ + L_{33}\,Y^2)\,\mathrm{d}l$$
$$f_{12} = f_{21} = \int(L_{23}\,XZ + L_{13}\,YZ - L_{12}\,Z^2 - L_{33}\,XY)\,\mathrm{d}l$$
$$f_{13} = f_{31} = \int(L_{12}\,YZ + L_{23}\,XY - L_{22}\,XZ - L_{13}\,Y^2)\,\mathrm{d}l$$
$$f_{14} = f_{41} = \int(L_{13}\,Y - L_{12}\,Z)\,\mathrm{d}l$$
$$f_{15} = f_{51} = \int(L_{23}\,Y - L_{22}\,Z)\,\mathrm{d}l$$
$$f_{16} = f_{61} = \int(L_{33}\,Y - L_{23}\,Z)\,\mathrm{d}l$$
$$f_{22} = \int(L_{11}\,Z^2 - 2L_{13}\,XZ + L_{33}\,X^2)\,\mathrm{d}l$$
$$f_{23} = f_{32} = \int(L_{12}\,XZ + L_{13}\,XY - L_{11}\,YZ - L_{23}\,X^2)\,\mathrm{d}l$$
$$f_{24} = f_{42} = \int(L_{11}\,Z - L_{13}\,X)\,\mathrm{d}l$$
$$f_{25} = f_{52} = \int(L_{12}\,Z - L_{23}\,X)\,\mathrm{d}l$$
$$f_{26} = f_{62} = \int(L_{13}\,Z - L_{33}\,X)\,\mathrm{d}l$$
$$f_{33} = \int(L_{11}\,Y^2 - 2L_{12}\,XY + L_{22}\,X^2)\,\mathrm{d}l$$
$$f_{34} = f_{43} = \int(L_{12}\,X - L_{11}\,Y)\,\mathrm{d}l$$
$$f_{35} = f_{53} = \int(L_{22}\,X - L_{12}\,Y)\,\mathrm{d}l$$

$$f_{36} = f_{63} = \int (L_{23} X - L_{13} Y)\, dl$$
$$f_{44} = \int (L_{11})\, dl$$
$$f_{45} = f_{54} = \int (L_{12})\, dl$$
$$f_{46} = f_{64} = \int (L_{13})\, dl$$
$$f_{55} = \int (L_{22})\, dl$$
$$f_{56} = f_{65} = \int (L_{23})\, dl$$
$$f_{66} = \int (L_{33})\, dl$$

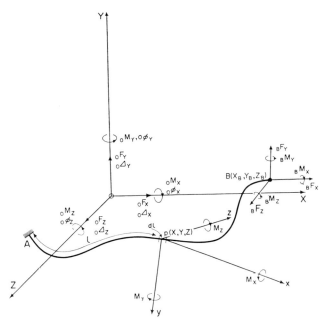

FIG. 12.5.   Inherently flexible duct.

and

$$L_{11} = k_1\, l_1^2 + k_2\, l_2^2 + k_3\, l_3^2$$
$$L_{22} = k_1\, m_1^2 + k_2\, m_2^2 + k_3\, m_3^2$$
$$L_{33} = k_1\, n_1^2 + k_2\, n_2^2 + k_3\, n_3^2$$
$$L_{12} = k_1\, l_1\, m_1 + k_2\, l_2\, m_2 + k_3\, l_3\, m_3$$
$$L_{13} = k_1\, l_1\, n_1 + k_2\, l_2\, n_2 + k_3\, l_3\, n_3$$
$$L_{23} = k_1\, m_1\, n_1 + k_2\, m_2\, n_2 + k_3\, m_3\, n_3$$

k_1 = torsional flexibility factor,

k_2 = in-plane bending flexibility factor,

k_3 = out-of-plane bending flexibility factor.

For ease of computation, the influence coefficients have been tabulated.[10] From the torsional properties of the duct $k_1 = 1·3$. The in-plane bending flexibility factor k_2 equals the value of K given by Gross,[4] while Vigness[7] has shown that k_3 also equals the value of K.

(c) *Application of the analysis to the gas outlet duct.* For the single plane gas outlet duct, Fig. 12.1, equations (12.1) reduce to three equations in unknowns $_0F_x$, $_0F_y$, $_0M_z$. From the typical design parameters shown in Fig. 12.1, the following may be derived.

Duct thickness, 1 in. (28–32 tons/in² U.T.S. material)

Duct factor λ, 0·08

Flexibility factor K, 16·4 for operating conditions
                     21·4 for zero internal pressure

Longitudinal stress factor ($\phi = 90°$), 1·96 for operating conditions
                     2·8 for zero internal pressure

Transverse stress factor ($\phi = 90°$), 6·0 for operating conditions
                     8·58 for zero internal pressure

Solution of the three equations gives the values of $_0F_x$, $_0F_y$, $_0M_z$ shown in Table 12.1. Two cases are considered, case (1) refers to operating conditions, while case (2) refers to an isolated duct with zero internal pressure, the reactor still being under power and at its operating temperature. Such a case would be given during the maintenance of a steam-raising unit, the duct isolating valve being closed.

TABLE 12.1.   LOADING EXERTED ON THE GAS OUTLET DUCT
BY THE REACTOR

Case	Temperatures (°F)	$_0F_x$ (tons)	$_0F_y$ (tons)	$_0M_z$ (tons in.)
1	Duct 750 Reactor 600	20	21·4	−3800
2	Duct 70 Reactor 600	6·9	10·8	400

From the values in Table 12.1 the bending moments at all significant points on the duct may be found, and hence the nominal maximum stress predicted by simple theory. Appropriate stress factors give the actual stresses, and Table 12.2 is a summary of maximum stresses developed in the duct due to the restrained thermal expansion and internal pressure. It is fortuitous that, at $\phi = 90°$ where maximum thermal expansion stresses occur, the stress factor for pressure *alone* equals unity. It is usual to assume that the duct wall is subjected to plane stress only, and the equivalent stress is based on the shear–strain energy (von Mises) theory of failure.

TABLE 12.2. GAS OUTLET DUCT STRESSES

Case	Temp. (°F)	Point considered	Loading considered	Max. princ. stresses (tons/in²)		Max. equiv. stress σ_e
				σ_l	σ_{tr}	(tons/in²)
1	750	Point P on bend $\phi = 90°$ outside surface (Fig. 1.1.)	Internal pressure	1·6	3·2	
			thermal expansions (operating)	3·4	10·3	
			Total	5·0	13·5	11·9
2	70	ditto	Thermal expansions (ducting isolated)	2·0	6·0	5·3

σ_l = longitudinal stress.
σ_{tr} = transverse or hoop stress.

12.4. STRUCTURAL ANALYSIS OF THE HINGED JOINT SYSTEM

Construction of the Hinge Joint

A typical hinge joint is shown in Fig. 12.6, the hydraulic cylinders of a fatigue test rig being seen on either side of the joint. Hinge joints are only intended to rotate in a plane perpendicular to the axis of the pins. The hinge arms transfer the axial pressure load and shear force across the joint, so that the bellows convolutions are not subjected to these forces. The design of the hinge arms and pins is straightforward, and with a 6 ft. diameter. duct system at 200 lb./in² they are subjected to a force of 370 tons. It is usual to employ hardened and tempered alloy steel for the pins, and to lubricate them with molybdenum disulphide which retains its lubricating properties for long periods at high temperatures.

The convolutions may be fabricated from $\frac{1}{8}$ in. thick hardened and tempered chromium–molybdenum steel, with a yield point of 40 tons/in². Their fabrication involves specialized techniques, and for the pressures and diameters with which we are concerned here the number of possible manufacturers is very limited. Bowden and Drumm[12] give detailed consideration to the design, construction and application of hinge joints.

FIG. 12.6.   Hinge joint for gas ducting.

Analysis of Convolution Stresses

The published literature on the analysis of convolution stresses and deflexions is by no means as extensive as that for duct bends, of the literature that is available, most of the papers relate to the simpler analytical problem of convolutions subjected to axial compression. Feely and Goryl[13] have considered the stress analysis of hinge joint convolutions, but the profile of convolution considered is not suitable for gas ducts in nuclear installations. Turner and Ford[14] have developed a theoretical analysis for varying convolution profile, but restricted their investigation to the case of axial compression. It may be concluded that no comprehensive analysis exists which could be used for determining the stress distribution in hinge joint convolutions, and provide a satisfactory acceptance basis. Acceptance of a specific design of hinge joint for use in the gas duct system is therefore based on prototype testing, which simulates the operating conditions for the twenty-year life of the station.

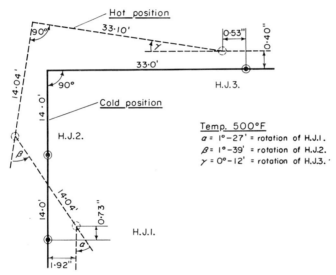

FIG. 12.7. Hinge-joint rotations.

Hinge-Joint Rotation

The gas inlet ducting (Fig. 12.1) illustrates the hinge-joint system, and from the dimensions and temperature distribution shown the displacements at *HJ* 1 and 3 may be obtained. For the purposes of hinge-joint rotation the gas inlet ducting is equivalent to the configurations shown in Fig. 12.7. Since all lengths and displacements are known, a trigonometrical solution gives the values of α, β, γ. It is usual to erect the ducting with the hinge joints preset by about half the calculated rotations to reduce the rotations imposed on the convolutions in the operating condition, given in Table 12.3.

TABLE 12.3. HINGE-JOINT ROTATIONS

Hinge joint	Calculated rotation	Preset rotation	Operating rotation
HJ.1	1° – 27′	0° – 45′	0° – 42′
HJ.2	1° – 39′	0° – 45′	0° – 54′
HJ.3	0° – 12′	0°	0° – 12′

The values given in Table 12.3 are based on the assumption that the ducting is undeflected by the bending moments due to the hinge joints. Sufficient accuracy may usually be obtained by the trigonometrical solution, but in a critical case the hinge-joint system may be analysed by the theory developed for the inherently flexible system. This requires deriving influence coefficients and flexibility factors for the hinge joints and utilizing test data for the spring rate of the joints obtained during prototype testing.

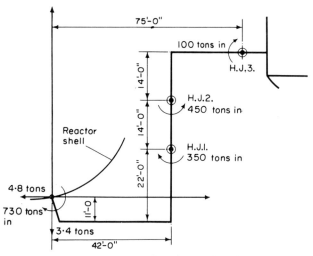

FIG. 12.8.   Reactor loading due to hinge joints.

Moment and Forces Exerted on the Reactor Due to Hinge-Joint Rotations

For a 6ft diameter hinge joint at 200 lb./in^2 pressure, the spring rate of the joint would be about 500 ton in. per degree of rotation. The moments exerted by the hinge joints for the operating rotations in Table 12.3 may thus be found, and are shown in Fig. 12.8.

The solution of three linear equations for the statically determinate system yields the moment and forces exerted on the reactor also shown in Fig. 12.8. Due to their small magnitude no calculations will be made of their effect on the reactor shell. The larger loading due to the upper ducting will be considered fully in Section 12.5.

12.5. STRESSES IN THE REACTOR PRESSURE VESSEL ADJACENT TO A DUCT OPENING

(a) *Due to Internal Pressure Only*

British Standard 1500 requires reinforcement of all openings in the reactor pressure vessel shell for the effects of internal pressure, and specifies rules by which this reinforcement may be calculated. Fig. 12.9 indicates a duct

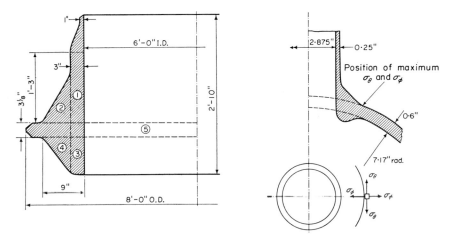

FIG. 12.9. Duct forging and photoelastic model.

forging which gives the required reinforcement determined approximately from the relationship: Areas $(1)+(2)+(3)+(4)$ must be equal to or greater than area (5). The concept of "replacement areas" theoretically gives stresses in the pierced shell equal to those in the unpierced if the following assumptions are made:

(1) The shell is assumed to be a flat plate.

(2) The shell is assumed to be uniformly stressed in all directions.

(3) All the reinforcement is assumed to act in the plane of the shell, and is concentrated at the edge of the hole.

Having satisfied the requirements of British Standard 1500, the validity of the above assumptions must be considered in determining the actual stress distribution around the spherical shell opening. In practice these assumptions are not all valid, and stress concentrations will occur around the opening.

Assumption (1). The work of Hicks[15] and Waters[16] is typical of the relevant analyses which are based on this assumption. Hicks states that this assumption is valid for the analysis of spherical shells when the radius of curvature of the vessel is large compared with the diameter of the hole. Waters similarly states that the openings in spherical shells should be small, but again does not specify limiting opening to vessel diameter ratios.

The paper by Penny[17] gives a theoretical analysis which does not require this assumption, and considers its effect when applied to gas duct openings in spherical pressure vessels with the sizes shown in Fig. 12.1. Here, the vessel diameter to opening diameter ratio equals 10·0 and the conclusion is drawn that large errors in the calculated stress factors can result from this assumption.

Assumption (2). This assumption is valid for a spherical pressure vessel.

Assumption (3). The reinforcing limits specified in British Standards 1500 tend to mitigate the effects of this assumption. However, the distribution of the reinforcement greatly influences the stress factors. It is considered that the profile of the duct forging in Fig. 12.9 gives the minimum practical stress factors, due to the reinforcement being approximately equal inside and outside the shell, and the use of generous radii at changes in direction of the profile. Balancing of the reinforcement inside and outside of the shell removes the bending stresses set up by the eccentric loading of the shell in the normal pad type reinforcement.

References 15, 16 and 17, do not apply to this optimum forging profile, for which no exact analytical analysis is yet available in the literature. For critical cases such as we are considering here recourse must be made to model strain gauge or photoelastic tests.

Typical photoelastic spherical model tests (see Chapter 13) are reported by Taylor[18], and for the model profile shown in Fig. 12.9, N–6A of Ref. 18, these tests gave maximum normal and tangential stresses of $\sigma_\theta = 1\cdot35\sigma$ and $\sigma_\phi = 1\cdot24\sigma$, respectively, where σ is the membrane pressure stress in the unpierced shell. The model profile is similar to that of the duct forging, but the effect on stress factors of scaling up the model to the dimensional ratios of the duct forging and reactor must be considered.

Table 12.4 shows the large increase over those for the model in diameter and diameter thickness ratios given by the reactor-duct forging intersection. It is to be expected that the increases in ratios D/h_v and d/h_n would result in considerably increased stress factors at the forging above those predicted by the model, while the increased D/d ratio would reduce the same stress factors.

With these effects under consideration, it is proposed to use stress factors 50 per cent greater than those obtained from the model test.

TABLE 12.4. DIMENSIONAL PARAMETERS OF MODEL N–6A
AND REACTOR

	Main vessel		Nozzle		Ratios		
	I.D. (D) (in.)	Thickness (h_v) (in.)	I.D. (d) (in.)	Thickness (h_n) (in.)	$\dfrac{D}{h_v}$	$\dfrac{d}{h_n}$	$\dfrac{D}{d}$
Model N–6A	14·3	0·6	2·875	0·25	24	11·5	5
Reactor	720	3·125	72	3	230	24	10

Hence, $\sigma_\theta = 2\cdot0\sigma$ and $\sigma_\phi = 1\cdot9\sigma$. For the operating pressure $\sigma = 5\cdot16$ tons/in², therefore $\sigma_\theta = 10\cdot3$ tons/in², $\sigma_\phi = 9\cdot8$ tons/in².

These values should be realistic for the duct forging, but it is emphasized that the increased stress factors above should not be used in an actual design problem, and are used only to illustrate the design procedure.

In a specific case model strain gauge or photoelastic tests should be made using the correct forging and reactor profiles.

(b) *Due to the Loading Imposed by the Duct*

Fig. 12.10 gives the loading imposed on the gas outlet duct forging for the two cases previously considered. The analysis of this type of spherical shell loading has been covered by Bijlaard[19, 20] and also Penny.[17] The latter author has basically applied the general methods enunciated by Zaremba.[21] Both Bijlaard and Penny have had to include certain assumptions or limitations in their analyses, and this restricts the accuracy of the stress distributions derived.

Bijlaard considers the effect of both a radial force and a bending moment externally applied to a duct forging. Bijlaard[20] states that the assumption of a rigid duct forging in the spherical shell, for all practical cases, gives conservative results for the stresses in the shell adjacent to the forging. Doubt exists as to the validity of this statement since the " rigid insert " assumption gives reduced values for σ_θ due to the restraining effect of the " rigid insert ", and increased values for σ_ϕ. It can be argued that the equivalent stress and the maximum stress are not appreciably altered, but the magnitudes of the individual stresses are in error.

Penny only considered the effect of the axi-symmetric radial force when dealing with externally applied loads, but his analysis does not require the assumption of a " rigid insert ". In certain cases, however, it is subject to approximations resulting from the assumptions of a semi-infinite and thin cylinder. The former assumption would not be necessary if the case of a

24

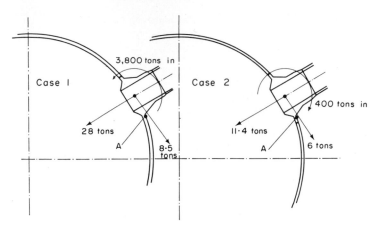

FIG. 12.10.   Loadings on the duct forging.

short cylinder were considered by the methods given in the discussion to
Zaremba.[21]   Penny's analysis therefore approximately gives the correct
magnitudes of the individual stresses for a pad type reinforced opening
subjected to a radial force.

The above summary of the analytical methods available shows that,
without model tests, the designer has little alternative but to use the work
of Bijlaard[19] and assume a rigid insert when dealing with both a radial

TABLE 12.5.   REACTOR SHELL STRESSES

Case	Temp. (°F)	Point considered	Loading considered	Max. princ. stresses (tons/in²)		Max. equiv. stress σ_e (tons/in²)
				σ_θ	σ_ϕ	
1	600	Point A outside surface of shell (Fig. 12.10.)	Internal pressure	10·3	9·8	
			Due to duct	1·1	3·5	
			Total	11·4	13·3	12·5
2	600	ditto	Internal pressure	10·3	9·8	
			Due to duct	−0·2	−0·6	
			Total	10·1	9·8	9·7

load and a bending moment applied to a reinforced opening with a profile of the duct forging considered here. Since the results of model tests subjected to external loadings are not yet available in the literature, use will be made of Bijlaard. Table 12.5 summarizes the stresses in the shell adjacent to the forging for the two loading cases of Fig. 12.10, and includes the previously derived pressure stresses.

12.6. ACCEPTANCE LIMITS FOR THE CALCULATED STRESSES

Sustained Stresses Compared to Thermal Stresses

Consider an element of a component subjected to stresses caused by pressure or dead-weight. When these stresses reach the yield point, non-elastic deformation will result, and this deformation will continue unless strain hardening or redistribution of stress takes place. This continued deformation is necessary since the *stress system* of the component must be in equilibrium with the external applied loading, which for pressure and dead-weight does not reduce with deformation. This concept gives rise to the term " *sustained stresses* ". In practice, strain-hardening and redistribution of stress almost always will take place. It is not considered good design practice to rely on such phenomena for sustained stresses when acceptance of a design is based solely on analysis and no recourse is made to experimental strain gauge tests. This philosophy should only be considered as referring to the complex shapes arising in pressure vessel or duct design.

When considering stresses due to differential thermal expansion, any yielding that may take place will reduce the thermal stresses. This is evident from the fact that for these stresses it is the thermal *strain system* that must be satisfied in the component, and the stress system need only give the equilibrium of internal forces.

An important extension of the strain system approach occurs when local areas, such as the pressure vessel shell-duct forging junction, are being considered. Here continuity of strain must exist between the components when the vessel is subjected to sustained internal pressure. Therefore, the stress system due to pressure in local areas has the same characteristics as thermal stresses.

The above approach must not be considered as universal to all local stress systems in all materials. Each system must be examined for its validity, important considerations are ductility and ratio of yield point to ultimate tensile strength in determining the degree of yielding that may safely be permitted.

The Strain-hardening Criteria for Thermal Stress

When dealing with thermal stresses, it must be appreciated that any yielding that takes place will set up a reversed stress system when the component cools down. The value of this system will approximately equal the difference between the thermal stress, calculated on assumed elastic conditions beyond the yield point, and the value of the yield point. Hence in order to prevent yielding both when the component is heated up and when it cools down, the *calculated* thermal stress should not exceed $1\cdot6\sigma_y$, where σ_y is the yield stress or proof stress in simple tension. For a fuller discussion of this approach, reference may be made to the work of Kerkhof.[22] Repeated yielding must not be permitted since it can cause strain-hardening and the phenomenon of stress corrosion.

The Fatigue Criteria for Thermal Stress

The possibility of fatigue failure due to thermal stresses must also be considered. We are only concerned with high strain fatigue, i.e. strains which are above the endurance limit in a relatively small number of cycles. Hence, the approach is that we are designing for a finite life and a given number of temperature cycles. The literature on high strain fatigue is now fairly comprehensive, and the work of Benham,[23] the Pressure Vessel Research Committee[24, 25] and the Babcock & Wilcox Co.[26] enables a fatigue criteria to be used. Coffin[27] has shown that mechanically induced fatigue strains have similar effects as those due to restrained thermal expansion. It is therefore permissible to utilize the mechanically induced fatigue data of Refs. 24 and 25 for the thermal stresses under consideration here.

Two types of fatigue test have been carried out for the Pressure Vessel Research Committee. Bowman and Dolan[24] carried out experiments on biaxially stressed flat plates, while Gross and Stout[25] utilized cantilever test specimens. The former test plates were freely supported around the edges of the top face and repeatedly loaded from zero to a maximum with hydraulic fluid pressure on the bottom face of the plate. The central zone of the top face developed biaxial tensile stresses with a 2:1 ratio. Both mill surface and notched plates were tested, the notches being crescent shaped with a depth of $\frac{1}{100}$ in. a root radius of $\frac{1}{100}$ in. and a length of $\frac{3}{8}$ in. They were intended to give a stress factor similar to that which might be obtained from irregularities present in commercial fabrication. The longitudinal axis of the notch was perpendicular to the maximum principal stress, and the development of a crack $\frac{3}{16}$ in. long on the surface was chosen as a criterion of failure. The cantilever tests were carried out using a ground finish, and were continued until complete fracture occurred.

Great care must be exercised by the designer when utilizing fatigue data obtained in laboratory tests for application to fabricated components, and the following effects must be considered.

(a) *Effect of temperature.* It has been found that at high temperatures the fatigue life tends to be slightly greater than at atmospheric temperatures, with equal strains imposed. No account is taken of this increased life when considering high-temperature components.

(b) *Effect of creep.* Use must not be made of fatigue results at a temperature where creep is likely to become significant, say above 750°F for killed carbon steel with good creep resisting properties. Fatigue under creep conditions is very complex, and further consideration is given to this effect in Section 12.8.

(c) *Effect of a weld.* It is found that the presence of a weld has no effect on the fatigue life, provided the weld is ground smooth with the plate surface. Normally, removal of the weld reinforcement is carried out for radiography and other purposes.

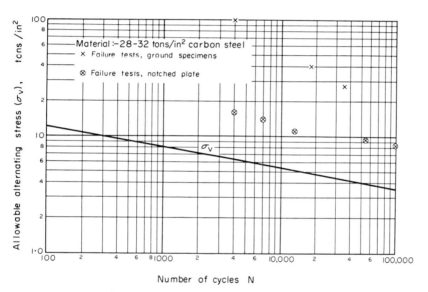

FIG. 12.11. Allowable values of σ_v.

(d) *Speed of cycling.* It was found from the cantilever tests that reducing the speed of cycling from 200 c.p.m. to 1·5 c.p.m. reduced the fatigue life by about 15 per cent. It is possible that service loadings involving cycles lasting weeks or months would reduce the fatigue life by 25 per cent or more. This question requires further consideration for nuclear reactors with a life of twenty years, and is akin to the extrapolation of short time creep and stress to rupture data.

Fig. 12.11 indicates the allowable alternating stresses for varying numbers of cycles, and also gives a selection of test results from Refs. 24 and 25. The test results were based on strain range to failure, the failure alternating stresses in Fig. 12.11 equal $\frac{1}{2} \times E \times$ (strain range to failure). The resulting stresses are fictitious beyond the proportional limit, and are used only for comparison with calculated stresses based on elastic theory irrespective of their value. The tests for ground specimens diverge upwards from the notched plate results as the alternating stress increased. This divergence is considered to be due to the strain hardening of the ground specimens under high strains. Similar strain hardening could not occur in the root of the notch of the plate specimens.

The design curve is positioned so that it gives a factor of safety of about 2 on the more applicable failure alternating stresses for notched plate. This design curve will adequately allow for those effects given above which have not yet been fully investigated either by theory or experiment.

The utilization of strain-cycling data to the type of loadings involved here has been covered by Langer,[28] where use is made of the Goodman diagram,[29] and the concept of cumulative fatigue.[30]

Cumulative fatigue must be considered since Cases (1) and (2) occur a different number of times in the design life of twenty years.

12.7. ACCEPTANCE OF THE CALCULATED STRESSES

Material Properties

The following average properties will be used:

Temperature (°F)	Ultimate stress (σ_u) (tons/in²)	Yield stress (σ_y) (tons/in²)
70	28	15
600	30	10
750	27	9

Duct Stresses (Table 12.2)

(a) *Strain-hardening criteria,* $\sigma_e < 1 \cdot 6 \sigma_y$. Maximum value of $\sigma_e = 11 \cdot 9$ tons/in² at 750°F and $1 \cdot 6 \sigma_y = 14 \cdot 4$ tons/in². Hence, the strain-hardening criteria is satisfied.

(b) *Fatigue criteria.* It is estimated that a maximum design value of 200 cycles should be taken for the complete shutting down of the unit, from its operating conditions, for a twenty-year life. Similarly, 1000 cycles are taken for isolation of the ducting from its operating conditions. Hence,

for Case (1), $N = 200 \quad \sigma_v = 10 \cdot 6$ tons/in²
for Case (2), $N = 1000 \quad \sigma_v = \ 8 \cdot 1$ tons/in² $\Big\}$ from Fig. 12.11.

Now alternating stress,

$$\sigma_a = \frac{\text{max. stress} - \text{min. stress}}{2}$$

and mean stress, $\sigma_m = \sigma_y - \sigma_a$. It may be shown that $\sigma_y - \sigma_a$ gives the value of the mean stress when the maximum stress exceeds σ_y.

Therefore

Case (1): $\sigma_a = \dfrac{11\cdot9 - 0}{2} = 6 \text{ tons/in}^2,$ $\quad \sigma_m = 9\cdot0 - 6\cdot0 = 3\cdot0 \text{ tons/in}^2$

Case (2): $\sigma_a = \dfrac{11\cdot9 - 5\cdot3}{2} = 3\cdot3 \text{ tons/in}^2,$ $\quad \sigma_m = 9\cdot0 - 3\cdot3 = 5\cdot7 \text{ tons/in}^2$

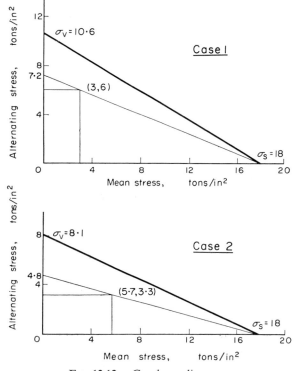

FIG. 12.12. Goodman diagrams.

Goodman diagrams for Cases (1) and (2) are given in Fig. 12.12. In these diagrams, ordinates represent alternating stresses with a maximum of σ_v, and abscissae represent mean stresses with a maximum of σ_s equal to $\frac{1}{2}(\sigma_u + \sigma_y)$. All points within the triangular diagrams represent safe combinations of alternating and mean stresses. From these diagrams the equivalent alternating stress for Case (1) equals 7·2 tons/in² and for case (2) equals 4·8 tons/in², and Fig. 12.11 gives the allowable number of cycles of 2000 and 20,000, respectively, for these equivalent stresses.

The check for cumulative fatigue requires the following condition to be satisfied:

$$\Sigma \frac{\text{actual cycles for a given equivalent alternating stress}}{\text{allowable cycles for this equivalent alternating stress}} < 0·8$$

The summation limit allows for the effects of the order in which the stress cycles are applied throughout the life of the component.

Here $\dfrac{200}{2000} + \dfrac{1000}{20,000} = 0·15$ which is less than 0·8.

Shell Adjacent to the Duct Forging (Table 12.5)

The check here follows precisely the same procedure as for the duct and only the results need be quoted.

(a) *Strain-hardening criteria.* $1·6\sigma_y = 16$ tons/in², which is greater than $\sigma_e = 12·5$ tons/in².

(b) *Fatigue criteria.* Equivalent alternating stresses for cases (1) and (2) are 7·7 and 2·5 tons/in², giving the allowable number of cycles of 1400 and infinity, respectively.

Hence the check for cumulative fatigue gives:

$$\frac{200}{1400} + \frac{1000}{\infty} = 0·14 \text{ which is less than } 0·8.$$

12.8. CREEP ANALYSIS OF SINGLE PLANE DUCT SYSTEMS

General Problem of Duct Creep Analysis

The complete stress analysis of a duct system should include a consideration of the possible effects of creep relaxation on the fatigue criterion used in the elastic analysis. Fatigue tests are carried out under conditions which do not include the effects of creep, and similar restrictions apply to the use of the Goodman diagram. The designer must therefore select a suitably creep-resisting material for the ducting, depending upon the temperature to which it will be submitted during the twenty-year life of the station. It is to be expected that 750° F forms the upper limit of temperature if the ducting is to be fabricated from killed carbon steel with optimum creep-resisting properties. If the effects of creep relaxation are considered in this manner, the fatigue criterion forms a valid check on stress cycling.

A comprehensive analysis of creep relaxation in ducting systems is not at present available, but the basis of such an analysis has been given by Robinson.[31] The work of this author is in general not applicable to an actual duct layout, since only symmetrical systems are considered, and the bends are idealized to square corners. Robinson's analysis may be extended to deal with non-symmetrical single-plane duct systems, but the creep flexibility factor for bends cannot at present be determined. This is a complex problem which needs investigation, and would require an analysis similar to that carried out by Turner and Ford[5] but using the strain rate–stress equation in place of the elastic relationship.

Creep Analysis of Non-symmetrical Single Plane Duct Systems (Bends not Considered)

(a) *Creep strain rate–stress relationship.* Of the many relationships proposed between creep strain rate and stress, the following is widely used:

$$= C\sigma^n \tag{12.2}$$

where C and n are constants for a given material and temperature. Equation (12.2) enables n to be evaluated for the duct material and temperature using reference values of creep rates at two different stress levels obtained from the literature. Then the creep strain rate at any stress level is given by

$$\dot{\varepsilon} = \dot{\varepsilon}_0 \left(\frac{\sigma}{\sigma_0}\right)^n \tag{12.3}$$

where $\dot{\varepsilon}_0$, σ_0, and n are known.

(b) *Second moment of area under creep conditions.* For an element of duct under a bending moment the elastic stress distribution is modified so that the creep rate is proportional to the distance from the neutral axis. Under these conditions an increased second moment of area must be used, and it may be shown that:

$$I_c = \frac{8I}{\sqrt{(\pi)}\left(3+\dfrac{1}{n}\right)} \frac{\left[1-\left(\dfrac{R_1}{R_2}\right)^3+\dfrac{1}{n}\right]}{\left[1-\left(\dfrac{R_1}{R_2}\right)^4\right]} \frac{\Gamma\left(1+\dfrac{1}{2n}\right)}{\Gamma\left(1\cdot5+\dfrac{1}{2n}\right)}$$

where R_1 and R_2 are the inside and outside radii of the duct, respectively, and Γ is the gamma function. Alternatively, the concept of a creep rate modulus may be used which is analogous to Young's modulus under elastic conditions. This approach has been used by Alexander[32] when analysing thermal and irradiation creep buckling effects.

(c) *Creep rotation under a bending moment.* Consider duct AB (Fig. 12.13) in plane XOY with origin taken at end B, and let element dl at point p be subjected to a bending moment due to elastic deflexions ($t = 0$). After

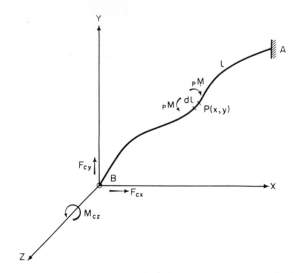

Fig. 12.13.   Duct reactions after time t under creep conditions.

time t, let maximum bending stress at mean radius r be σ and bending moment at p be pM.

Now for creep conditions:

$$\text{rate of change of curvature} = \frac{\text{rate of change of maximum creep strain}}{\text{distance from neutral axis}}$$

therefore

$$\dot{\kappa} = \frac{\dot{\varepsilon}}{r}$$

But from equation (12.3)

$$\dot{\varepsilon} = \dot{\varepsilon}_0 \left(\frac{\sigma}{\sigma_0} \right)^n$$

therefore

$$\dot{\kappa} = \frac{\dot{\varepsilon}_0}{r} \left(\frac{\sigma}{\sigma_0} \right)^n$$

Also

$$\sigma = \frac{pMr}{I_c} \quad \text{and} \quad d\phi = \kappa \, dl$$

where $d\phi$ = creep rotation of element dl in time dt.

If

$$D = \frac{\dot{\varepsilon}_0}{r} \left(\frac{r}{\sigma_0 I_c} \right)^n$$

Then

$$\dot{\phi} = D \cdot {}_pM^n \, dl \tag{12.4}$$

(d) *Bending moment at any point on the duct after time* t *under creep conditions.* For the initial elastic state:

$$EI \cdot \Delta = A \cdot F$$

where

$$\Delta = \begin{bmatrix} {}_o\Delta \\ {}_o\phi \end{bmatrix},$$

$$F = \begin{bmatrix} {}_oF \\ {}_oM \end{bmatrix},$$

A = matrix of influence coefficients.
For the residual displacements after time t:

$$EI_c(\Delta - \Delta_C) = A \cdot F_C$$

where Δ_C = matrix of creep displacements at origin after time t,

$\quad F_C$ = matrix of reactions at origin after time t.

thus

$$F_C = \frac{I_c}{I} \cdot F - EI_c A^{-1} \Delta_C$$

and

$$\dot{F}_C = -EI_c A^{-1} \dot{\Delta}_C$$

But from (12.4)

$$\dot{\Delta}_C = D \int_0^l B \, {}_pM^n \, dl$$

where $B = \begin{bmatrix} y \\ -x \\ 1 \end{bmatrix}$

Therefore

$$\dot{F}_C = -EI_c \, DA^{-1} \int_0^l B \, {}_pM^n \, dl$$

But ${}_pM = B'F_C$, thus ${}_p\dot{M} = B'\dot{F}_C$

therefore

$$_p\dot{M} = -EI_c \, DB'A^{-1} \int_0^l B \, {}_pM^n \, dl$$

and
$$\int_0^l {}_pM\,dl = -EI_cD\int_0^l \mathbf{B}'\,dl\,.\,\mathbf{A}^{-1}\int_0^l \mathbf{B}\,{}_pM^n\,dl$$

and
$$\int_0^l \left[{}_p\dot{M} + EI_cD\int_0^l \mathbf{B}'\,dl\,.\,\mathbf{A}^{-1}\mathbf{B}\,{}_pM^n \right]dl = 0$$

A possible solution is given by the integrand equals zero, and leads to:

$$_pM = \frac{{}_pM_0}{\left[1+(n-1)\,{}_pM_0^{n-1}\,EI_cD\int_0^l \mathbf{B}'\,dl\,.\,\mathbf{A}^{-1}\mathbf{B}\,.\,t\right]^{1/n-1}} \qquad (12.5)$$

where pM_0 = value of pM when $t = 0$, obtained from the elastic analysis.

Equation (12.5), when modified to allow for the creep flexibility of the bends, would enable the designer to undertake a comprehensive creep analysis for the twenty-year life of the station. It is considered that such an analysis would only be necessary for more advanced gas conditions than are at present being used in Stage I reactors.

REFERENCES

1. BRITISH STANDARD 1500, Fusion welded pressure vessels (1958).
2. Petroleum Refinery Piping Code 1959. American Standards Assoc. (A.S.A. B 31.3).
3. L. BESKIN, Bending of curved thin tubes. *J. Appl. Mech.* **12**, No. 1 (1945).
4. N. GROSS, Experiments on short-radius pipe bends. *Proc. Inst. Mech. Engrs.* B **1B**, No. 10 (1952–53).
5. C. E. TURNER and H. FORD, Examination of the theories for calculating the stresses in pipe bends subjected to in-plane bending. *Proc. Inst. Mech. Engrs.* **171**, No. 15 (1957).
6. N. GROSS and H. FORD, The flexibility of short-radius pipe bends. *Proc. Inst. Mech. Engrs.* B **1**, No. 10 (1952–53).
7. I. VIGNESS, Elastic properties of curved tubes. *Trans. Amer. Soc. Mech. Engrs.* **65** (1943).
8. E. C. RODABAUGH and H. H. GEORGE, Effect of internal pressure on flexibility and stress intensification factors of curved pipe or welding elbows. *Trans. Amer. Soc. Mech. Engrs.* **79**, 939 (1957).
9. S. TIMOSHENKO, *Theory of Plates and Shells.* McGraw-Hill, London (1940).
10. M. W. KELLOGG, Co., *Design of Piping Systems.* John Wiley, New York and London (1956).
11. P. B. MORICE, *Linear Structural Analysis.* Thames & Hudson, London (1959).
12. A. T. BOWDEN and J. C. DRUMM, Design and testing of large gas ducts. *Proc. Inst. Mech. Engrs.* **174**, No. 3 (1960).
13. F. J. FEELY and W. M. GORYL, Stress studies on piping expansion bellows. *J. Appl. Mech.* **17**, No. 1 (1950).
14. C. E. TURNER and H. FORD, Stress and deflection studies of pipeline expansion bellows. *Proc. Inst. Mech. Engrs.* **171**, No. 15 (1957).
15. R. HICKS, Asymmetrically ring reinforced circular hole in a uniformly end loaded flat plate with reference to pressure vessel design. *Proc. Inst. Mech. Engrs.* **173**, No. 11 (1959).

16. E. O. WATERS, Theoretical stresses near a circular opening in a flat plate reinforced with a cylindrical outlet. *Weld. Res. Counc. Bull.* No. 51, p. 1 (1959).
17. R. K. PENNY, Stress concentrations at the junction of a spherical pressure vessel and cylindrical duct. *Symposium on Nuclear Reactor Containment Buildings and Pressure Vessels.* Royal College of Science and Technology, Glasgow (1960).
18. C. E. TAYLOR, N. C. LIND and J. W. SCHWEIKER, A three-dimensional photoelastic study of stresses around reinforced outlets in pressure vessels. *Weld. Res. Counc. Bull.* No. 51, p. 26 (1959).
19. P. P. BIJLAARD, Computation of the stresses from local loads in spherical pressure vessels or pressure vessel heads. *Weld. Res. Counc. Bull.* No. 34 (1957).
20. P. P. BIJLAARD, Stresses in spherical vessels from local loads transferred by a pipe. *Weld. Res. Counc. Bull.* No. 50 (1959).
21. W. A. ZAREMBA, Elastic interactions at the junction of an assembly of axi-symmetric shells. *J. Mech. Engng. Sci.* **1**, No. 3 (1959).
22. W. P. KERKHOF, Some principles of design for pressure vessels and boilers made of low alloy steel. *J. W. Scotland Iron Steel Inst.* **64** (1956).
23. P. P. BENHAM, Fatigue of metals caused by a relatively few cycles of high load or strain amplitude. *Met. Revs.* **3**, Inst. Metals. (1958).
24. C. E. BOWMAN and T. J. DOLAN, Studies of the biaxial fatigue properties of pressure vessel steels. *Weld. J.* Res. suppl. Jan. (1955).
25. J. H. GROSS and R. D. STOUT, Plastic fatigue properties of high strength pressure vessel steels. *Weld. J.* Res. suppl. April (1955).
26. R. U. BLASER, J. T. TUCKER and L. F. KOOISTRA, Biaxial fatigue tests on flat plate specimens. *Weld. J.* Res. suppl. March (1952).
27. L. F. COFFIN, The problem of thermal stress fatigue in austenitic steels at elevated temperatures. A.S.T.M. Special Technical Publication No. 165 (1954).
28. B. F. LANGER, Design values for thermal stress in ductile materials. *Weld. J.* Res. suppl. Sept. (1958).
29. J. MARIN, Interpretation of fatigue strengths for combined stresses. *Proceedings of the International Conference of Fatigue of Metals.* Institute of Mechanical Engineers (1956).
30. M. A. MINER, Cumulative damage in fatigue. *Trans. Amer. Soc. Mech. Engrs.* **67** (1945).
31. E. L. ROBINSON, Steam piping design to minimize creep concentrations. *Trans. Amer. Soc. Mech. Engrs.* **77**, No. 7 (1955).
32. J. M. ALEXANDER, Approximate theory for the thermal and irradiation creep buckling of a uranium fuel rod and its magnesium can. *J. Mech. Engng. Sci.* **1**, No. 3 (1959).

CHAPTER 13

APPLICATION OF EXPERIMENTAL
STRESS ANALYSIS

J. R. RYDZEWSKI

13.1. INTRODUCTION

THERE always arise structural problems which engineers are called upon to solve for which there exist no satisfactory theoretical methods of analysis. Even if such methods do exist it is often found that the structure may be highly complex because of its geometry, its boundary conditions or its system of loading. Under such circumstances, an experimental approach to the problem can be of great value.[1]

As its name implies, experimental stress analysis involves the carrying out of an experiment either on the full-scale structure (the prototype) or on a scale model of the structure.

When thinking about structural models it is useful to recognize two extreme categories:

 (i) in which the model is in all respects a scale replica of the prototype; and

 (ii) in which the model becomes a physical representation of a mathematical abstraction of the prototype.

The first is self-explanatory, while the second simply means that the model inherits all the assumptions about the behaviour of the prototype that would normally have been made in a theoretical analysis (e.g. the linear–elastic behaviour of concrete). In this case, the model can be looked on as an inexpensive computer.

Needless to say, most practical cases lie somewhere between these extremes.

Model analysis may be applied to the whole or to a part of the structure for a complete study of its structural behaviour, or it may be used simply to check the validity of some simplifying assumptions in a theoretical solution of the problem.

Entire volumes have been and still can be written on the subject of model analysis in all its theoretical and practical detail. In this introductory survey emphasis will be laid on fundamental principles and on techniques, such as photoelasticity, which have an important application in the study of nuclear reactor structures, but which are not as frequently mentioned in technical literature, as, say, are electrical-resistance strain gauging methods.

The reader who wishes to pursue certain aspects of the subject further will be referred to specialized texts.

13.2. DIMENSIONAL ANALYSIS

Before a designer can turn his attention to the manufacture, the loading and the analysis of a model of a particular structure, it is essential for him to have a firm understanding of how the information he hopes to derive from his model will apply to the prototype. This fundamental aspect of model analysis will now be treated in some detail.

The only systematic method of investigating this relation is by means of the relatively new discipline of dimensional analysis. In it, information about a physical phenomenon is deduced from the single premise that the phenomenon can be described by a dimensionally correct equation among certain variables.

In classical mechanics it has been found convenient to select arbitrarily the physical quantities of mass (M), length (L) and time (T) as the " fundamental units " of measurement.

The *dimensions* of a physical magnitude are the powers of the fundamental units in the expression for the derived unit used to specify that magnitude. Thus a magnitude P is specified by the statement

$$P = nU$$

where U is the unit and n the numeric.

Hence for

$$P = n(M^a L^b T^c)$$

a, b and c are the dimensions of P.

It can be shown[2] that every derived magnitude is expressible as some constant multiplied by arbitrary powers of the " fundamental units ", for instance,

$$S = k(M^d L^e T^f).$$

Once it has been decided which derived physical magnitudes are involved in a particular problem, it is convenient to present their dimensions in tabular form. If, for example, there are n variables (physical magnitudes) P_i ($i = 1, 2, \ldots n$) involved in the physical problem and if the dimensions, referred to M, L and T, of P_i are a_i, b_i, c_i, then we have

	P_1	P_2	.	.	.	.	P_n
M	a_1	a_2	.	.	.	.	a_n
L	b_1	b_2	.	.	.	.	b_n
T	c_1	c_2	.	.	.	.	c_n

The above table is known as the *dimensional matrix* of the problem.

Now it can be proved[3] that a sufficient condition for an equation expressing a physical phenomenon to be dimensionally homogeneous is that it can be reduced to a relation between a complete set of dimensionless products. This is, in fact, the well-known Buckingham's π-Theorem.

Let there be a dimensionless product of the form

$$\pi = (P_1)^{k_1} . (P_2)^{k_2} \ldots (P_n)^{k_n}$$

$$= (M^{a_1} L^{b_1} T^{c_1})^{k_1} . (M^{a_2} L^{b_2} T^{c_2})^{k_2} \ldots (M^{a_n} L^{b_n} T^{c_n})^{k_n}$$

$$= (M)^{a_1 k_1 + \ldots + a_n k_n} . (L)^{b_1 k_1 + \ldots + b_n k_n} . (T)^{c_1 k_1 + \ldots + c_n k_n}$$

$$= (M)^0 (L)^0 (T)^0, \text{ since } \pi \text{ is dimensionless.}$$

Equating indices results in the equations

$$a_1 k_1 + a_2 k_2 + \ldots + a_n k_n = 0$$
$$b_1 k_1 + b_2 k_2 + \ldots + b_n k_n = 0 \qquad (13.1)$$
$$c_1 k_1 + c_2 k_2 + \ldots + c_n k_n = 0,$$

in which, it is observed, the coefficients a_1, b_1, c_1 are the rows of the dimensional matrix.

Any solution to the above equations (13.1) will result in a dimensionless product. However, we are after a *complete set* of dimensionless products, which means that each product in the set must be independent of the others in the set and, in addition, that every *other* dimensionless product of the variables of the problem can be formed from products of powers of the dimensionless products *in* the complete set.

From the theory of equations it is known that, disregarding the trivial solution $k_i = 0$, equations (13.1) have $(n-r)$ linearly independent solutions, r being the rank of the matrix of the coefficients of (13.1) or, in this context, of the dimensional matrix.

In the most general case there is, of course, a great number of such complete sets obtained by taking any $(n-r)$ independent dimensionless products.

25

Returning to model experiments, it is possible to establish a hierarchy of variables associated with the problem. The physical quantity required (stress, displacement, reaction, etc.) becomes the dependent variable of the problem. Also, one distinguishes among the remaining (independent) variables those which are easy to control experimentally (e.g. it is usually easier in a model experiment to alter the loading than, say, the dimensions or Young's modulus).

There is obviously a need for a systematic method of finding a suitable complete set of dimensionless products. A most satisfactory one, due to Langhaar,[3] will now be demonstrated on a fictitious problem involving the physical magnitudes, A, B, C, D, E and F from which dimensionless products of the form

$$\pi = A^{k_1} . B^{k_2} . C^{k_3} . D^{k_4} . E^{k_5} . F^{k_6} \qquad (13.2)$$

will be derived. The method will be presented step by step.

Step 1. The dimensional matrix of the variables of the problem is drawn up, placing the dependent variable (the quantity required) first, followed by the other variables beginning with those which are easiest to regulate during the experiment, say,

	(1)	(2)	(3)	(4)	(5)	(6)
	A	B	C	D	E	F
M	1	1	−1	0	0	−2
L	3	2	1	−1	−4	0
T	−1	−2	2	0	3	1

Step 2. The rank of the dimensional matrix is found, making sure that the non-zero determinant is at the right-hand side of the matrix. Here the rank is 3 since the determinant formed from the dimensions of D, E and F is non-zero; its value is 6.

Step 3. Equations of the type (13.1) are formed, specifying the condition that π in equation (13.2) must be dimensionless. Here,

$$\left. \begin{array}{l} k_1 + k_2 - k_3 - 2k_6 = 0 \\[2mm] 3k_1 + 2k_2 + k_3 - k_4 - 4k_5 = 0 \\[2mm] -k_1 - 2k_2 + 2k_3 + 3k_5 + k_6 = 0 \end{array} \right\} \qquad (13.3)$$

Step 4. There are $(n-r)$ linearly independent solutions possible (here 3) and thus arbitrary but convenient values can be given to k_1, k_2, . . . k_{n-r} and equations (13.3) can then be solved for the remaining k_i.

Here k_4, k_5 and k_6 are expressed in terms of k_1, k_2 and k_3 giving

$$\left.\begin{aligned} k_4 &= \tfrac{7}{3}k_1 + 3k_3 \\ k_5 &= \tfrac{1}{6}k_1 + \tfrac{1}{2}k_2 - \tfrac{1}{2}k_3 \\ k_6 &= \tfrac{1}{2}k_1 + \tfrac{1}{2}k_2 - \tfrac{1}{2}k_3 \end{aligned}\right\} \tag{13.4}$$

Step 5. Arbitrary values are now assigned to k_1 k_2, and k_3. It is convenient to take in turn one of the k_i as unity with the others equal to zero. This is best illustrated on our example.

For the first solution take $\quad k_1 = 1$ with $k_2 = k_3 = 0$.

For the second solution take $k_2 = 1$ with $k_1 = k_3 = 0$.

For the third solution take $\quad k_3 = 1$ with $k_1 = k_2 = 0$.

Step 6. Using the above values in equation (13.4) it is now possible to construct the matrix of solutions,

	A	B	C	D	E	F
π_1	1	0	0	$\tfrac{7}{3}$	$\tfrac{1}{6}$	$\tfrac{1}{2}$
π_2	0	1	0	0	$\tfrac{1}{2}$	$\tfrac{1}{2}$
π_3	0	0	1	3	$-\tfrac{1}{2}$	$-\tfrac{1}{2}$

Thus the particular physical phenomenon under investigation can be described by a law of the form

$$\phi(A^6 D^{14} E F^3, \quad B^2 E F, \quad C^2 D^6 E^{-1} F^{-1}) = 0$$

It can be noted that the fact that A, B and C appear only once in the above set of dimensionless products demonstrates their linear independence; it is impossible to form one from a combination of the other two.

13.3. THE PROBLEM OF ELASTIC STRUCTURES

It will be useful to compile, if only once, a complete list of the variables that enter into the general problem of an elastic structure subjected to static, dynamic and thermal effects.

To simplify the list that follows it will be understood throughout that any particular physical quantity can be expressed by the value of this quantity at one point and by numerical ratios between it and the values at all other points. As these ratios are, of course, dimensionless, they do not affect the problem of the derivation of complete sets of dimensionless products.

The following quantities will describe the general elastic problem:

The Cartesian co-ordinates, x, y, z;
a leading dimension, l;
the modulus of elasticity, E;
the Poisson's ratio, v;
the specific gravity, ρ;
the specific heat, c;
the coefficient of linear expansion, α;
the coefficient of thermal conductivity, k;
the acceleration due to gravity, g;
the concentrated forces, P;
the line forces, Q;
the surface forces, R;
the prescribed displacements, u_0;
the initial internal stresses, σ_0;
the dynamic body forces caused by an acceleration, γ;
the temperature, θ;
the time, t;
the stresses, σ.

It is convenient for this problem to take as "fundamental units" mass M, length L, time T, temperature θ and in addition a heat quantity H expressed in terms of work; H can be legitimately included as a "fundamental unit" since the problem of a heat transfer is not envisaged.

The dimensional matrix of the twenty-two variables listed above with respect to M, L, T, θ and H is:

	σ	u	x	y	z	t	l	E	v	ρ	c	a	k	g	P	Q	R	u_0	σ_0	γ	θ
M	1	0	0	0	0	0	0	1	0	1	-1	0	0	0	1	1	1	0	1	0	0
L	-1	1	1	1	1	0	1	-1	0	-3	0	0	-1	1	1	0	-1	1	-1	1	0
T	-2	0	0	0	0	1	0	-2	0	0	0	0	-1	-2	-2	-2	-2	0	-2	-2	0
θ	0	0	0	0	0	0	0	0	0	0	-1	-1	-1	0	0	0	0	0	0	0	1
H	0	0	0	0	0	0	0	0	0	0	1	0	1	0	0	0	0	0	0	0	0

This is a matrix of rank 5 so that it is possible to form $21 - 5 = 16$ independent dimensionless products. It is not proposed to do this here, but interested readers are referred to the work of Beaujoint[4] who has thoroughly investigated this general problem.

13.4. THE RELATION BETWEEN MODEL AND PROTOTYPE

To take the discussion further without undue complexity, the case of a statically loaded structure will now be considered. The example taken will be one in which the state of stress, σ, can be described by P, x, y, z, l, E and v from the list previously drawn up.

Dimensional analysis performed on these physical quantities results in the statement that the physical law, applicable equally to prototype and model, will take the form of

$$F_1\left(\frac{\sigma}{E}, \ \frac{x}{l}, \ \frac{y}{l}, \ \frac{z}{l}, \ \frac{P}{El^2}, \ \text{ and mere } ratios\right) = 0$$

Taking the term containing the dependent variable σ out of the functional gives

$$\frac{\sigma}{E} = f_1\left(\frac{x}{l}, \ \frac{y}{l}, \ \frac{z}{l}, \ \frac{P}{El^2}, \ \text{ and } ratios\right)$$

Now in the above two expressions the nature of the functionals F_1 and f_1 is not known. Yet this will not matter if it can be so arranged that the terms in the brackets on which the unknown functionals operate are made the same for both model and prototype. If this is so, one can write

$$\frac{\left(\dfrac{\sigma}{E}\right)_m}{\left(\dfrac{\sigma}{E}\right)_p} = \frac{f_1(\ )_m}{f_1(\ )_p} = 1$$

or

$$\frac{\sigma_p}{\sigma_m} = \frac{E_p}{E_m}$$

Turning to the terms in the brackets of $f_1(\ )$ it is seen that making x/l, y/l and z/l the same for both assumes that equivalent (or homologous) points are considered on model and prototype, while the *ratios* ensure similarity in geometry and load application. It is also necessary to have identical values of Poisson's ratio and in addition to have

$$\frac{P_m}{P_p} = \frac{E_m \, l_m^2}{E_p \, l_p^2}$$

This last requirement may not always be easy to satisfy.

However, in a large proportion of structures, in which displacements are small enough not to affect the geometrical configuration, a linear relation can justifiably be assumed between applied load and stress, strain, displacement and reactive forces.

Once the assumption of this linearity has been made for a structure it is impossible for the term containing the load P to remain concealed behind the unknown functional, so that it has to be placed outside the bracket to show the direct proportionality now required,

i.e.
$$\frac{\sigma}{E} = \frac{P}{El^2} f_2\left(\frac{x}{l}, \frac{y}{l}, \frac{z}{l}, \text{ and } ratios\right)$$

The most significant thing to notice is that the modulus of elasticity, E, now disappears from the above equation. If, as before, the contents of the brackets of $f_2( )$ are made the same for model and prototype, it follows that

$$\left(\frac{\sigma l^2}{P}\right)_m = \left(\frac{\sigma l^2}{P}\right)_p$$

or
$$\sigma_p = \sigma_m \cdot \frac{(P_p)(l_m)^2}{(P_m)(l_p)}$$

Thus for linear structures one is not restricted by the modulus of elasticity in one's choice of model material.

The expression for displacement, u, will in this case be

$$u_p = u_m \frac{(P_p)(E_m)(l_m)}{(P_m)(E_p)(l_p)}$$

A word has to be said now about the practical difficulties involved in attempting to ensure the geometrical similarity for model and prototype and also the identity of Poisson's ratios for the two materials.

Taking the latter problem first, it is soon discovered that, as a rule, model materials tend to have higher values of Poisson's ratio than most engineering materials. Here are some typical values:

Material	Poisson's ratio
Concrete	0·15
Steel	0·31
Perspex	0·40
Rubber	0·50

It is difficult to generalize about this problem. Where it is possible, from a theoretical analysis, to apply corrections for inequality in Poisson's ratio, this should be done. However, it has been found from experience that in a great number of structural problems any difference in stresses due to differences in Poisson's ratio between model and prototype is completely masked by the usual allowable experimental error of, say, 3–5 per cent.

The problem of geometrical similarity of model and prototype can be awkward when, for instance, a structure is made of members the cross-sections of which are difficult to reproduce on the scale of the model (e.g. rolled steel joists). Where bending is regarded as the main cause of stress, it has been found convenient to replace the exact cross-sectional dimensions of the various members by their second moments of area, I. Thus, with d being the depth of the beam, the problem of beam-bending could be described by

$$f_1\left(\frac{d}{l}, \frac{\sigma I}{Pl^2}\right) = 0$$

or

$$f_2\left(\frac{u}{l}, \frac{Pl^2}{EI}\right) = 0$$

In a short introductory chapter it is impossible to include worked examples. However, readers interested in the application of the methods outlined above are referred to Langhaar,[3] Goodier,[5] Charlton[6] and Durelli, Phillips and Tsao.[7]

13.5. STRESSES FROM STRAINS

The state of stress at any point is most conveniently specified by the magnitudes of the principal stresses and their directions. Alternatively, it can be expressed by the components of normal and shear stress along three orthogonal axes. Since in experiments on models the quantity measured is usually a displacement or, preferably, a strain, and since these measurements generally refer to the surface of the model, a brief reminder of the stress–strain relations in two dimensions will not be out of place.

Here the quantities required are the two principal stresses, σ_1 and σ_2, and their direction $\theta_{1,2}$ with respect to some datum. As it is strain that is being measured, it is first necessary to derive an expression for the principal strains ε_1 and ε_2 and their directions $\theta_{1,2}$.

With three unknown quantities required, it is obvious that measurement of strain at a point in three different directions will provide enough data for a complete solution.

Referring to Fig. 13.1, let a, b and c be three strain gauges measuring strain in three directions making angles of θ_a, θ_b and θ_c with the given datum, here the x-axis.

Any text on strength of materials or elasticity derives the relation between strain ε_θ in any direction θ and the three rectangular components of strain as

$$\varepsilon_\theta = \varepsilon_x \cos^2\theta + \varepsilon_y \sin^2\theta + \tfrac{1}{2}\gamma_{xy}\sin 2\theta$$

Thus, for the case being considered, three equations of the form

$$\varepsilon_a = \varepsilon_x \cos^2\theta_a + \varepsilon_y \sin^2\theta_a + \tfrac{1}{2}\gamma_{xy}\sin 2\theta_a$$

can be formed and solved simultaneously for ε_x, ε_y and γ_{xy}. Now the principal strains are given by

$$\varepsilon_{1,2} = \tfrac{1}{2}(\varepsilon_x + \varepsilon_y) \pm \tfrac{1}{2}\sqrt{[(\varepsilon_x - \varepsilon_y)^2 + \gamma_{xy}^2]}$$

while

$$\tan 2\theta_{1,2} = \frac{\gamma_{xy}}{\varepsilon_x - \varepsilon_y}$$

It is now only necessary to recall that the principal stresses are given by

$$\sigma_1 = \frac{E(\varepsilon_1 + v\varepsilon_2)}{1 - v^2}$$

and

$$\sigma_2 = \frac{E(\varepsilon_2 + v\varepsilon_1)}{1 - v^2}$$

to complete the calculation.

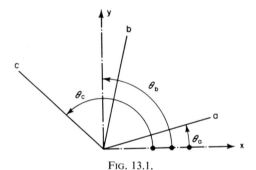

FIG. 13.1.

13.6. MEASUREMENT OF STRAIN

A stage has been reached in this chapter at which, given the model, the engineer is about to consider methods of measuring strains on it. To preserve the intended brevity of the chapter the problems of model manufacture and model loading cannot be gone into. But it would be as well to emphasize in passing the value of a skilled and experienced technician.

Returning to the general problem of strain measurement, it is obvious from the definition of strain that what is to be measured is the change in length of a known length in a given direction.

Any measuring device has a given *deformation sensitivity*, S_D, which is defined as the smallest value of the measured quantity that can be read by the instrument. Most instruments incorporate some form of magnifying device to increase their deformation sensitivity.

Once the sensitivity of measuring changes of length is known, it is only necessary to know over what length these changes are measured in order to evaluate the *strain sensitivity* of the instrument, i.e. for a gauge length L the strain sensitivity, S_S, is defined as

$$S_S = \frac{\text{deformation sensitivity}}{\text{base length}} = \frac{S_D}{L}$$

Needless to say, the longer the permissible base length, the easier it is to manufacture a sensitive strain gauge. However, with small models and a possibility of rapid variation of stress from point to point, it is important to have short gauge lengths *and* high strain sensitivity.

To give the reader some idea of values of strain sensitivity encountered in practice, Table 13.1 gives some typical values.

TABLE 13.1

Type of gauge	S_D (in. $\times 10^{-6}$)	Base length (in.)	$S_S \times 10^{-6}$
Micrometer	100	1	100
Dial gauge	100	1	100
DEMEC	80	8	10
Huggenberger	8	1	8
Johansson	5	2	2·5
Maihak (acoustic)	1·2	0·8	1·5
Hickson (pneumatic)	2·4	0·4	6
Hickson (replica)	10	0·4	25
Grids on rubber	100	0·25	400
Photogrids	5	0·25	20
Electric resistance	5	any length	5

A much more detailed table, from which some of the values above were taken, is given by Durelli, Phillips and Tsao.[7]

13.7. SOME COMMON METHODS OF STRAIN MEASUREMENT

(i) *Mechanical Gauges*

A great deal of ingenuity and effort has gone into the design of purely mechanical as well as mechanical–optical devices for increasing the sensitivity of strain gauges.

Two purely mechanical gauges are shown in Fig. 13.2. The DEMEC gauge was designed primarily for work on large-scale models and prototypes, hence its long base length of 8 in. In it the movable point acts as a lever actuating a dial gauge reading to 0·0001 in. The Huggenberger gauge has a much more complex system of levers and is at the same time much more sensitive and delicate than the DEMEC gauge.

The Johansson gauge employs the simple yet ingenious principle of a twisted metal strip in tension. A pointer attached to the strip moves across a scale when tension is applied to the strip.

A very full treatment of mechanical strain gauges and their development is given by Donnell and Savage.[8] Durelli, Phillips and Tsao[7] also devote a short chapter to this topic.

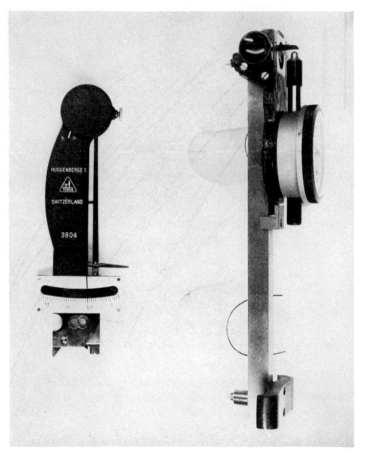

FIG. 13.2. Two types of mechanical strain gauges: *right*, the DEMEC gauge; *left*, the Huggenberger extensometer.

(ii) *Acoustic Gauges*

The principle of the acoustic strain gauges, invented by Schaeffer in the 1930's, is essentially that of a violin string, the frequency of vibration (the tone) of which varies with the tension in the string. The wire, which can be plucked by electromagnetic means, is stretched over the gauge length. Strain in the model alters the tension in the wire and hence its tone, which is transmitted electrically to the observer who can compare it with the tone of a standard wire to which he can apply known tensions.

The acoustic gauge is a very good example of a transducer, i.e. a device by means of which one physical quantity is converted into another. Here apart from the tension of the wire being converted into its periodic displacement (vibration), this in turn is converted into an electrical signal.

When it is added that electrical frequency measurements can be made very accurately indeed, it can be seen that this is, in fact, a very elegant method of strain measurement. Its chief drawback is the cost of the equipment and the fact that very short base lengths are difficult to arrange.

(iii) *Electrical Resistance Strain Gauges*

The possibility of devising transducers which would convert changes of a linear dimension directly into changes of electrical quantities had been realized for a long time and has resulted in the electric-inductance, electric-capacitance and electrical-resistance types of gauges. Each type has a chapter devoted to it in Hetényi's *Handbook of Experimental Stress Analysis*. However, the success of the electrical-resistance strain gauge has made the other two of largely academic interest. For this reason the brief remarks that follow will be confined to the E.R.S. gauge.

For a length of wire, L, its resistance, R, is related to its specific resistance, ρ, and its cross-sectional area, A, in the following manner

$$R = \frac{\rho L}{A}$$

To investigate the variation in resistance caused by variations in the other three quantities, it is first convenient to take the logarithms of both sides of the equation, thus

$$\log R = \log \rho + \log L - \log A$$

Differentiation gives

$$\frac{\delta R}{R} = \frac{\delta \rho}{\rho} + \frac{\delta L}{L} - \frac{\delta A}{A}$$

From elasticity, the relation between longitudinal and cross-sectional changes in dimension is

$$\frac{\delta A}{A} = -2v\frac{\delta L}{L}$$

where v is the Poisson's ratio.

Thus

$$\frac{\delta R}{R} = \frac{\delta L}{L}(1 + 2v) + \frac{\delta\rho}{\rho}$$

or

$$\frac{\delta R}{R}\bigg/\frac{\delta L}{L} = 1 + 2v + \frac{\delta\rho}{\rho}\bigg/\frac{\delta L}{L}$$

Now in an electrical resistance strain gauge it is so arranged that the wire, the change of resistance of which can be accurately measured, follows accurately the surface strain of the structure.

The ratio $(\delta R/R)/(\delta L/L)$, denoted by K_s, is known as the gauge factor. Its value is usually about 2.

Detailed information about E.R.S. strain gauges and methods of measurement of changes of resistance are given in many texts, e.g. Dohrenwend and Mehaffey[4] or Murray and Stein.[10]

Latest research on E.R.S. gauges has been concerned mainly with their application for thermal stress investigations.[11] Here the problem is not only that of satisfactory bond between the gauge and the structure, but also that of electrical resistance stability of the gauge material at elevated temperatures. For steady state thermal problems strain gauges and adhesives are reliable for temperatures up to 250°C. However, their suitability for rapidly varying thermal stresses is questionable, since the gauge is separated from the model by its backing material and the adhesive, both of which are unlikely to have the same thermal properties as the model.

The development of gauges which use semiconductors instead of resistance wire is of great interest since gauge factors as high as 200 have been achieved.

(iv) *Pneumatic Extensometers*

If a compressible fluid under constant pressure is first made to pass through a fixed orifice and then through one with a variable throat area, the pressure differential between the two orifices is a function of their relative sizes.

This principle has been employed for measurement of extension since 1930. A typical apparatus of the period is illustrated and described by Savage and Donnell.[8] Although great accuracy of measurement was possible the instrument was rather bulky and subsequently became overshadowed by the electrical-resistance strain gauge.

A recent investigation at the Royal Aircraft Establishment at Farnborough into the behaviour of aircraft structures subjected to simulated kinetic heating has led Hickson[12] to design a pneumatic extensometer with which transient thermal strains can be accurately measured at temperatures as high as 900°C.

Diagrammatically the extensometer is illustrated in Fig. 13.3. Nitrogen from a high-pressure cylinder is passed at a pressure P_2 and absolute temperature T_2 through the fixed orifice of cross-sectional area a_2. It is then led by means of a hypodermic tube along the surface of the model to allow it to attain the temperature, T_1, of the model. The gas then discharges at a pressure P_1 through the second orifice with a variable throat area a_1 which depends on the relative positions of the point at which the nozzle is attached to the model (A) and the small baffle (B) also attached to the model.

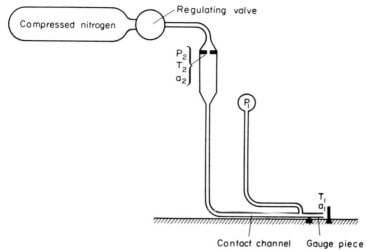

FIG. 13.3.   Basic circuit of Hickson's pneumatic extensometer.

In order to make the flow of gas independent of the atmospheric pressure, sonic speeds are employed when, for constant mass flow

$$\frac{C_1 a_1 P_1}{\sqrt{T_1}} = \frac{C_2 a_2 P_2}{\sqrt{T_2}}$$

Here C_1 and C_2 are the nozzle coefficients.

The gauge is fabricated from the same material as the model or prototype on which measurements are being taken and it is attached to it by spot welding.

On account of its robust construction and remote control, there are possibilities of using this type of gauge on irradiated parts of nuclear reactor structures.

(v) Grid and Replica Techniques

One of the simplest ways of obtaining experimentally the strain in a plane model is to observe the deformation after loading of a grid previously inscribed on the surface of the model.

Various techniques of marking the grid, from scratching the lines by hand to depositing them by photographic means, have been employed; likewise, different methods of measuring the displacement of the grid lines have been developed to suit different conditions. They are described in detail by Durelli, Phillips and Tsao.[7] Of special interest is the use of models made of rubber sheet which give large displacements. Here by drawing small circles on the unstrained model it is possible to obtain a good indication of the stress distribution simply by measuring the ellipses into which the circles deform.

The simple grid idea has recently been turned by Hickson[13] into an accurate method of measuring both elastic and plastic strain.

His method, applicable at the moment mainly to metal structures, uses a random grid scratched by hand with rouge paper. A replica of this grid is taken, before and after loading, by applying, with small impact, a platten coated with a low melting point alloy which is fused at the point of impact. Comparison of the two replicas in a microscope with a micrometer head yields information from which strain can be calculated.

(vi) *Brittle Lacquers*

A very useful method of determining the principal directions of stress on the surfaces of more complex models is to coat them with a thin layer of some brittle lacquer, the property of which is to develop cracks perpendicular to the direction of the maximum tensile stress.

Great use of this method, which has been extended to quantitative evaluation of the state of stress, has been made by Durelli;[7] it has also been given full description by Hetényi.[14]

13.8. PHOTOELASTICITY: DOUBLE REFRACTION

It was discovered nearly 150 years ago that a plate of glass when subjected to stress and viewed in polarized light exhibited a pattern of coloured fringes. As these fringes disappeared with the removal of stress, some relation was suspected between the optical and elastic phenomena. A comparison was drawn between the stressed glass plate and a natural crystal, such as calcite, which possesses the optical property of double refraction. Briefly, this means that a ray of light entering a crystal splits into two components at right angles which travel through the crystal with different velocities, i.e. the refractive indices of the crystal are different for these two orthogonal directions which coincide with the principal axes of the crystal in that plane.

It happens to be experimentally rather difficult, though not impossible, to measure independently the velocities of the two rays which, in the language of optics, are oppositely polarized. Difficulties do not arise when the interest is confined to the measurement of the relative retardation of one ray on the other. Here the approach is to begin with polarized light of a definite wavelength (this can be expressed as a sinusoidal vibration), and to combine the

two rays emerging from the crystal or stressed glass plate so that an inter-
ference fringe pattern results from their interaction.

The operation described above is carried out in a polariscope. Diagrammatically, Fig. 13.4 shows a doubly refracting crystal in a plane crossed
polariscope. A parallel beam of light is passed through a polariser so that,
say, only the vertical vibrations of the light are transmitted. These can be
expressed as a wave-form,

$$a \sin \omega t \tag{13.5}$$

This vertically plane-polarized light enters the crystal which, in a general
case, will have its optical axes inclined at some angle θ to the polarizing axis.

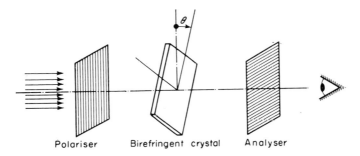

Polariser   Birefringent crystal   Analyser

Fig. 13.4.   Plane crossed polariscope.

Immediately the ray of light will be split into two components along these
optical axes. On leaving the crystal, one ray will be retarded by a phase
angle ϕ relative to the other.

Finally, the two rays pass through a second polarizing sheet, called the
analyser, which in this example would have its polarizing axis horizontal.
Thus the light reaching the observer's eye now consists only of the horizontal
components of the two rays, and it is the interaction of these that gives rise
to the appearance of the dark and light fringes. To give meaning to these,
it is useful to investigate under what conditions fringes (i.e. extinction of
light) could occur in a plane crossed polariscope.

Having started with a simple sinusoidal wave-form (13.5) it is easily
shown[15, 16] that the light reaching the observer can be represented by the
expression

$$\left[a \cdot \sin 2\theta \sin \frac{\phi}{2} \right] \left[\cos \left(\omega t + \frac{\phi}{2} \right) \right].$$

In it the first square bracket represents the amplitude of the vibration, while
the second is a periodic function, the value of which varies from $+1$ to -1.

Since in the wave theory of light on which this analysis is based the intensity of illumination is proportional to the square of the amplitude of the vibration of the light, i.e.

$$\left(a^2 \sin^2 2\theta \sin^2 \frac{\phi}{2} \right)$$

extinction of light will occur when this function is zero.

This condition will be met when either

(a) $2\theta = 0,\ \pi,\ 2\pi,\ 3\pi$, etc.

or   (b) $\phi = 0,\ 2\pi,\ 4\pi,\ 6\pi$, etc.

In physical terms condition (a) means that extinction of light occurs when the optical axes of the crystal are parallel to the axes of polarization. Condition (b) shows that light will also be extinguished when the relative retardation of the two oppositely polarized rays, on passing through the crystal, is zero or an integral number of wavelengths. Here, it is convenient to make a transformation from angular to linear measure by recalling that

$$\frac{\phi}{2\pi} = \frac{r}{\lambda}$$

where r is the relative retardation of the two rays and λ is the wavelength of the light. Condition (b) can therefore be rewritten as

$$r = n\lambda$$

for extinction of light to occur.

13.9. PHOTOELASTICITY: THE STRESS–OPTIC RELATIONS

In the above section the phenomenon of double refraction (or birefringence) was developed for a natural crystal.

It was conclusively shown by early investigators that stresses in certain transparent materials, such as glass, had the effect of making these materials behave optically like double-refracting crystals. The optical effect was found to relate to the state of stress in the following three ways.

(1) At any point on the stressed plate the axes of temporary double refraction coincide with the principal axes of stress at that point.

(2) The relative retardation of the two oppositely polarized rays on passing through the plate is proportional to the difference of the principal stresses $(\sigma_1 - \sigma_2)$, at any point. This is known as the *Stress–Optic law*.

(3) Only the stresses in the plane normal to the direction of the beam of light are responsible for the temporary double refraction.

Considering the first two of the above relations, together with the previously derived conditions for extinction of light when a birefringent material is viewed in a plane crossed polariscope, it is readily seen that two distinct sets of dark bands (or fringes) will be observed in the stressed plate.

The first, known as the *isoclinics*, will be the loci of points at which the principal directions of stress have an equal inclination to some reference datum. Isoclinics of different parameters are revealed by rotating the stressed plate in the plane polariscope or, more simply, by rotating together the polarizer and analyser with respect to the plate. It should be noted that the conditions of extinction that give rise to the isoclinics do not involve the wavelength of light. Thus in white light the isoclinics appear black.

The second set of fringes will be the contours of the principal stress difference $(\sigma_1 - \sigma_2)$. Mathematically, the Stress–Optic law can be expressed as

$$r = n\lambda = Ct(\sigma_1 - \sigma_2) \tag{13.6}$$

where C is the stress–optic constant of the material and t the thickness of the plate.

By rewriting (13.6) as

$$(\sigma_1 - \sigma_2) = n\frac{\lambda}{Ct} \tag{13.7}$$

it is obvious that the contours of principal stress differences are dependent on the wavelength of light used. In white light, which early observers used in their experiments, they appear as coloured fringes and as a result the name of *isochromatics* was given to them.

It may be noted in passing that the fringe corresponding to zero value of $(\sigma_1 - \sigma_2)$, or zero relative retardation, will be black in white light, i.e. in such places the dark background of the crossed polariscope remains unaffected by the stresses in the plate.

In modern photoelasticity, where accurate measurements of relative retardation are necessary, it is usual to employ monochromatic light. In Britain it is customary to use green light by isolating the pronounced green band emanating from a mercury-vapour lamp. In the United States the yellow light of sodium-vapour lamps is preferred. An example of a fringe pattern in a perforated plate (part of a reactor grillage) is shown in Fig. 13.5.

For a given wavelength of light and a given material one may introduce another constant, f, known as the *material fringe value*, by putting

$$f = \frac{\lambda}{C}$$

Equation (13.7) now becomes

$$(\sigma_1 - \sigma_2) = n\frac{f}{t} \tag{13.8}$$

When a model of constant thickness is used a further simplification is possible by introducing the *model fringe value*, F, where

$$F = \frac{\lambda}{Ct}$$

N.R.E.

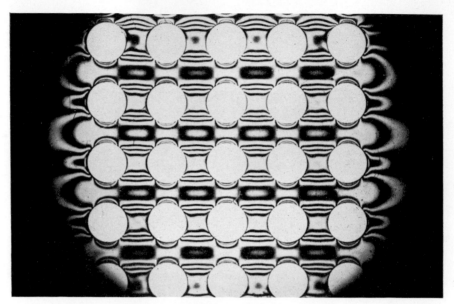

Fig. 13.5. Photoelastic fringe pattern in model of reactor grillage plate.

It is evident that f is measured in units of stress per fringe per unit thickness, while F as stress per fringe. The material fringe value f is, for a given material, most conveniently determined from a calibration experiment by observing the *fringe order n* at some point where the state of stress is known. An example is the observation of fringes at the centre of a diametrically compressed disc. With the symbols used in Fig. 13.6 it can be shown that at the centre

$$(\sigma_1 - \sigma_2)_0 = \frac{8P}{\pi t_0 D}$$

If n is the number of fringes counted at that point

$$n \frac{f}{t_0} = \frac{8P}{\pi t_0 D}$$

or

$$f = \frac{8P}{\pi n D}$$

Then, of course, for a model of thickness t,

$$F = \frac{f}{t}$$

When using monochromatic light in a plane polariscope, it is sometimes found that the isoclinics tend to obscure the isochromatics (or *fringes* as they are commonly called nowadays). A convenient way of eliminating the isoclinics from a fringe pattern is to use circularly polarized light. The analysis of the passage of light through a birefringent material in a circular polariscope is beyond the scope of this introductory chapter. Full details are given by Jessop and Harris.[15]

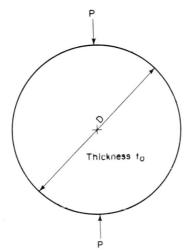

FIG. 13.6.   Disc in diametral compression.

To summarize, the foregoing discussion has shown that for the two-dimensional case, photoelastic observations yield directly the principal stress difference $(\sigma_1 - \sigma_2)$, and the principal stress directions, $\theta_{1,2}$. This is not the complete stress solution and means of finding supplementary information about the stresses will be discussed in a later section after the description of the " frozen stress " phenomenon, which is here of great assistance.

13.10.   "FROZEN STRESS" PHOTOELASTICITY

It was discovered in the late 1930's that certain transparent plastics when subjected to stress at an elevated temperature and subsequently cooled, while still under the action of the stresses, exhibited the photoelastic effect after the removal of the loads which produced the stresses.

The physical chemistry of this phenomenon is as yet not fully known but it does appear to be associated with materials, like the epoxy resins, which have long-chain molecules.

The " stress-freezing " process had the immediate advantage that complicated experiments could be carried out away from the limited space of

26*   N.R.E.

the polariscope. What is more, this was coupled with greatly increased stress–optic sensitivity of the materials, so that to produce the same fringe pattern a much smaller load was required. A comparative list of properties of Araldite B* (C N 501 in the United States) which is a very popular photoelastic material, is given in Table 13.2.

TABLE 13.2.   PROPERTIES OF " ARALDITE B "

	Material fringe value, f, (lb./in^2/fringe/in.)	Modulus of elasticity (lb./in^2)	Poisson's ratio
20°C	57	450000	0·36
120°C	1·32	2000	0·48

It was also discovered that a model with " frozen-in " stresses could be cut without disturbing the stress pattern, provided no excessive heat was generated in the process of cutting. Thus slices could be cut from the model to provide additional information about the stress distribution.

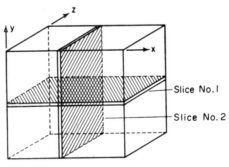

FIG. 13.7.

Referring to Fig. 13.7, it is seen that in a general three-dimensional state of stress, slice No. 1, cut in the xz-plane, when viewed in the polariscope from the y-direction, will show fringes of the difference of the *secondary principal stresses*, $(\sigma_1 - \sigma_2)_{xz}$, and their isoclinics. Similar information is obtained for the yz-plane from the second slice.

The term *secondary principal stresses* was introduced since, as the co-ordinate system is here arbitrary, there is no guarantee that the x- and y-directions coincide with *the* principal directions of stress. Yet within each

* Recently renamed " Araldite CT 200 " in Great Britain.

plane (or slice) there will be directions in which normal stresses have maximum and minimum values and it is these which give rise to the photoelastic effect in that plane.

The application of the " slicing method " to obtain a complete stress solution to certain problems will be described in a later section after another photoelastic technique is introduced.

13.11. REFLEXION PHOTOELASTICITY

So far we have dealt with photoelastic methods relying on the transmission polariscope, i.e. light was passed through the stressed model or through a slice cut from it. However, it is quite in order to place a mirror behind the model and to observe the photoelastic effect in the reflected light.

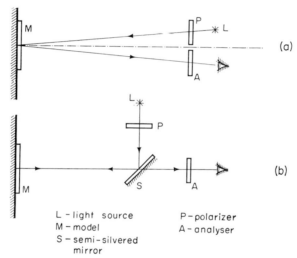

L – light source P – polarizer
M – model   A – analyser
S – semi-silvered
  mirror

FIG. 13.8. Two types of reflexion polariscopes.

Two commonly used arrangements are illustrated in Figs. 13.8 (a) and (b). In the first the incident and reflected rays make a small angle with the normal to the stressed plate, while in the second the two ray paths are normal, but use is made of a semi-silvered mirror in observing the stress pattern. Since the light travels twice through the thickness of the model, twice as many fringes will be observed as would have been in a transmission polariscope.

The main application of the reflexion technique lies in the exploration of surface stresses in metal structures. Here, a layer of photoelastic material is bonded to the previously polished surface and the reflexion polariscope is brought to the structure for observations. Stress concentrations round rivets in aircraft structures have been investigated in this manner.

A simple modification of this method is the " compass gauge ". It consists of a thin annular disc of photoelastic material and is attached, usually by means of an impact adhesive, to the unstrained model at a point at which the state of stress is being investigated. After loading the model the gauge is viewed through a plane polarizer when the isoclinic pattern in the disc will immediately indicate the principal directions of stress at the point. With this information the principal stresses can be obtained by measurement of strain along these directions.

13.12. STRESS SOLUTIONS THROUGH PHOTOELASTICITY

For problems of plane stress the state of stress at a point can be fully described either by the two orthogonal components of normal stress σ_x, σ_y and the accompanying shear stress τ_{xy}, or by the principal stresses σ_1, σ_2 and their directions $\theta_{1,2}$.

Considering for the moment the latter case, it is easily seen from Fig. 13.9 that in the principal directions the state of stress σ_1, σ_2 can be decomposed into a system consisting of a hydrostatic pressure σ_2 and one of unidirectional stress (known as the deviator stress), $(\sigma_1 - \sigma_2)$.

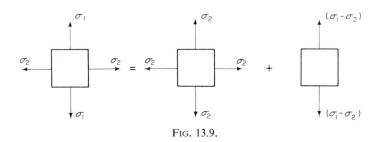

FIG. 13.9.

Now photoelastic observations give directly only $(\sigma_1 - \sigma_2)$ and $\theta_{1,2}$ and cannot, by the definition of the Stress–Optic law, distinguish between different intensities of hydrostatic pressure distributions. This means that additional information is necessary to complete the stress solution.

Let it be pointed out at once that at a free boundary, or at one where the applied or reactive stresses are known, the photoelastic data are sufficient to solve the problem. In very many cases, such as those dealing with stress concentrations at openings or notches, this, in fact, is the problem.

However, once the boundary values are known, it is possible to determine the stresses at interior points by a numerical integration of the differential equations of equilibrium. These can be in curvilinear or rectangular coordinates. In the latter case, they are

$$\frac{\partial \sigma_x}{\partial x} + \frac{\partial \tau_{xy}}{\partial y} = 0 \qquad (13.9)$$

$$\frac{\partial \sigma_y}{\partial y} + \frac{\partial \tau_{xy}}{\partial x} = 0 \qquad (13.10)$$

for zero body forces.

If, in the example of Fig. 13.10, it were of interest to obtain the full stress solution along the x-axis, the first of the above equations would be rewritten as

$$\Delta \sigma_x = -\frac{\Delta \tau_{xy}}{\Delta y} . \Delta x$$

Now, τ_{xy} at any point is given by

$$\tau_{xy} = \tfrac{1}{2}(\sigma_1 - \sigma_2) \sin 2\theta$$

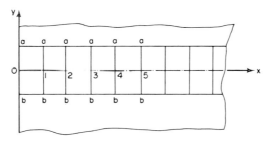

FIG. 13.10. Grid for shear difference method.

the initial value of σ_x at 0 is known and the variation in shear along vertical lines *ab* for successive positions 1, 2, 3, etc., along the x-axis is easily determined. Hence, the numerical integration of equation (13.9) presents no difficulty.

Another approach, when the stresses are known at all points along the boundary of a two-dimensional model, is to recall from the theory of elasticity that the distribution of the sum of the principal stresses at internal points obeys the Laplace law, i.e.

$$\left(\frac{\partial^2}{\partial x^2} + \frac{\partial^2}{\partial y^2} \right)(\sigma_1 + \sigma_2) = 0$$

or, more concisely,

$$\nabla^2 (\sigma_1 + \sigma_2) = 0$$

Thus the sum of the principal stresses at internal points can be determined from the boundary values by relaxation or by use of an electrical resistance network analogue.

Yet another method of, what in photoelastic language is called the *separation of principal stresses*, makes use of the " frozen-stress " phenomenon. Consider the thin plate shown in Fig. 13.11 and assume that the stresses have been " frozen-in ". At any point, p, the values of $(\sigma_1 - \sigma_2)$ and $\theta_{1,2}$ can be obtained in the usual way. If, now, a slice in the *xz*-plane is cut so that it contains the point p, and if light is passed through this slice in the *y*-direction, the stress pattern will at once yield the σ_x stress, which will be one of the secondary principal stresses in that slice, the other being zero. The σ_y stresses, being parallel to the axes of the polariscope, will not affect the stress pattern.

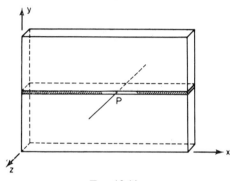

FIG. 13.11.

The elastic solution is now complete since

$$(\sigma_1 + \sigma_2) = 2\sigma_x - (\sigma_1 - \sigma_2)\cos 2\theta \tag{13.11}$$

There are many other methods of separating the principal stresses; most of these are described in the texts by Frocht[16] and Jessop and Harris.[15] It may be said in passing that research work is now being done on photoelastic methods which can give sufficient direct information for a complete stress solution of two-dimensional problems. In this connection the work of Post[17] in the United States could be mentioned.

For details of photoelastic solutions to three-dimensional elastic problems the reader is referred to the paper by Frocht and Guernsey.[18]

13.13. APPLICATION OF PHOTOELASTICITY IN DESIGN OF REACTOR STRUCTURES

In the highly evolved state photoelasticity finds itself today, it can safely be said that provided it is possible to manufacture and load the photoelastic model of a structure a full elastic solution can be obtained for it. A good

FIG. 13.12. Photoelastic model of the Hinkley Point pressure vessel.

example is the model of the Hinkley Point pressure vessel, shown in Fig. 13.12, on which photoelastic studies have been made at University College of London University.

Other typical examples of work connected with nuclear reactor structures are given in Refs. 19, 20, 21 and Ref. 18 of Chapter 12.

13.14. CONCLUSION

Basically the aim of this chapter has been to give the reader some idea of the general scope of model analysis. Since such a great variety of different methods and techniques are now available to the engineer, emphasis has been laid on fundamental concepts which are sometimes omitted in more specialized texts.

Model analysis can be a very useful tool in the hands of the designer; it should not, however, act as a veil behind which an ignorance of structural principles can be concealed.

REFERENCES

1. B. F. LANGER, Experimental mechanics of nuclear power reactors. *Proc. Soc. Exp. Stress Anal.* **17,** No. 2 (1960).
2. C. M. FOCKEN, *Dimensional Methods and their Application.* Arnold, London (1953).
3. H. L. LANGHAAR, *Dimensional Analysis and Theory of Models.* John Wiley (1951).
4. N. BEAUJOINT, *Similitude and Theory of Models.* RILEM Bulletin No. 7, Paris, June (1960).
5. J. N. GOODIER, *Handbook of Experimental Stress Analysis* (edited by M. Hetényi), Appendix II. John Wiley (1950).
6. T. M. CHARLTON, *Model Analysis of Structures.* Spon (1954).
7. A. J. DURELLI, E. A. PHILLIPS and C. H. TSAO, *Introduction to the Theoretical and Experimental Analysis of Stress and Strain.* McGraw-Hill (1958).
8. L. H. DONNELL and W. T. SAVAGE, *Handbook of Experimental Stress Analysis* (edited by N. HETÉNYI), Ch. 3. John Wiley (1950).
9. C. O. DOHRENWEND and W. R. MEHAFFEY, *Handbook of Experimental Stress Analysis* (edited by N. HETÉNYI), Ch. 5. John Wiley (1950).
10. W. H. MURRAY and P. K. STEIN, *Strain Gauge Techniques.* Stein Engineering Services, U.S.A.
11. G. F. BROSIUS and D. HARTLEY, Evaluation of high temperature strain gauges. *Proc. Soc. Exp. Stress Anal.* **17,** No. 1 (1959).
12. V. M. HICKSON, *Special Techniques in Experimental Stress Analysis.* Int. Congress of Experimental Mechanics, New York (1961).
13. V. M. HICKSON, A replica technique for measuring static strains. *J. Mech. Eng. Sci.* **1,** No. 2 (1959).
14. M. HETÉNYI, *Handbook of Experimental Stress Analysis* (edited by M. HETÉNYI), Ch. 14. John Wiley (1950).
15. H. T. JESSOP and F. C. HARRIS, *Photoelasticity, Principles and Methods.* Cleaver-Hume Press, London (1949).
16. M. M. FROCHT, *Photoelasticity,* vol. I. John Wiley (1941).
17. D. POST, Photoelastic evaluation of individual principal stresses by large field absolute retardation measurement. *Proc. Soc. Exp. Stress. Anal.* **13,** No. 2 (1956).
18. M. M. FROCHT and R. GUERNSEY, *A Special Investigation to Develop a General Method for Three-Dimensional Photoelastic Stress Analysis.* N.A.C.A. Report 1148 (1953), U.S.A.
19. C. E. TAYLOR and J. W. SCHWEIKER, A three-dimensional photoelastic investigation of the stresses near a reinforced opening in a reactor pressure vessel. *Proc. Soc. Exp. Stress Anal.* **17,** No. 1 (1959).
20. N. M. LEVEN and R. C. SAMPSON, Photoelastic stress and deformation analysis of nuclear reactor components. *Proc. Soc. Exp. Stress Anal.* **17,** No. 1 (1959).
21. C. SNELL and H. T. JESSOP, Photoelastic exploration of the stresses in a design for a full-bore closure for a reactor pressure vessel. *J. Mech. Eng. Sci.* **1,** No. 2 (1959).

APPENDIX

CONCRETE PRESSURE VESSELS—REVIEW NOTE

P. B. MORICE

AT THE present time all the nuclear power reactors built in Britain for electricity generation have been contained in steel pressure vessels. A pressure vessel surrounding the reactor is necessary in carbon dioxide cooled systems, since a reasonable rate of heat exchange is only possible at gas pressures of the order of 200 p.s.i. The steel vessel is, however, very inefficient as a radiation shield and a surrounding mass of concrete with a minimum thickness of the order of 9 ft has been used for biological protection.

The development of British power reactors has been rapid and, whilst earlier stations such as Berkeley have reactors producing 140 megawatts, only a year or two later stations such as Hinkley Point will have reactors working at about twice this power. Such developments are brought about partly by increased dimensions of the reactor core and consequently of the pressure vessel, and also by increased gas pressures. The diameter of the Hinkley vessels is 67 ft and they are constructed from 3 in. steel plate and have a 9 ft thick concrete shield.

Further increases in reactor dimensions are no doubt possible using steel pressure vessels, but the technical problems of welding and annealing very thick steel plates make the costs rise rapidly with size and alternative methods are worth looking for.

An obvious choice is to make use of shielding concrete to act also as the structural material of the containment vessel. There is less difficulty in constructing thick-walled members in concrete than in steel, but since concrete is essentially a material with strength in compression rather than in tension, its resistance to internal pressure requires reinforcement and, if cracks are to be prevented under load, negative pressure forces. These can conveniently be provided by prestressing.

It was for these reasons that the French Atomic Energy Board (C.E.A.) designed and built two prestressed concrete pressure vessels at Marcoule in 1958.[1]

Figure A–1 shows the geometry and dimensions of the vessels, where it is seen that inverted domical ends were used to produce a zone of compressive stress without artificial prestressing devices, thus giving an uninterrupted area

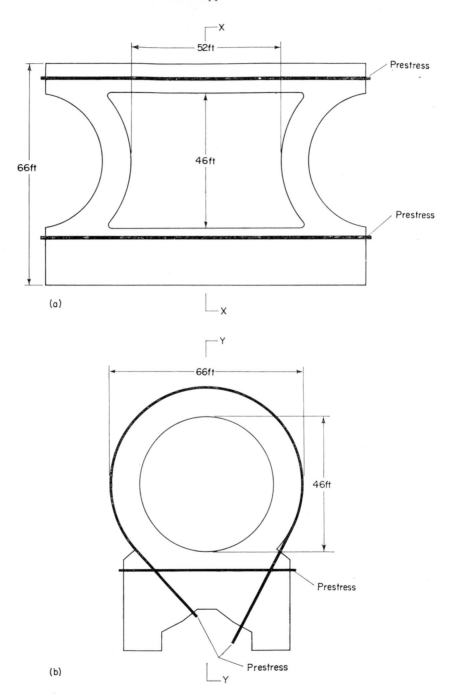

FIG. A.1.   Diagrammatic representation of the Marcoule pressure vessel.

for the gas ducts and other openings which are always necessary. Gas tightness of the vessel was ensured by a steel liner $1\frac{1}{4}$ in. thick. The vessel and its associated structure when completed weighed approximately 75,000 tons.

Model and full-scale tests were carried out on the Marcoule vessels. One-tenth scale concrete models failed at 800 p.s.i. when designed for a working pressure of 215 p.s.i., which indicates an adequate factor of safety for this type of structure.

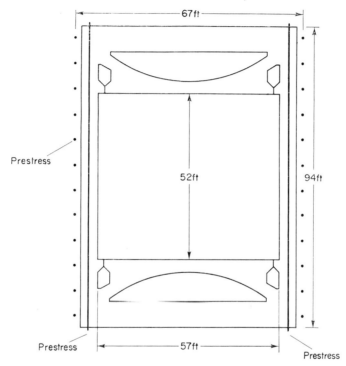

FIG. A.2. Diagrammatic representation of the Simon-Carves experimental pressure vessel.

The completed vessels were tested to twice the working pressure.

More recently[2] the Simon-Carves Atomic Energy Group have reported tests on a 1:6 model of a design for a prestressed concrete pressure vessel which would be somewhat larger than those at Marcoule. Figure A–2 shows the geometry and dimensions, where it is seen that domical ends are again used, but in addition radial stiffness is added by flat diaphragms. A thin steel liner was provided for gas tightness. The vessel is intended to stand with the cylindrical axis vertical instead of horizontal as at Marcoule.

The advantages prompting this investigation were primarily capital economy, easier construction with less skilled labour, and a more satisfactory mechanism of failure under load than that of a steel vessel, with adequate warning of overload and non-explosive release of pressure at failure.

The model was designed for a working pressure of 150 p.s.i. and it was required to have an ultimate strength of 375 p.s.i. In fact, the pressure which would cause destruction of the vessel was in excess of 555 p.s.i. The model was, incidentally, tested under varying temperature conditions as well as pressure.

Temperature effects may well be of great importance in concrete vessels with thick walls and, whilst ultimate failure loads are not likely to be affected, cracking could occur at lower loads. It seems clear that, with the increasing reactor sizes required for economical electricity generation, prestressed con-

FIG. A.3   Artist's impression of Oldbusy Nuclear Power Station which will use prestressed concrete pressure vessels.

crete structures will provide the most satisfactory solution to the containment vessel problem unless dramatic improvements occur in steel constructional techniques.

There is still a great deal to learn about the design and performance of concrete vessels and even more to be done to develop economic and efficient constructional techniques but, in principle, size limitations are not likely to be so restrictive as in steel. This suggests that it may be economical to consider much larger vessels and place the heat exchangers (steam raising units) as well as the reactor inside the vessel, which would very considerably reduce the power absorbed in gas circulation and also allow of a simplification in heat exchanger structural design, since they would not have to withstand significant gas pressures. Only small diameter steam pipe, charging and control rod openings would then be required. This feature has, in fact, been adopted for the Oldbury Nuclear Power Station (Fig. A3), the Contract for which has recently been placed with The Nuclear Power Group by the C.E.G.B. Other prestressed concrete vessels are currently in the design stage for the proposed Wilfa Station in North Wales.

The provision of flat diaphragms at the ends of the Simon-Carves vessel and the infill concrete used to provide a flat floor over the dome means that, as far as the overall concrete volume is concerned, there is relatively little difference from a solid flat ended vessel. It seems probable that the structural shapes will, in fact, be simplified to a form dependent upon the convenience of the mechanical space requirements within the vessel. Most simple shapes can be adequately provided with prestress, but the economics of such systems still remain to be sorted out and, indeed, lie in the realm of constructional and design techniques requiring development.

One important characteristic of the concrete vessel is that it is " thick walled " and the usual assumptions of the elastic and thermal theories of thin shells and plates may not be satisfactory for its analysis. This is particularly the case if cracks at working loads are to be completely avoided. Thick shell theory is not well-worn ground and in the other field where it is required—arch dams—progress is only now being made. Three-dimensional relaxation methods provide one possible technique, whilst variational combinations of onion peel type solutions using, for example, the matrix progression method outlined in Chapter 7, may be more rapidly convergent and more convenient for computation. This is particularly the case when discontinuities have to be included in the structure.

Little is yet known of the stress concentration effects caused by openings in thick walled shells and this also provides a field for further study.

Ultimate load studies of concrete vessels will be necessary, but it is likely that, with adequate amounts of mild steel reinforcement, thick shell effects will not cause great difficulty in analysis.

Gas tightness will remain an important problem, but it is to be hoped that an alternative membrane to the complicated and expensive steel liner will be found.

The effect of installing both reactor and heat exchangers within a large concrete pressure vessel may well lower the working temperature on the inner wall of the vessel and consequently reduce the problems associated with thick shell temperature stresses and widen the range of materials which could be used for construction of the gas tight membrane. Indeed, with the right kind of mechanical properties in the membrane it might well be possible to allow pressure vessels to work with the limited degree of cracking which is normally associated with structural concrete.

REFERENCES

1. J. BELLIER and M. TOURASSE, Prestressed concrete pressure vessels at Marcoule Nuclear Centre. Cement and Concrete Association Bb21, Oct. 1960, 28 pp.
2. A. L. L. BAKER, M. L. A. MONCRIEF, I. W. HANNAH and S. GILL, The design, construction and testing of a prestressed concrete reactor pressure vessel model. *Proc. I.C.E.* **20**, 555–586 (1961).

INDEX